The Bookshelf
for Boys and Girls

Prepared under the Supervision of

THE EDITORIAL BOARD
OF THE UNIVERSITY SOCIETY

VOLUME II

Happy Hours in Storyland

THE UNIVERSITY SOCIETY, INC.

Educational Publishers since 1897

NEW YORK

1970

ACKNOWLEDGEMENTS Volume II

Grateful acknowledgement and thanks are extended to the following publishers, authors, periodicals, and individuals for permission to reprint copyrighted material:

American Junior Red Cross News—"When the Mail Came Through" by Armstrong Sperry.

Margaret Wise Brown—"Never Worked and Never Will."

Jonathan Cape Limited—"Stopping by Woods on a Snowy Evening" by Robert Frost, from *Complete Poems.* "How Bambi Found the Meadow" from *Bambi* by Felix Salten.

Child Life Magazine—"Mr. Scrunch" by Helen and Alf Evers. "All Mutt" by Helen Train Hilles.

William Weber Coblentz—"The Horse That Came From Heaven" by Catherine Cate Coblentz, from *Animal Pioneers* published 1936, by Little, Brown & Co.

Council Against Intolerance in America—"Fung's Fourth" and "Willie's Good Recess" by Lavinia Davis.

Coward-McCann, Inc.—"No Room" by Rose Dobbs, illustrated by Fritz Eichenberg. Reprinted by permission of Coward-McCann, Inc., copyright, 1944, by Rose Dobbs. "Karoo, the Kangaroo" by Kurt Wiese, copyright, 1929, by Coward-McCann, Inc. Reprinted by permission of Coward-McCann, Inc.

Dodd, Mead & Co.—"Barnum's First Circus" by Laura Benét, from *Barnum's First Circus* by Laura Benét, copyright, 1949, by Dodd, Mead & Company, Inc. Reprinted by permission of Dodd, Mead & Company, Inc.

Doubleday & Company, Inc.—"Mr. A and Mr. P" and "The Baker's Daughter" by Margery W. Bianco, with illustrations by Grace Paull, from *A Street of Little Shops,* copyright, 1932, by Margery Williams Bianco, reprinted by permission of Doubleday & Company, Inc. "The Animal Store" by Rachel Field, from *Taxis and Toadstools* by Rachel Field, copyright, 1926, by Doubleday & Company, Inc. Illustration on page 90, by Barbara Cooney, from *American Folk Songs for Children* by Ruth C. Seeger, illustrated by Barbara Cooney, copyright, 1948, by Ruth Crawford Seeger, reprinted by permission of Doubleday & Company, Inc.

Ruth Sawyer Durand—"The Christmas Apple" from *This Way to Christmas,* by Ruth Sawyer, copyright, 1944, by Ruth Sawyer Durand, published by Harper and Brothers.

Helen and Alf Evers—"Mr. Scrunch."

Marjorie Fischer—"Rococo Skates."

Doris Gates—"The Seventh Pup."

Harcourt, Brace and Company, Inc.—"The Middle Bear" from *The Middle Moffat,* by Eleanor Estes, copyright, 1942, by Harcourt, Brace and Company, Inc. "A Miserable Merry Christmas" from *Boy on Horseback,* by Lincoln Steffens, copyright, 1931, 1935, by Harcourt, Brace and Company, Inc.

Harper and Brothers—"The Skunk in Tante Odette's Oven" from *The Talking Cat* by Natalie Savage Carlson, illustrated by Roger Duvoisin, copyright, 1952, by Natalie Savage Carlson, published by Harper and Brothers. "The Christmas Apple" by Ruth Sawyer, from *This Way to Christmas* by Ruth Sawyer, copyright, 1944, by Ruth Sawyer Durand. "Circus Parade" by James S. Tippett, from *A World to Know* by James S. Tippett, copyright, 1933, by Harper and Brothers. "Indians in the House" from *The Little House on the Prairie* by Laura Ingalls Wilder, copyright, 1935, by Harper and Brothers. "Surprise" from *On the Banks of Plum Creek* by Laura Ingalls Wilder, copyright, 1937, by Harper and Brothers.

Helen Train Hilles—"All Mutt."

Henry Holt & Company, Inc.—"Elizabeth Ann Fails an Examination" by Dorothy Canfield Fisher, from *Understood Betsy* by Dorothy Canfield, copyright, 1917, 1946, by Henry Holt & Company, Inc., copyright, 1944, by Dorothy Canfield. Used by permission of the publishers. "Stopping by Woods on a Snowy Evening" by Robert Frost, from *Complete Poems by Robert Frost,* copyright, 1930, 1949, by Henry Holt & Company, Inc. Used by permission of the publishers. "Silver" by Walter de la Mare, from *Collected Poems* by Walter de la Mare, copyright, 1920, by Henry Holt & Company, Inc., copyright, 1948, by Walter de la Mare. Used by permission of the publishers. "Theme in Yellow" by Carl Sandburg, from *Chicago Poems* by Carl Sandburg, copyright, 1916, by Henry Holt & Company, Inc., copyright, 1944, by Carl Sandburg. Used by permission of the publishers.

Alfred A. Knopf, Inc.—For illustration in full color by Maurice Brevannes, for "The Teacup Whale" from *The Treasure Bag,* compiled by Lena Barksdale, illustrated by Maurice Brevannes, copyright, 1947, by Alfred A. Knopf, Inc.

Lois Lenski—"A Tree of Apples" by Lois Lenski, from *Blueberry Corners,* published by J. B. Lippincott Company, copyright, 1940, by Lois Lenski. Used by permission of the author.

Gladys Francis Lewis—"The Black Stallion and the Red Mare."

J. B. Lippincott Company—"Poetry" by Eleanor Farjeon, from *Eleanor Farjeon's Poems for Children,* copyright, 1951, by Eleanor Farjeon. Reprinted by permission of the publishers, J. P. Lippincott Company. "Ring Around the World" by Annette Wynne, from *All Through the Year* by Annette Wynne, copyright, 1921, by J. B. Lippincott Company. Reprinted by permission of the publishers, J. B. Lippincott Company.

Longmans, Green and Co.—"How Many Donkeys?" by Alice Geer Kelsey, from *Once the Hodja* by Alice Geer Kelsey, copyright, 1943, by Longmans, Green & Co., Inc.

Mary Ellen Lynde and The New York Times—"Queen Anne's Lace" by Mary Leslie Newton.

Oxford University Press—Illustrations on Pages 86, 87, 98, and 331 by Pelagie Doane from *A Small Child's Book of Verse* compiled and illustrated by Pelagie Doane, copyright, 1948, by Oxford University Press, Inc.

Rand McNally & Company—"Pony Penning Day" from *Misty of Chincoteague* by Marguerite Henry, copyright, 1947, by Rand McNally & Company, as condensed for the book *24 Horses: A Treasury of Stories*, collected by Frances Cavanah and Ruth Weir, copyright, 1950, by Rand McNally & Company. "Space Ship to the Moon" by E. C. Reichart from *Space Ship to the Moon* by E. C. Reichert, copyright, 1952, by Rand McNally & Company, publishers.

Random House, Inc.—"The Happy Cure" by Rose Dobbs, from *Once Upon a Time*, compiled by Rose Dobbs, copyright, 1950, by Random House, Inc. Illustrations by Flavia Gág for "The Happy Cure" and "How Many Donkeys?" from *Once Upon a Time*, copyright, 1950, by Random House, Inc.

Rinehart & Company, Inc.—"The Teacup Whale" by Lydia Gibson, copyright, 1934, by Rinehart & Company, Inc. and reprinted by their permission.

Charles Scribner's Sons—"His First Bronc" by Will James. Reprinted from *Young Cowboy* by Will James, copyright, 1935, by Charles Scribner's Sons. Used by permission of the publishers. "The Family Who Had Never Had Roller Skates" by Hildegard Woodward. Reprinted from *Time Was* by Hildegard Woodward, copyright, 1941, by Charles Scribner's Sons. Used by permission of the publishers.

Simon and Schuster, Inc.—"How Bambi Found the Meadow" adapted from *Bambi* by Felix Salten, copyright 1928. Reprinted by permission of Simon & Schuster, Inc., publishers.

Society of Authors—"Silver" by Walter de la Mare, from *Collected Poems* by Walter de la Mare, copyright, 1920, by Henry Holt & Company, Inc., copyright, 1948, by Walter de la Mare. Used by permission of the publishers.

Armstrong Sperry—"When the Mail Came Through."

Story Parade, Inc.—Reprinted by permission: "Almost an Ambush" by Le Grand Henderson, copyright, 1944, by Story Parade, Inc. "The Big Green Umbrella" by Elizabeth Coatsworth, copyright, 1944, by Story Parade, Inc. "Caleb's Luck" by Laura Benét, copyright, 1938, by Story Parade, Inc. "Champion Fire 'n Feathers" by Lavinia Davis, copyright, 1939, by Story Parade, Inc. "The Dog Who Chose a Prince" by Catherine C. Coblentz, copyright, 1946, by Story Parade, Inc. "High Water in Arkansas" by Charles J. Finger, copyright, 1938, by Story Parade, Inc. "Katie Meets Buffalo Bill" by Katherine Koch, copyright, 1945, by Story Parade, Inc. "Mother Makes Christmas" by Cornelia Meigs, copyright, 1937, by Story Parade, Inc. "Oscar, the Trained Seal" by Mabel Neikirk, illustrated by William O'Brian, copyright, 1939, by Story Parade, Inc. "Pino and Paint" by Dan Noonan, copyright, 1947, by Story Parade, Inc. "Such a Kind World" by Mabel Leigh Hunt, copyright, 1946, by Story Parade, Inc.

Vanguard Press—"The 500 Hats of Bartholomew Cubbins" by Dr. Seuss, copyright, 1938, by Dr. Seuss. Reprinted by permission of Vanguard Press, Inc.

The Viking Press, Inc.—"Blue Rocking Chair Tells a Story" from *Country Stop* by Carolyn Sherwin Bailey, illustrated by Grace Paull, copyright, 1942, by Carolyn Sherwin Bailey and Grace Paull. Reprinted by permission of The Viking Press, Inc., New York. "The Doughnuts" by Robert McCloskey, from *Homer Price*, copyright, 1943, by Robert McCloskey. Reprinted by permission of The Viking Press, Inc., New York. "Little Rain" by Elizabeth Madox Roberts, from *Under the Tree* by Elizabeth Madox Roberts, copyright, 1922, by B. W. Huebsch, Inc., 1950, by Ivor S. Roberts. Reprinted by permission of The Viking Press, Inc., New York.

Carolyn Wells, Estate of—"The Animals' Fair."

The Westminster Press—Illustrations by Ninon on pages 332 and 384 from *For a Child: Great Poems Old and New*, collected by Wilma McFarland, illustrated by Ninon, copyright, 1947, by W. L. Jenkins, published by The Westminster Press.

Whittlesey House—"Kentucky Birthday," "Little Fox Lost," "To a Christmas Tree," by Frances Frost from *The Little Whistler*, copyright, 1949, by the McGraw-Hill Book Company, Inc. Published by Whittlesey House and reprinted with their permission.

In a few instances, where no acknowledgement is made, the compilers have made every effort to find sources and get permissions from them to reprint, but without success.

A Word to Parents about this Volume

HAPPY HOURS IN STORYLAND

IT ISN'T EASY—in fact, it is impossible—to keep a child who loves to read from reading. But it *is* possible to provide him with *good* reading. And by good we mean stories and poems which fulfill all of the following requirements:

The child must *enjoy* them.

They must appeal to the child's interests and understanding at his particular stage of development when he reads them, and they must, in one way or another, contribute something constructive to that development.

They must meet the approval of educators whose standards of literary and artistic taste are of the highest.

The stories and poems, as well as the illustrations, in this volume are, we believe, of this caliber. They have all been selected because they provide *wholesome fare* for the child with an insatiable appetite for reading. And even more to their credit, perhaps, is their appeal to children who do *not* naturally take to reading. There is such variety of material here that even the most uninterested child is sure to be intrigued by *something* in the book. And once intrigued, he will want to sample more, to investigate further. Many a child to whom ordinary reading comes hard has been known to respond enthusiastically to reading as invitingly presented as this.

The Aesop's Fables, with which the book opens, are short so as not to strain the child's attention. They are told in simple words. The "lessons" they teach are universal and will not make the child feel he is being preached at.

The next section, "Cheerful Tales and Verse," contains many humorous selections especially chosen to appeal to the funny-bone of young children. The same is true of the later humorous section, "Fun and Laughter."

The "Poems for Pleasure" will endear themselves particularly to the sensitive child. All children of this early reading age will love the "Animal Stories."

"Children in America Then and Now" provides the child with stories of life in America all the way from Indian days to the space-ship era of today. Here are many of the fundamentals of life in America all presented in the form of *stories* so that children will absorb the facts with *interest*.

"Christmas in Story and Verse," containing Christmas selections on a slightly older level than those in Volume I, brings this volume to a glowing and appropriate end. The child who has this volume for his own to browse through will indeed have before him many happy hours of storyland reading.

Table of Contents

NOTE: The **Section Headings** follow the order of their appearance in the book. But under each **Section Heading** the titles of stories, rhymes, etc. appear in *alphabetical* order to make them easier to locate.

ALPHABETICAL INDEX of the **contents of all 9 volumes** will be found *at the end* of Volume 9.

Poems for Pleasure

Animal Stories

Time for Laughter

Children in America Then and Now

Christmas Stories and Christmas Verses

Illustrators of this Volume

ELINORE BLAISDELL, *The Months; Seven Times One; Color; The Stork and the Holy Babe*

MAURICE BREVANNES, *The Teacup Whale*

PETER BURCHARD, *The Black Stallion and the Red Mare*

BESS B. CLEAVELAND, *The Fox and the Crow* (frontispiece)

BARBARA COONEY, *Song; Little Fox Lost; Stopping by Woods on a Snowy Evening; The Friendly Beasts*

LAWRENCE DARROW, *What Do We Plant When We Plant a Tree?*

HARRY DAUGHERTY, *The Dog Who Chose a Prince; The Horse That Came from Heaven; Pony Penning Day; Waukewa's Eagle*

MARGUERITE DAVIS, *The Seven Little Tigers and the Aged Cook; The Monkeys and the Crocodile; Mrs. Snipkin and Mrs. Wobblechin*

PELAGIE DOANE, *Queen Anne's Lace; The Sandpiper; Theme in Yellow*

ROGER DUVOISIN, *The Skunk in Tante Odette's Oven*

FRITZ EICHENBERG, *No Room*

PHOEBE ERICKSON, *Karoo, the Kangaroo; Bambi*

HELEN EVERS, *Mr. Scrunch*

FLAVIA GÁG, *The Happy Cure; How Many Donkeys?*

LYDIA GIBSON, *The Teacup Whale*

MARGUERITE GAYER, *The Lamb; Fung's Fourth; Away in a Manger; Our Christmas Tree*

HARPER JOHNSON, *The Sugar Plum Tree; Space Ship to the Moon*

URSULA KOERING, *Such a Kind World; Almost an Ambush; Caleb's Luck; Katie Meets Buffalo Bill; Indians in the House; Barnum's First Circus; The Christmas Apple; Surprise; Mother Makes Christmas; When The Mail Came Through*

EDWARD LEAR, *The Duck and the Kangaroo; Nonsense Limericks; The Pobble Who Has No Toes*

LOIS LENSKI, *A Tree of Apples*

ROBERT McCLOSKEY, *The Doughnuts*

WILLIAM MOYERS, *The Seventh Pup; Pino and Paint; Champion Fire 'N' Feathers; His First Bronc; High Water in Arkansas; A Miserable Merry Christmas*

NINON, *The Gift; We Will Sing a New Song*

WILLIAM B. O'BRIAN, *Oscar the Trained Seal*

GRACE PAULL, *The Baker's Daughter; Mr. A and Mr. P*

VIRGINIA RUPP, *Willie's Good Recess*

DR. SEUSS, *The 500 Hats of Bartholomew Cubbins*

MARY STEVENS, *Never Worked and Never Will; Ring Around The World; Kentucky Birthday; The Animal Store; All Mutt; Stories from the Peterkin Papers; The Middle Bear; Blue Rocking Chair Tells a Story; Elizabeth Ann Fails in an Examination; Rococo Skates; Young Lucretia; Christmas Every Day*

SIGISMUND VIDBERGS, *The Camel and the Pig; The Council of Animals; The Lion and the Goat*

KURT WIESE, *Aesop's Fables; The Big Green Umbrella*

HILDEGARD WOODWARD, *Poetry; Little Rain; Autumn; Silver; The Family Who Had Never Had Roller Skates*

Aesop's
and Other Fables

Aesop's Fables

THE FOX AND THE CROW

ONE DAY a Crow who had found a piece of cheese was flying toward the top of a tall tree where she hoped to enjoy her prize alone. Along came a Fox who smelled the delicious cheese and determined to have it for himself. "If I plan this right, I shall have cheese for supper," he thought.

So he went to the foot of the tree and began to speak in his politest tones. "Good day, Mistress Crow," he said, "how well you are looking today!"

The Crow was very much pleased, but of course could not reply because of the cheese she held in her beak.

"How glossy your wings are, and how smooth your feathers," the Fox went on. "Indeed, you are the loveliest of birds."

The Crow was even more pleased by this and believed every word of it. Still she said nothing, but she swelled with inward pride and flapped her wings to show her pleasure.

Then the Fox said: "I have heard that you have, besides, a wonderful voice. I should like so much to hear you sing, for if your voice matched the beauty of your plumage, then you would indeed be the most wonderful of feathered creatures.

Won't you sing just a few notes for me that I may greet you as Queen of Song?"

These words flattered the vain Crow. She had often been told that her voice was rusty, but here was someone who appreciated her. She lifted up her head and began to caw her best. The moment she opened her beak, down dropped the piece of cheese!

Quick as a flash the wily Fox snatched it up before it touched the ground. "Thank you, that was all I wanted," said he as he gobbled up the cheese.

As he walked away licking his chops, the Fox offered these words of advice to the saddened Crow: "In the future perhaps you won't be so ready to believe all the good things you hear about yourself." With an insolent flick of his tail the clever Fox sauntered off into the forest.

Do not trust flatterers!

THE ANT AND THE GRASSHOPPER

Out in the fields on a warm sunny day an Ant was busy gathering grains of wheat and corn for his winter's food. A Grasshopper, chirping and dancing to his heart's content, saw the Ant at work and laughed, "Why not sing and dance with me instead of toiling all day long?"

"I am working to store up food for the long cold winter," replied the Ant. "Perhaps you will wish some time that you had laid some away too."

"Why worry about winter when we have so much now?" said the Grasshopper, and went on his merry way. The Ant said nothing but went on busily working.

When winter came the poor Grasshopper was almost dead of hunger for the ground was hard and the snow had covered all his food.

Sadly he came to the house of the Ant and begged for something to eat. "What," cried the Ant, "did you store nothing away when the weather was sunny and warm? What did you do all summer long?"

"I was so busy singing and dancing," said the Grasshopper, "that I had no time to store up food, and before I knew it the summer had gone."

"Singing and dancing, were you!" scoffed the Ant, turning his back on the Grasshopper. "Then sing and dance now!"

The poor Grasshopper crept away silently, regretting he had been so foolish during the summer in not providing for the winter that he knew must come.

It is wise to put something away for tomorrow's rainy day.

3

THE COUNTRY MAID AND HER MILK PAIL

ONE DAY a milkmaid was on her way to market carrying a pail of milk on her head. As she walked along she said to herself: "With the money I get after I sell this milk, I shall buy some eggs. Say I'll have a hundred eggs. My old hens will hatch them into chickens and when the chickens are old enough, I'll sell them in the market."

"Then," she went on, "I'll have enough money to buy myself a pretty new silk dress. It will be—let me see—green. I look my prettiest in green, so it will be of green silk."

"I'll wear my beautiful green silk dress at the fair," she said to herself, "and I shall look so beautiful that all the young men at the fair will beg me to dance with them. Many of them will ask my hand in marriage. Of course I shall marry the handsomest and the wealthiest one. We shall have an elegant wedding. How my friends will envy me!"

With this vain thought the milkmaid tossed her head haughtily just as if she were already wearing her bridal finery, and down from her head toppled the pail spilling milk all over the dusty road. And with it flew all her dreams of glory. There was nothing—no money, no eggs, no chickens, and no green dress.

Don't count your chickens before they are hatched!

THE WIND AND THE SUN

THE WIND and the Sun once had a quarrel as to which of them was the stronger. They boasted of the wonderful things they could do and each believed himself to be the more powerful.

Cried the Sun: "I bring the summer and ripen the fruits and grains. I cover the earth with flowers!"

"And I," cried the Wind, "can move ships at sea, uproot trees, and I bring the winter!"

So they quarrelled, and while they were arguing with much bluster and heat, they saw a traveler walking along a country road, wearing a great cloak.

"Do you see that traveler plodding along the highway?" asked the Wind. "Let us see which of us is strong enough to make him take off his cloak. The one who can do that first shall be the winner."

"Agreed," said the Sun.

The Wind was the first to try, so the Sun went behind a cloud. At once the Wind sent a howling blast against the traveler. The blast sent the leaves flying through the air, raised clouds of dust in

the road, bent the tops of trees to the ground and even tore up a sturdy oak by its roots.

But the harder the Wind blew, the colder it became and the more tightly did the traveler wrap his cloak about him. At last the Wind gave up in despair. He could not get the cloak off.

Then it was the Sun's turn. He came out from behind a black cloud and, little by little, darted his warm beams upon the traveler's head and back. In the pleasant warmth, the traveler opened his cloak, letting it hang loosely from his shoulders. The Sun's rays grew warmer and soon the man stopped to mop the sweat from his face.

"Ah," said the traveler, "it is getting so hot I might as well be in an oven!" At that he threw off his cloak, and carrying it on his arm, lay down under a shady tree to cool himself off. So the gentle rays of the Sun succeeded where the blustering Wind was unable to do what he tried. After that the Wind never claimed to be stronger than the Sun.

Gentleness often accomplishes more than force.

BELLING THE CAT

ONCE upon a time a large family of Mice lived in the barn of a well-to-do farmer. His barn was stacked with corn, and grain and hay and the Mice might have lived there in great peace and comfort with all that good food at hand except for one thing.

The farmer had a Cat—a sleek, sharp-eyed Cat whose green eyes glared brightly in the dark. Besides, his paws were so well padded that no one could hear him when he walked. The Mice never knew when the Cat might pounce out upon them from the shadows; so their every meal was eaten in fear and trembling.

Even the youngest and bravest Mouse, its little heart beating pit-a-pat, scarcely dared to scurry across the floor, and all the Mice began to grow thin.

The Mice pondered and worried and worried and pondered but they could not think of a plan to outwit the Cat. At last one evening when the Mice were gathered in a safe hole where the Cat could not reach them, they held a meeting to consider what measures to take to outwit their enemy.

Some Mice said this, some said that. But finally, a young Mouse, looking very important, rose to speak.

"You will all agree," he said, "that our chief danger lies in the sly and treacherous way our enemy approaches us. Now

if we had a signal to warn us of his coming, we could easily escape. I have thought of a wonderful plan," continued the young Mouse. "Why not tie a bell around the Cat's neck so we can hear him when he walks. We could use the old cowbell in the barn."

"What a wonderful plan! Why haven't we ever thought of it before?" applauded the Mice. They went on excitedly praising the plan until a wise old Mouse who had kept silent all the while rose to his feet and said, "That is all very well now that we are all agreed about a bell. Indeed, with a bell about the Cat's neck to warn us, we shall all be safe. However, there is one question I must ask. Which of you is going to put the bell on the Cat?"

There was a great silence. The Mice looked at one another and nobody spoke, not even the smart young Mouse. Then the old Mouse said, "It is easy to propose impossible remedies."

Many things are easier said than done.

THE MILLER, HIS SON, AND THEIR DONKEY

A MILLER and his Son were taking their Donkey to market one day to sell him. They walked with the Donkey in the middle, the Man and Boy on either side of him. As they ambled along, the Father and Son stopped often to wipe the sweat from their brows for the road was steep and the sun was hot.

They had not gone far when they met a Farmer returning from town, who looked at them and laughed. "Of all the idiocies! To trudge along on foot when you have a perfectly good animal to carry you. What's a Donkey for if not to ride upon?" he exclaimed.

"I guess there's something in what you say," agreed the Miller. So he lifted his Son to the Donkey's back and they went on their way. They had not gone very far when they came up to a group of old men talking very earnestly among themselves.

sun while you ride. Why, he can hardly keep up with you!"

The Miller stopped to ponder. What was he to do? At last, to satisfy the women, he picked up the Boy and sat him up in front of him on the Donkey's back.

"Just what I've been saying all along—what's the world coming to?" cried one of them. "Children have no respect for their parents these days. See this great lazy lout of a Boy riding in comfort while his poor old Father must walk in the dust and heat."

Thereupon the Miller told his Son to get off and he himself climbed upon the Donkey's back. Soon they met a group of women with their children.

"You lazy old fellow!" cried several tongues at once. "You should be ashamed to let your little Son trudge in the hot

They continued on their way and soon were entering the outskirts of the market town.

Everyone they met stopped to point a finger at them and to cry "For shame, for shame!"

"Now," wondered the bewildered Miller, "what's wrong this time?"

"What, indeed?" said one. "It's easy to see you've never given a thought to that poor animal. Just because he can't speak for himself, is that any reason why you and your lazy hulk of a boy should abuse him? Why you two are better able to

8

carry the Donkey than he is to carry you."

"We hadn't thought of that!" said the Miller and his Son, and they both jumped off the Donkey. What were they to do now? They thought and thought and at last decided upon a plan.

They made the little beast lie down on his back with his feet in the air. The Father cut down a long pole which he tied to the Donkey's four feet. Then the Father and Son swung the pole to their shoulders and carried the Donkey this way toward the market.

This was such an odd sight that crowds of shouting, laughing people ran out to see it. They followed them until the three reached a little bridge that crossed a rushing stream. Here, the Donkey, not liking the idea of being carried at all, and frightened by the noise and clamor, brayed loudly and started thrashing about.

In the struggle he freed one of his feet and kicked out, causing the Boy to drop his end of the pole.

In the excitement that followed, the Donkey slipped off the pole and fell over the bridge into the swirling water below.

As his forefeet were still tied, the poor animal could not swim and so he disappeared from sight.

By trying to please everyone he met, the poor Miller learned the sad lesson that he had pleased no one, not himself, not his Son, and not even the poor Donkey.

If you try to please everyone, you may end up by pleasing no one.

THE FOX AND THE STORK

ONE DAY a Fox invited a Stork to have dinner with him, and the Stork accepted the invitation. At dinner, the Fox, who enjoyed practical jokes, put before the Stork nothing but a shallow plate of thin soup.

With her long sharp beak it was as much as the Stork could do to get even a taste of the soup, while the Fox, chuckling to himself, quickly lapped it up with his broad tongue. At the end of the meal, the Stork was as hungry as she had been when she began.

Then said the Fox, "My dear Stork, I am sorry to see you did not eat anything. Was the soup not seasoned to your taste?"

"Pray, do not apologize," said the Stork. "I have had a most interesting evening. And now you must do me the honor of paying *me* a visit. Will you dine with me a week from tonight?"

"Thank you," said the Fox. "I will do so with pleasure."

True to his appointment, the Fox arrived at the Stork's home and sat down

to dinner. But when it was served, the Fox found to his dismay a long-necked jar with a narrow mouth was placed before him. It was so tall and narrow that the Fox could not get his snout into it.

The Stork, readily thrusting her long beak into the jar, enjoyed her dinner while the Fox had to content himself with licking the outside of the jar.

Said the Stork, "I hope you are enjoying your dinner every bit as much as I did mine when I visited you." Unable to satisfy his hunger, the Fox retired with as good grace as he could. He realized that he could hardly find fault with his hostess, the Stork, who had only paid him back as he deserved.

Treat others as you would have them treat you.

THE GOOSE THAT LAID THE GOLDEN EGG

ONE DAY a Farmer went to the nest of his Goose to see if she had laid an egg. To his great wonder and delight he found that instead of an ordinary egg, she had laid an egg of pure gold. He rushed to the house in great excitement to show his wife the treasure he had found and she too was overjoyed.

Every day thereafter the Farmer visited the nest, and every day he found the Goose had laid a beautiful glittering golden egg.

The Farmer took the eggs to market and soon began to get rich. But it was not long before he grew impatient with the Goose because she gave him only a single golden egg a day. He was not getting rich quickly enough.

Then one day, after he had finished counting his money, the idea came to him that he could get all the golden treasure at once by killing the Goose and cutting it open. But when the deed was done, not a single golden egg did he find, and his marvelous Goose was dead.

The greedy who always want more often lose all.

THE CITY MOUSE AND THE COUNTRY MOUSE

ONCE upon a time a Country Mouse invited her friend, a City Mouse, to visit her. The Country Mouse lived in a barn on very simple food. All she had to offer her guest from the city were cheese parings, nuts, barley, dried peas, and bread crumbs. But she served them freely and with good-will.

The City Mouse sampled everything politely, but when she had finished her meal, she wiped her whiskers delicately and said, "My dear, I do feel sorry for you having to put up with such poor food. But of course you cannot expect anything better in the country. You should see how *I* live! I have all sorts of fine things to eat every day. Come with me to the city and I'll show you. When you have been in town one week, you'll wonder how you could ever have stood country life."

The Country Mouse felt rather ashamed of her simple home after that and readily agreed to go off with the City Mouse to visit her. It was almost midnight when they crept into the huge brick house where the City Mouse lived.

"You will surely want some refreshments after our long journey," said the City Mouse taking her friend into the grand dining-room.

There they found the remains of a splendid feast and soon they were busily nibbling away at cakes and jellies and raisins and candies. The City Mouse, playing the hostess, kept urging her friend to try this delicacy and that rich morsel. The eyes of the Country Mouse grew big and round. Never had she seen or tasted such food. And so much of it! She sighed contentedly. "This is really wonderful," she said, her mouth full of rich golden cheese. "How lucky I am to have such a devoted friend. I should like to live here forever."

She had scarcely finished speaking when she heard a loud barking and growling. "What's that?" asked the Country Mouse.

"Oh, those are only the master's dogs," replied the City Mouse. "But run for your life. We can come back after they've gone." And she jumped off the table and scampered down the handiest mouse hole, with the Country Mouse behind her, just an inch ahead of one of the dogs.

"We'll wait here till it's quiet again upstairs, and then we can return to our feast," whispered the City Mouse.

But the Country Mouse, her heart still fluttering with fright, shook her head. At last, when everything seemed quiet, the Country Mouse stole out of their hiding place and bade her friend goodby, saying, "You are welcome to all the fine food you can get, my dear. As for me, I'd rather nibble my dried crusts in peace and safety than eat the daintiest feast in fear and trembling."

A crust eaten in peace is preferable to a feast partaken in fear and danger.

THE LION AND THE MOUSE

ONE DAY a Lion lay asleep in the jungle. A tiny Mouse, running about in the grass and not noticing where he was going, ran over the Lion's head and down his nose.

The Lion awoke with a loud roar, and down came his paw over the little Mouse. The great beast was about to open his huge jaws to swallow the tiny creature when "Pardon me, O King, I beg of you," cried the frightened Mouse. "If you will only forgive me this time, I shall never forget your kindness. I meant no harm and I certainly didn't want to disturb Your Majesty. If you will spare my life, perhaps I may be able to do you a good turn, too."

The Lion began to laugh, and he laughed and laughed. "How could a tiny creature like you ever do anything to help *me?*" And he shook with laughter.

"Oh well," he shrugged, looking down at the frightened Mouse, "you're not so much of a meal anyway." He took his paw off the poor little prisoner and the

Mouse quickly scampered away.

Some time after this, some hunters, trying to capture the Lion alive so they could carry him to their king, set up rope nets in the jungle. The Lion, who was hunting for some food, fell into the trap. He roared and thrashed about trying to free himself but with every move he made, the ropes bound him tighter.

The unhappy Lion feared he could never escape, and he roared pitifully. His thunderous bellows echoed through the jungle. The tiny Mouse, scurrying about far away, heard the Lion's roars. "That may be the very Lion who once freed me," he said, remembering his promise.

And he ran to see whether he could help.

Discovering the sad state the Lion was in, the Mouse said to him, "Stop, Stop! You must not roar. If you make so much noise, the hunters will come and capture you. I'll get you out of this trap."

With his sharp little teeth the Mouse gnawed at the ropes until they broke. When the Lion had stepped out of the net and was free once more, the Mouse said, "Now, was I not right?"

"Thank you, good Mouse," said the Lion gently. "You did help me even though I am big and you are so little. I see now that kindness is always worth while."

Even the strong sometimes need the friendship of the weak.

THE HARE AND THE TORTOISE

ONCE there was a Hare who used to laugh scornfully at a Tortoise because he plodded along so slowly. "You never can get anywhere with those short legs of yours. Look at my long legs! They're so swift no one would dare race me."

All the animals of field and forest were tired of hearing the Hare brag. At last the Tortoise said, "If we were to run a race, I'm sure I would beat you."

The animals were astonished for they knew the Tortoise was the slowest of them all, and the Hare, bursting into loud laughter, cried, "What a joke! That slow-poke thinks he can beat me! Come on, then, Mr. Tortoise, you shall see what my feet are made of. Why I can beat you before you are even half-started!"

"You'd better not be too sure," cautioned the Tortoise.

All the big and little animals gathered to watch the race. At the signal the Hare leaped forward in a great bound and soon left the plodding Tortoise far behind him on the dusty road. Looking back, the Hare could not even see the Tortoise after a little while.

"Hum-m, I've as good as won this race already," he thought. "There's really no reason to hurry." So, as the sun was very warm, he decided to rest a bit under a shady tree. "I'll come in away ahead of

that Tortoise, anyhow," he told himself.

Soon he was sound asleep. The little rest stretched into a good long nap.

Meantime the Tortoise jogged steadily along on the hot, dusty road, ever so slowly, but surely, and soon he passed the Hare who was still peacefully sleeping.

Quietly the Tortoise plodded on nearing the goal. When the Hare finally woke up with a start, he saw the Tortoise just reaching the finish line far ahead and he could hear all the animals cheering the winner.

Boastful and careless, the Hare had lost the race. Now he would never again be able to count on his speed.

Perseverance wins the race.

THE DOG IN THE MANGER

A Dog, once looking for a quiet and comfortable place to take a nap, jumped into a manger in a stable and lay there cosily on the hay. He was awakened by the cattle which came in tired and hungry after a hard day's work in the field.

One by one, a Horse, a Cow, a Sheep, and a Goat approached the manger to eat the hay. But the Dog would not let them get near it, he snarled and snapped as if it were filled with the finest of meat and bones, all for himself. He kept growling at them and would not let them have as much as a mouthful of hay.

Then an Ox came and looked in, and the Dog barked at him, too.

"You selfish fellow," said the Ox. "You cannot eat the hay, and yet you won't let us who are so hungry for it eat it either."

Do not begrudge to others what you cannot enjoy yourself.

THE FOX AND THE GRAPES

ONE hot summer's day a Fox was strolling through an orchard. He was famished and very thirsty too. Just then he spied a beautiful bunch of sun-ripened grapes hanging high on a vine trained along the branches of a tall tree. The grapes were bursting with juice and the Fox's mouth watered.

"Just the thing to quench my thirst," thought he as he jumped for them. But he missed by a long way. So he walked off a short distance and took a running leap toward the luscious cluster only to fall short once more.

Again and again he jumped, but each time he just missed the delicious prize. At last, worn out with his useless efforts, the Fox stalked off, nose in the air, muttering scornfully, "Well, I never wanted those grapes anyway. I am sure they are sour."

Some people pretend to despise what they cannot have.

THE WOLF IN SHEEP'S CLOTHING

A WOLF, once upon a time, found it so hard to get close enough to attack a flock of Sheep that he often went hungry. For a long time the Shepherd had guarded his Lambs and Sheep so carefully that the Wolf was becoming desperate.

a little distance apart from the rest of the flock, the Wolf in sheep's clothing made a good meal off her. For a while he succeeded in deceiving the other Sheep and enjoying hearty meals.

Even the Shepherd was fooled by the

One night the Wolf found a sheepskin that had been thrown away and forgotten. The Wolf resolved to disguise himself and so gain an easy living. Quickly he slipped the sheepskin over his own hide and next morning strolled into the pasture with the grazing Sheep as if he were one of them.

Soon the Lamb that had belonged to the Sheep whose skin the Wolf was wearing began to follow the Wolf. Leading her

Wolf in disguise, for when evening came, the Wolf in Sheep's clothing was shut up with the Sheep in their fold.

But it happened that the Shepherd had a longing for mutton broth for his supper that night. Picking up a knife, he went to the fold, and reaching in, seized the first animal he came to. Mistaking the Wolf for a Sheep, the Shepherd killed him on the spot.

Appearances are often deceiving.

THE BUNDLE OF STICKS

THERE was once a Farmer with several Sons who could never agree among themselves. He had often told them how foolish they were to be always quarreling, but they kept on and paid no attention to his advice.

One day the Father called his Sons before him and showed them a bundle of sticks tied tightly together. "See which one of you can break this bundle in two," he commanded.

Each Son in turn took the bundle in his hands and tried his best to break it. They all tried, but in vain, for the bundle was so strong that not one of them could even bend it. At last they gave it back to their Father saying, "We cannot break it."

Then the Father untied the bundle and gave a single stick to each of his Sons. "Now see what you can do," he said. Each one broke his stick with the greatest ease.

"My Sons," said the wise Father, "you, like these sticks, will be strong if you stand together; but once you quarrel and become separated, then you are destroyed."

In unity there is strength.

ONCE there was a young Shepherd Boy who watched his Father's flock of Sheep from morning till night in a lonely pasture. The pasture was on the slope of a mountain near a dark forest.

All day the Boy would watch his Sheep, and as the days went by he used to wish that something might happen to make watching Sheep less dull. "It would be fun if Wolves came and attacked the Sheep. Then everyone would come rushing out and there would be far more excitement around here," he thought.

One warm summer day, as the Sheep were quietly grazing, he decided he would play a trick on his neighbors and see what would happen. He rushed down toward the village, waving his arms and crying out at the top of his voice, "Wolf, Wolf! Help! The Wolves are after my Lambs!"

Down below in the village, the men and boys dropped their work and stopped everything they were doing. They seized their axes and pitchforks and rushed toward the pasture to get after the Wolf, who, they thought, would be killing the Sheep.

But while they were still a little distance away, they could see the Sheep quietly cropping the grass. As they came toward the Shepherd Boy asking "Where is the Wolf?" he burst out laughing. "Ha, Ha! I fooled you that time. There was no Wolf!"

The villagers were very angry because they had had to leave their work, and run to the pasture on such a warm day. They warned the Boy he must never do such a thing again.

For a long time he did not. But one day, he was lonelier than ever. So again he shouted at the very top of his lungs, "Wolf! Wolf!"

Again the men and boys of the village dropped their work and whatever they were doing. Again they seized their axes and pitchforks and rushed to the pasture to help the Shepherd Boy.

And just as before, when they came to the pasture, there were the Sheep peacefully grazing as though nothing could ever disturb them. The Boy laughed loudly, "It was only a joke!" This time the villagers were angrier than before. They told him he must never try to fool them again.

So the Boy promised.

But one day, as he sat under a tree watching his Sheep, he saw a big gray Wolf come slinking out of the dark forest. The Shepherd Boy was dreadfully frightened, and ran toward the village shouting more loudly than ever before, "Wolf! Wolf! Wolf!"

He shouted again with all his might, "WOLF! WOLF! WOLF!" But the villagers, who had been fooled twice, did not want to be fooled again. There had been no Wolf when the Boy had shouted for help before, and they did not believe there was one now. So they just smiled and went on with their work.

The Shepherd Boy kept on shouting, but the villagers paid no attention. The hungry Wolf killed Sheep after Sheep, but there was nothing the Boy could do.

The Boy had cried "Wolf" once too often. But he had learned a sad lesson.

Those who lie are not believed even when they tell the truth.

Other Fables

THE CAMEL AND THE PIG

A Camel said, "There is nothing like being tall! See how tall I am."

A Pig who heard these words said, "*I think there is nothing like being short. See how short I am!*"

The Camel said, "Well, if I fail to prove how much better it is to be tall than short, I will give you my hump."

The Pig said, "If I fail to prove that it is better to be short than tall, I will give you my snout."

"Agreed!" said the Camel.

"Just so!" said the Pig.

They came to a garden enclosed by a low wall without any opening. The Camel stood outside the wall, and, reaching the plants within by means of his long neck, made a breakfast on them. Then he turned to the Pig, who had been standing at the bottom of the wall without being able even to look at the good things in the garden. "Now, would you rather be tall or short?" the Camel asked him.

The Pig shook his head sadly, and the two walked on. Soon they came to a garden enclosed by a high wall with a wicket gate at one end. The Pig entered by the gate, and, after having eaten his fill of the vegetables within, came out laughing at the poor Camel who had had to stay outside because he was too tall to get in to the garden by the gate. "Now, would you rather be tall or short?" the Pig asked the Camel.

They both thought the matter over and came to the conclusion that the Camel should keep his hump and the Pig his snout, observing:

*Tall is good where tall will do;
But short is just as useful too.*

22

THE OAK AND THE REED

By Jean de La Fontaine

A STOUT Oak, looking down on a slim Reed, said, "Nature has certainly been unkind to you. She has made you so frail that the gentlest breeze can sway you, the smallest bird can bend you. Look at me: I am so strong I can weather a tempest, even a hurricane! But poor little you—if you lived nearer to me, beneath the shelter of my strength, I could save you from the storms that are so cruel to you. But, alas, nature has left you unprotected along the marshy borders of the stream. She has indeed been unjust to you."

"I appreciate your concern," replied the Reed, "but I do not need your pity. You have your defenses but I have mine too."

At that very moment a great north wind rushed down and flung itself in fury on the Oak and on the Reed. Swaying in the blast the Reed bent her head before it. But the Oak, defying the wind, stood straight and unbending in the very teeth of the tempest.

The mighty wind, redoubling its efforts, smote the Oak with furious force and, tearing it up by its stubborn roots, laid it low.

Having done its worst, the storm passed on, and in the quiet that followed the Reed raised its slender head and looked sadly at the giant Oak whose stately crown lay in the waters of the stream.

It is often well to bend before a storm to avoid being broken by it.

THE COUNCIL OF ANIMALS

ONCE upon a time a great many different kinds of animals lived in the same forest. Each one thought he was better than the others.

"See how courageous I am!" boasted the Lion. "It is my courage that makes me the king of beasts."

"What good is courage," scoffed the Fox, "if you don't know how to use it? I'm the clever one around here, and sly too. That's how I get so much to eat."

The Peacock, spreading his tail into a great beautifully-colored fan, gazed with admiration at his reflection in a pond. "Neither strength nor cleverness can compare with beauty," he remarked. "It is my magnificent beauty that makes everyone in the forest envy me and bow down before me."

"But the thing that counts the most is value," trumpeted the Elephant. "Look at these ivory tusks of mine. They are

worth a fortune. They make me the most valuable animal in the forest."

A little Toad who lived secure in a crack of the big rock close by, and who felt he had nothing to be particularly conceited about himself, listened to the boasting of the other animals.

"But see," he remarked, "how vain all these boasts are! The Lion's courage leads him to venture into dangerous places so that the hunter kills him. The Fox's cleverness doesn't help him a bit when he has been trapped for his fur. As for the beauty of the Peacock's tail and the value of the Elephant's tusk, these are both things that men covet and crave and will pay any price to obtain. Hence the ruin of the Peacock and the Elephant."

Boasting is vain and may defeat itself.

THE ADVANTAGE OF KNOWLEDGE

By Jean de La Fontaine

A RICH man and a poor man lived side by side in a town of olden France. The rich man had a fine house and garden, horses and carriages, and many servants to wait on him. But he was ignorant and stupid. The other man, though poor in gold and silver, was rich in knowledge and understanding. His learning and wisdom gave him the means for understanding people and for appreciating the difference between ugliness and beauty, and between evil and good.

The two men argued endlessly. The rich man said that money counted more than anything else in the world because if you had money you could buy whatever you wanted with it. "What good is all your wisdom," he often asked his neighbor, "if you haven't the money to buy the things you need?"

The wise poor man was too wise to try to explain his point of view to the stupid rich man who was quite incapable of understanding it.

One day war broke out. The whole town was in ruins after the fighting stopped, and both men, stripped of everything and fleeing for their lives, had to seek refuge in another place.

The rich man, without his money or his belongings, was poor indeed, for he now had nothing. Wherever he went he was scorned for his ignorance and stupidity.

But the wise man still had his learning and his wisdom. Nothing could ever take from him the rich store of knowledge in his mind and in his heart. Everywhere he went he was received with honor.

Knowledge is power.

THE LION AND THE GOAT

A GREEDY Lion had been eating up the animals of a certain country as fast as he could catch them.

The Goat, who was the chief of the animals, decided one day that this must stop. "I shall have to find a way of sending that Lion out of the country," he said to himself.

Crawling into a large cave opening onto the roadside, the Goat lay in wait, hoping the Lion would soon come by.

Sure enough, on his way to the village not long afterward, the Lion passed the cave and saw the Goat with his flowing beard and curved horns.

"What are you doing there?" asked the Lion.

"Oh," replied the Goat, "I have been

waiting for you. You see, I have eaten up a hundred Elephants, a hundred Tigers, and a hundred Wolves, but only ninety-nine Lions. I need just one more Lion to make it a hundred. The gods are good to me to have sent you here." And the Goat shook his horns and stroked his beard before making a leap as though to spring upon the Lion.

Hastily the Lion retreated. "This creature looks like a Goat," he said to himself, "but he doesn't talk like one. He is probably some wicked spirit in the form of a Goat. Caution is often the better part of valor; I think I shall not proceed to the village but return to my home in the woods—fast."

"I am sorry you are in such a hurry," said the Goat from his cave. "Will you be back tomorrow?"

"I will not," replied the Lion, running faster.

"Then I shall have to come looking for you in the wood," said the Goat.

But as he disappeared, the Lion called back, "You won't find me in the wood, or here, or anywhere else in this country, ever again!"

Fear makes even the bravest cowardly.

THE ROOSTER AND THE SUN

THERE was once a Rooster who lived in a country of the far East. Early every morning he crowed loudly, "Cock-a-doodle-do!" And he was sure his crowing was the signal by which the sun rose every day.

With enormous pride he puffed himself out, thinking "How important I am! If it were not for my crowing, the sun would not know when to rise."

One night he decided to find out what would happen if he failed to give the sun his signal. So toward dawn, just before the time when he usually began crowing, he rolled over, shut his eyes, and went to sleep again.

When he awoke there was the sun shining brightly as ever. But the Rooster refused to believe that the sun would have known when to rise without help of some kind from him. "I know what must have happened," he told himself. "Some other Rooster imitated my voice and the sun thought it was my crowing he heard."

Believing one falsehood leads to believing others.

Cheerful Tales
and Verses

How Cats Came to Purr

By John Bennett

A BOY having a Pet Cat which he Wished to Feed, Said to Her. "Come, Cat, Drink this Dish of Cream; it will Keep your Fur as Soft as Silk, and Make you Purr like a Coffee-Mill."

He had no sooner said this than the Cat, with a Great Glare of her Green Eyes, bristled her Tail like a Gun-Swab, and went over the Back Fence, head first —pop!—as Mad as a Wet Hen.

And this is how she came to do so:

The story is an old one—very, very old. It may be Persian; it may be not: that is of very little moment. It is so old that if all the nine lives of all the cats that have ever lived in the world were set up together in a line, the other end of it would just reach back to the time when this occurred.

And this is the story:

Many, many years ago, in a country which was quite as far from anywhere else as the entire distance thither and back, there was a huge cat that ground the coffee in the King's kitchen, and otherwise assisted with the meals.

This cat was, in truth, the actual and very father of all subsequent cats, and his name was Sooty Will, for his hair was as black as a night in a coal-hole. He was ninety years old, and his mustaches were like whisk-brooms. But the most singular thing about him was that in all his life he

had never once purred nor humped up his back, although his master often stroked him. The fact was that he never had learned to purr, nor had any reason, so far as he knew, for humping up his back. And being the father of all the cats, there was no one to tell him how. It remained for him to acquire a reason, and from his example to devise a habit which cats have followed from that time forth, and no doubt will forever follow.

28

The King of the country had long been at war with one of his neighbors; but one morning he sent back a messenger to say that he had beaten his foeman at last, and that he was coming home for an early breakfast as hungry as three bears. "Have batter-cake and coffee," he directed, "hot and plenty of 'em!"

At that the turnspits capered and yelped with glee, for batter-cakes and coffee are not cooked upon spits, and so they were free to sally forth into the city streets and watch the King's home-coming in a grand parade.

But the cat sat down on his tail in the corner and looked cross. "Scat!" said he, with an angry caterwaul. "It is not fair that you should go and that I should not."

"Oh, yes, it is," said the gleeful turnspits; "turn and turn about is fair play: you saw the rat that was killed in the parlor."

"Turn about fair play, indeed!" cried the cat. "Then all of you get to your spits; I am sure that is turn about!"

"Nay," said the turnspits, wagging their tails and laughing. "That is over and over again, which is not fair play. 'Tis the coffee-mill that is turn and turn about. So turn about to your mill, Sooty Will; we are off to see the King!"

With that they pranced out into the court-yard, turning hand-springs, head-springs, and heel-springs as they went, and, after giving three hearty and vociferous cheers in a grand chorus at the bottom of the garden, went capering away for their holiday.

The cat spat at their vanishing heels, sat down on his tail in the chimney-corner, and was very glum indeed.

Just then the cook looked in from the pantry. "Hullo!" he said gruffly. "Come, hurry up the coffee!" That was the way he always gave his orders.

The black cat's whiskers bristled. He

turned to the mill with a fierce frown, his long tail going to and fro like that of a tiger in its lair; for Sooty Will had a temper like hot gunpowder, that was apt to go off sizz, whizz, bang! and no one to save the pieces. Yet, at least while the cook was by, he turned the mill furiously, as if with a right goodwill.

Meantime, out in the city, a glorious day came on. The sun went buzzing up the pink-and-yellow sky with a sound like that of a walking-doll's works, or of a big Dutch clock behind a door; banners waved from the castled heights, and bugles sang from every tower; the city gates rang with the cheers of the enthusiastic crowd. Up from cellars, down from lofts, off work-benches, and out at the doors of their masters' shops, dodging the thwacks of their masters' straps, "pop-popping" like corks from the necks of so many bottles, came apprentices, shop-boys, knaves and scullions, crying: "God save the King! Hurrah, Hurrah! Masters and work may go to Rome; our tasks shall wait on our own sweet wills; 'tis holiday when the King comes home. God save the King! Hurrah!"

Then came the procession. There were first three regiments of trumpeters, all blowing different tunes; then fifteen regiments of mounted infantry on coal-black horses, forty squadrons of green-and-blue dragoons, and a thousand drummers and fifers in scarlet and blue and gold, making a thundering din with their rootle-te-tootle-te-tootle-te-rootle; and pretty well up to the front in the ranks was the King himself, bowing and smiling to the populace, with his hand on his breast; and after him the army, all in shining armor, just enough pounded to be picturesque, miles on miles of splendid men, all bearing the trophies of glorious war, and armed with lances, and bows and arrows, falchions, morgensterns, martels-de-fer, and other choice implements of justifiable homicide, and the reverse, such as

30

hautboys and sackbuts and accordions and dudelsacks and Scotch bagpipes—a glorious sight!

And, as has been said before, the city gates rang with the cheers of the crowd, crimson banners waved over the city's pinnacled summits, and bugles blew, trumpets brayed, and drums beat until it seemed that wild uproar and rich display had reached its high millennium.

The black cat turned the coffee-mill. "My oh! My oh!" he said. "It certainly is not fair that those bench-legged turnspits with feet like so much leather should see the King marching home in his glory, while I, who go shod, as it were, in velvet, should hear only the sound through the scullery windows. It is not fair. It is no

doubt true that 'The cat may mew, and the dog shall have his day,' but I have as much right to my day as he; and has it not been said from immemorial time that 'A cat may look at a king'? Indeed it has, quite as much as that the dog may have his day. I will not stand it; it is not fair. A cat may look at a king; and if any cat may look at a king, why, I am the cat who may. There are no other cats in the world; I am the only one. Poh! The cook may shout till his breath gives out, he cannot frighten me; for once I am going to have my fling!"

So he forthwith swallowed the coffee-mill, box, handle, drawer-knobs, coffee-well, and all, and was off to see the King.

So far, so good. But, ah! the sad and undeniable truth, that brightest joys too soon must end! Triumphs cannot last for-ever, even in a land of legends. There comes a reckoning.

When the procession was past and gone, as all processions pass and go, van-ishing down the shores of forgetfulness; when barons, marquises, dukes, and dons were gone, with their pennants and ban-ners; when the last lancers had gone prancing past and were lost to sight down the circuitous avenue, Sooty Will, with drooping tail, stood by the palace gate, dejected. He was sour and silent and glum. Indeed, who would not be, with a coffee-mill on his conscience? To own up to the entire truth, the cat was feeling decidedly unwell. When suddenly the cook popped his head in at the scullery entry, crying, "How now, how now, you vagabonds! The war is done, but the breakfast is not. Hurry up, scurry up, scamper and trot! The cakes are all cooked and are piping hot! Then why is the coffee so slow?"

The King was in the dining-hall, in dressing-gown and slippers, irately call-ing for his breakfast!

The shamefaced, guilty cat ran hastily down the scullery stairs and hid under the refrigerator, with such a deep inward sensation of remorse that he dared not look the kind cook in the face. It now really seemed to him as if everything had gone wrong with the world, especially his own insides. This any one will readily believe who has ever swallowed a coffee-mill. He began to weep copiously.

The cook came into the kitchen. "Where is the coffee?" he said. Then, catching sight of the secluded cat, he stooped, crying, "Where is the coffee?"

The cat sobbed audibly. "Some one must have come into the kitchen while I ran out to look at the King!" he gasped, for there seemed to him no way out of the scrape but by telling a plausible un-truth. "Some one must have come into the kitchen and stolen it!" And with that, choking upon the handle of the mill, which projected into his throat, he burst into inarticulate sobs.

The cook, who was, in truth, a very kind-hearted man, sought to reassure the poor cat. "There; it is unfortunate, very; but do not weep; thieves thrive in kings' houses!" he said, and, stooping, he began to stroke the drooping cat's back to show he held the weeping creature blameless.

Sooty Will's heart leaped into his throat.

"Oh, oh!" he half gasped, "oh, oh! If he rubs his great hands down my back he will feel the corners of the coffee-mill through my ribs as sure as fate! Oh, oh! I am a gone cat!" And with that, in an agony of apprehension lest his guilt and his falsehood be thus presently detected, he humped up his back as high in the air as he could, so that the corners of the mill might not make bumps in his sides and that the mill might thus remain un-discovered.

But, alas! he forgot that coffee-mills turn. As he humped up his back to cover his guilt, the coffee-mill inside rolled over, and, as it rolled, began to grind—*rr-rr-rr-rr-rr-rr-rr-rr-rr-rr!*

"Oh, oh! You have swallowed the mill!" cried the cook.

"No, no," cried the cat, "I was only thinking aloud."

At that out stepped the Genius that Lived under the Great Ovens, and, with his finger pointed at the cat, said in a frightful voice, husky with wood-ashes: "Miserable and pusillanimous beast! By telling a falsehood to cover a wrong you have only made bad matters worse. For betraying man's kindness to cover your day Sooty Will could never abide having his back stroked without humping it up to conceal the mill within him; and never did he hump up his back but the coffee-mill began slowly to grind, *rr-rr-rr-rr!* inside him; so that, even in the prime of life, before his declining days had come, being seized upon by a great re-

shame, a curse shall be upon you and all your kind until the end of the world. Whenever men stroke you in kindness, remembrance of your guilt shall make you hump up your back with shame, as you did to avoid being found out. And in order that the reason for this curse shall never be forgotten, whenever man is kind to a cat the sound of the grinding of a coffee-mill inside shall perpetually remind him of your guilt and shame!"

With that the Genius vanished in a cloud of smoke.

And it was even as he said. From that morse for these things that might never be amended, he retired to a home for aged and reputable cats, and there, so far as the records reveal, lived the remainder of his days in charity and repentance.

But the curse has come down even to the present day—as the Genius that Lived under the Great Ovens said—and still maintains, though cats have probably forgotten the facts, and so, when stroked, hump up their backs and purr as if these actions were a matter of pride instead of being a blot upon their family record.

The Seven Little Tigers and the Aged Cook

By Laura E. Richards

SEVEN little tigers they sat them in a row,
Their seven little dinners for to eat;
And each of the troop had a little plate of soup,
The effect of which was singularly neat.

They were feeling rather cross, for they hadn't any sauce,
To eat with their pudding or their pie;
So they rumpled up their hair, in a spasm of despair,
And vowed that the aged cook should die.

Then they called the aged cook, and a frying-pan they took,
To fry him very nicely for their supper;
He was ninety-six years old, on authority I'm told,
And his name was Peter Sparrow-piper Tupper.

"Mr. Sparrow-piper Tup, we intend on you to sup!"
Said the eldest little tiger very sweetly;
But this naughty aged cook, just remarking, "Only look!"
Chopped the little tiger's head off very neatly.

Then he said unto the rest, "It has always been confessed
That a tiger's better eating than a man;
So I'll fry him for you now, and you will find, I trow,
That to eat him will be much the better plan."

So they tried it in a trice, and found that it was nice,
And with rapture they embracèd one another;
And they said, "By hook or crook, we must keep this aged cook;
So we'll ask him to become our elder brother!"

(Which they accordingly did.)

34

Mr. Scrunch

THE STORY OF AN INVENTOR AND HIS ANIMAL FRIENDS

Written and Illustrated by Helen and Alf Evers

Mr. JASPER SCRUNCH was a very famous inventor. Kindness shone from his pink face, which was set off by white hair and whiskers.

But Mr. Scrunch was clever as well as kind. So he had spent his life inventing thousands of machines to help people and to make them happier. His machines

made it easier for people to work, easier for them to play, and even easier for them to do nothing at all.

Mr. Scrunch invented a dresser and undresser. This clever machine, which looked like a comfortable chair, could take off or put on the clothes of anyone

sitting in it, in a few seconds. It could also sew on missing buttons, mend tears, and remove spots and stains while it dressed or undressed.

This machine was sold all over the world, except in those uncivilized places, such as the South Sea Islands, where people don't wear enough clothes to make it worth while.

Mr. Scrunch was also the inventor of a sled which could coast uphill even faster than it could downhill.

A few more of Mr. Scrunch's inventions were a self-making bed, a rocking chair which rocked itself, and for very *lazy* people, a game-playing machine, which played baseball, tennis, cards, or croquet for them.

These inventions made Mr. Scrunch rich.

But Mr. Scrunch worked so very, very hard at inventing things to keep other people from working that he became very tired. His friends insisted that he take a vacation.

So the inventor bought a quiet little farm, on a quiet little road near a quiet little village, and went there to take a long rest. When Mr. Scrunch reached the farm, he hired two men to do the farm work. Then he sat down on the steps and did nothing for ten minutes.

As Mr. Scrunch sat on the steps, doing

36

nothing, he saw four little pigs racing round and round the barn. One of the pigs was always last, because he had very short legs. Mr. Scrunch felt sorry for him.

So he coaxed the pig into the house with a bowl of milk and a banana. Then, while the pig was busy eating, Mr. Scrunch thought hard and invented something to help the short-legged pig run faster. The invention was remarkably simple. It was just four little stilts with straps to hold them in place.

First, kind Mr. Scrunch tested the stilts himself. It was so much fun that he hated to take them off.

Then he put the stilts on the pig. Away went the little pig, tumbling down at every step. Down went chairs and tables, lamps and pictures.

And down went Mr. Scrunch. The pig raced faster and faster as he learned how to manage the stilts. At last he vanished through the open door.

Mr. Scrunch sat on the floor, a picture frame around his neck and a lamp cord around his legs.

"Dear me!" he murmured. "That worked altogether too well, but never mind, it has given me a *tremendous idea.*"

"All these years," said Mr. Scrunch unwinding the lamp cord, "I have been inventing things to help people, but I have never thought of making inventions to help animals do their work and enjoy their play. Someone must do it," he said solemnly, "and that someone will be me."

So the inventor removed the picture frame from his neck and began .

First, he invented prettier and more comfortable hats for the horses to wear in hot weather.

Then he invented an automatic fly-swatter, to save the horses the trouble of swishing their tails all day in hot weather. As the swatter revolved, it produced a gentle breeze which kept the horses cool, even on the hottest day.

Mr. Scrunch hated to see the hens sleeping at night clinging to their hard roost. So he invented comfortable beds with soft pillows for them.

He invented little sails for the ducks to use on the pond, so that they would not have to work so hard at swimming.

And finally Mr. Scrunch invented a grazing machine for Belle, the old cow.

For a long time Mr. Scrunch had felt

sorry for cows, because they had to work so hard grazing. It didn't seem right to him that cows should spend most of the day with their faces practically on the ground, tugging away at the grass and sometimes picking up insects, thorns, sand, or even stones, by mistake.

So Mr. Scrunch invented a machine, something like a lawn mower, with a fan in front and a basket on top, to be strapped to Belle. As Belle walked, the mower cut the grass, the fan blew everything but the grass away, and all Belle had to do was to eat from the basket right in front of her mouth.

But when the horses had their hats and automatic fly swatters they had so little to do, when they were in the pasture in the summer, that they couldn't stand it.

So they jumped over the fence into Mr.

Scrunch's fine cornfield and ate and ate cornstalks until they became very sick.

Then the veterinary had to come and cure them with some bitter medicine.

When the hens tried their new beds they found them so comfortable that they couldn't get up in the morning and get to work laying eggs.

When the ducks were fitted out with their sails a breeze came up, and they just whirled round and round the ponds like tops until they became dizzy.

And Belle, the cow, loved the old way of grazing and hated Mr. Scrunch's grazing machine so much that when she first tried it she became so angry that she raced across the fields, kicking her heels in the air, with Mr. Scrunch after her.

She crossed the road and raced right through the poppies and roses in Mrs. Green's garden, leaving a smooth path behind her and chopped-up flowers flying through the air.

On she went through Mr. Jenkins' vegetable patch, mowing down the neat rows of carrots and lettuce.

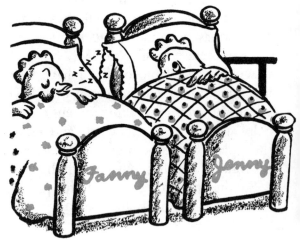

And on she raced across the lawn where Mrs. Anderson had spread her best cloths and napkins to bleach in the sun.

The chopped-up bits of white cloth swirled in the air around Belle like snowflakes in a blizzard.

At last, with a crash that could be heard for miles, Belle smashed the grazing machine against a stone wall. Then she felt much better.

Mr. Scrunch came up, puffing and panting. First he paid Mrs. Green, Mrs. Anderson, and Mr. Jenkins, who had arrived full of anger and threats, for the damage done by the grazing machine.

As he led Belle home, Mr. Scrunch patted her affectionately.

"Dear me," he murmured. "This is all too bad, but never mind, it has given me an idea for a tremendous invention to help animals."

For days Mr. Scrunch slaved away at his invention, hardly stopping to eat or sleep. It looked like an immense box, with a sort of coffee mill on top. When it was finished he put it in the barnyard and called all the animals together.

Mr. Scrunch took the stilts from the pig, the sails from the ducks, the beds from the henhouse, and the hats and automatic fly swatters from the horses. He put them all, one by one, in the top of the machine. Then he pressed a button.

There was a sighing, wheezing noise from inside the machine. A little puff of blue smoke popped out, hovered over the machine for a moment, and slowly sailed away.

This was all that was left of Mr. Scrunch's invention for animals.

"Hurrah," cried Mr. Scrunch, "for the last and best of my inventions for animals —Scrunch's Universal Uninventor for Useless Inventions!"

Then Mr. Scrunch put one arm around

Belle and the other on one of the horses. A chicken flew to the top of his head and a happy duck to his shoulder, while a pig rubbed his side against the inventor's legs.

"At last," said Mr. Scrunch in a voice made unsteady by emotion, "at last I have invented something that has helped all of you and made you happy. All my work has not been in vain."

And then kind Mr. Scrunch, with a smile on his face, went to the house, sat down on the steps, and did nothing at all for a long, long time.

A Legend of Lake Okeefinokee

By Laura E. Richards

There once was a frog,
And he lived in a bog,
On the banks of Lake Okeefinokee.
And the words of the song
That he sang all day long
Were, "Croakety croakety croaky."

Said the frog, "I have found
That my life's daily round
In this place is exceedingly poky.
So no longer I'll stop,
But I swiftly will hop
Away from Lake Okeefinokee."

Now a bad mocking-bird
By mischance overheard
The words of the frog as he spokee.
And he said, "All my life
Frog and I've been at strife,
As we lived by Lake Okeefinokee.

"Now I see at a glance
Here's a capital chance
For to play him a practical jokee;
So I'll venture to say
That he shall not to-day
Leave the banks of Lake Okeefinokee."

So this bad mocking-bird,
Without saying a word,
He flew to a tree which was oaky;
And loudly he sang,
Till the whole forest rang,
"Oh! Croakety croakety croaky!"

As he warbled this song,
Master Frog came along,
A-filling his pipe for to smokee;
And he said, " 'Tis some frog
Has escaped from the bog
Of Okeefinokee-finokee.

"I am filled with amaze
To hear a frog raise
His voice on the top of an oaky;
But if frogs can climb trees,
I may still find some ease
On the banks of Lake Okeefinokee."

So he climbed up the tree;
But, alas, down fell he!
And his lovely green neck it was brokee;
And the sad truth to say,
Never more did he stray
From the banks of Lake Okeefinokee.

And the bad mocking-bird
Said, "How very absurd
And delightful a practical jokee!"
But I'm happy to say
He was drowned the next day
In the waters of Okeefinokee.

No Room

Retold by Rose Dobbs

Not so long ago, perhaps in your father's time, if not, then in his father's time, there lived a selfish old peasant and his wife in the smallest hut the world had ever seen. It was a one-room hut. In it there was space only for bare necessities: a bed, a bench, a couple of stools, a table, a cupboard. The old man never made anyone welcome, so he did not find it necessary to increase his meagre possessions. It happened, however, that times grew hard. Work became scarce, and soon Hunger and Want began to poke their skinny fingers and gaunt faces into many a window and doorway.

One day the peasant received a letter from his daughter. The letter asked if the daughter, her husband, and their little baby might not come and stay with the old couple. The husband was out of work and things were going badly with them.

"Stay with us!" cried the selfish peasant. "Now, here is a thing. Where shall we put three people in this small hut that has no room?"

"They can sleep in our bed," said the wife, "and we will make ourselves a nice soft bed of straw on the floor."

"We will do nothing of the kind," protested the peasant. "I am an old man and sleeping on straw will be none too good for my weary bones."

"See," urged the wife, "you will be able to take long rests, and I will have time to keep you comfortable, for our son-in-law will do the work in the fields, our daughter help in the house, and—"

"Enough!" cried the old man. "I'll hear no more about it. We cannot afford in these hard times to give food and lodging to three."

The wife's heart was troubled, but nothing would move the selfish old man. Soon, however, came another letter, more pleading, more urgent, and the poor old mother could not let it go unanswered.

"Well, then," said she, "in these hard times how bitter it is if parents will not help their own children."

"In these hard times," said the old man tartly, "how bitter it is if children who are young and strong and healthy will yield to laziness and add to the burdens of their poor old parents."

"Now let us stop throwing empty words back and forth," said the old woman. "Let us ask the Wise Man's advice and let us abide by it."

And because she kept at him, the old man grudgingly consented.

Now in that village there was no judge or magistrate or police force. The people were governed by the counsel of a Wise Man. According to legend, dreadful punishment befell any who dared to disobey him, but as no one within living memory had ever disobeyed him, no one knew what the punishment might be. And truth to tell, no one cared to find out.

So early the next morning, the selfish old peasant set out for the Wise Man's house. After a long, long walk he reached it and stood at the door twirling his cap.

The Wise Man was seated in front of his fire, reading a big, black book.

my old woman and I, living as best we can in these hard times in a very little hut with no room to spare and—" he hesitated—"and our daughter and her lazy husband who will not work, and their child ask leave to come and stay with us."

The Wise Man looked steadily at him.

"What shall I do?" asked the peasant.

"Peace to this house and to all within it," said the peasant.

"And may you find peace," said the Wise Man. "Come in, my friend."

A sigh that came from the peasant's very soul escaped him as he came in.

"Alas," he wailed, "how can I know the meaning of the word? Here we are,

"Hm. Take your daughter and her husband and their little baby into your hut," said the Wise Man shortly.

The old peasant could not believe his ears, but he did not dare question the Wise Man, so with heavy feet he trudged wearily and wrathfully home and with many grumblings and mutterings wrote

43

to his daughter—and shortly afterwards all three arrived.

The young husband gathered big armfuls of soft straw and made a bed on the floor for the old couple. He rose early each morning and worked all day long in the forest and fields. The daughter cooked, and cleaned the hut, and took care of the baby. The peasant had nothing to do but demand attention. He was waited on hand and foot; nevertheless he filled the little hut with his wails and lamentations. He complained until his wife could bear it no longer.

"Go then," said she, "again to the Wise Man. Tell him how things are."

So he went, and he stood once more before the Wise Man, and he said:

"Peace to this house and to all in it."

"And may you find peace," said the Wise Man.

"Alas," sighed the peasant, "how can I know the meaning of the word? Not only must I crowd three lusty persons into my little hut and give them food and lodging besides, but my old bones must toss and creak all night long on a bed of prickly straw. Ah, woe is me! How unhappy is my old age!"

"Your daughter's husband does not help you so that you may rest now and then in the day?" asked the Wise Man.

The peasant hemmed and hawed and mumbled a few indistinct words.

"And your daughter does nothing, and the little child—"

"Oh the child," cried the peasant, "he is a nuisance. That's what he is. Learning to crawl and always under foot, and in a hut as small as mine there is no room for a baby to crawl."

"Hm." The Wise Man looked steadily at the peasant. "Tell me," he said suddenly, "have you a rooster?"

"Oh yes," said the peasant. "I have a rooster and four hens and six chicks."

"Take the rooster and the hens and the chicks into the hut," said the Wise Man and returned to his big, black book.

The peasant's jaw dropped. He stood there a few moments in dismay but the Wise Man did not once lift his eyes so at last the peasant trudged wearily home.

And that night he took the rooster and the hens and the chicks into the hut.

The rooster did not like this arrangement. He much preferred to strut outdoors. The hens, after the manner of women, were too busy minding the chicks to care one way or another. But the selfish old man found life harder than before. The rooster perched on the mantelpiece, the hens roosted underneath the table and the chicks beneath their wings.

Soon the little hut was quiet. It seemed to the peasant he had no sooner fallen into a deep sleep when a sound like the very crack of doom shook the little hut.

He sprang up from his bed of straw. A thin trickle of light showed him the rooster, stretched to his full height, and crowing for all he was worth. The rooster had a job to do. The peasant tore his hair, but the rooster kept on crowing, louder and louder, until he was sure he had called up the day. The peasant moaned and groaned and said he would not go through another night like this. So after breakfast his wife sent him back to the Wise Man.

"Peace to this house and to all within it," he said, when he stood again outside the door.

"And may you find peace," said the Wise Man.

The peasant wrung his hands. "Surely I do not question your wisdom," he said, "but the fowls, they give a man no peace by day, no peace by night. There is no room for *my* family in the little hut, much less for the rooster and *his* family. There has been some mistake, yes?"

"Hm." The Wise Man looked at him steadily. "No, no mistake has been made," he said. "Tell me, have you a goat?"

"Oh yes," said the peasant.

"Well, then, take the goat into the hut," said the Wise Man and returned to his big black book.

The peasant stood rooted to the spot. The clock ticked the minutes away, but the Wise Man did not once raise his eyes.

Finally the peasant turned away and with leaden feet stumbled home. After that he tried to make the best of things for a while, for he did not dare complain again to the Wise Man. But when early one morning he was awakened as usual by the rooster's trumpeting blasts to find the goat chewing his beard, the four hens roosting on his stomach and the six baby chicks sleeping on his chest, he sprang to his feet, scattering his unwelcome bed-fellows and crying "Something must be done," he flew to the Wise Man.

The Wise Man listened patiently to the peasant's woeful tale. Then he said, "Tell me, my friend, have you a pig?"

"A p-pig?" the peasant stuttered. "Yes," he said unhappily, "I have a pig."

"Well then, take the pig into the hut."

So there was nothing for it but to take the pig into the hut. And now to the crowing and cackling and cheeping and maa-maaing there was added the grunt, grunt, grunting of the pig. The old woman and the daughter did not seem to mind much. The young man worked hard all day and quickly fell asleep at night. But the old peasant was in a fix. He had time to spare and he mooned about the hut all day. He could not take a step but that he stumbled over one creature or stretch forth his hand for his pipe but that another nipped at him. This went on for some time, until one day he went again to the Wise Man and now his sorrowful tale was longer than from seed time to harvest. The Wise Man looked at him steadily, and said at last, "Hmm. Yes. Of course. Have you a lamb and a goose?"

The old man did not answer.

"Have you a lamb and a goose?" asked the Wise Man again, sternly.

"Yes," muttered the peasant.

"Take the lamb and the goose in."

With weighted steps the peasant finally reached home and took the lamb and the goose into the hut. The bed was pushed up against the wall as far as it would go; the table was squeezed into a corner; the stools were put under it; and the lamb and the goose made themselves at home. The old woman and the daughter took all this calmly. There was too much for them to do to worry about the situation or to fret over the Wise Man's advice. But the old man groaned and moaned and moaned and groaned, louder and louder each day, until his whining voice drowned out all the other sounds: the crowing and cackling and cheeping; the ma-a-ing and grunting and ba-a-ing; and the constant quack, quack, quacking. Finally the old woman said:

"It is not nearly as hard as you say, but if you are so unhappy, try once more to see the Wise Man."

So the peasant tried once more.

"Tell me," said the Wise Man after he had listened to all the peasant had to say, "tell me, have you a donkey?"

"Oh," cried the peasant in despair, and began to flee down the road. The Wise Man called him back in a voice of thunder. For the seventh time the peasant stood before him.

"I asked you if you had a donkey?"

"Yes," cried the peasant and, growing

reckless, he added rudely, "and a fine cow, too—a big, brown cow with a long tail. And what do you think of that?"

"I think that is fine," said the Wise Man. "Take the donkey and the cow into the hut at once, and don't let me see you again until you have something worthwhile to say."

The peasant found himself trembling as he looked into the Wise Man's blazing eyes. A sharp wind arose whipping up dark clouds which hid the sun. The peasant's teeth began to chatter and his knees knocked together. He took to his heels and did not stop running until he sank, panting, on the doorstep of his little hut.

"Well," said the wife cheerfully when she heard the news, "we will do the best we can. It's a little crowded but the animals are good company and at least the cow will be here in the warm hut to be milked in the morning and not out in the cold barn."

The cow was gentle, but she *was* big, and she *did* have a long, swishy tail, and *she* certainly needed space. The baby now had no room at all in which to crawl. The other animals tried to keep out of the cow's way; the old woman and her daughter barely squeezed through from the stove to the table. The peasant's lamentations kept up, increasing in vigor, and these, with the protests of the animals, filled the little hut near to bursting.

One night as they lay in their bed, the young man said to his wife, "I have heard it said that a bit of rhyme if it comes from the heart has magic power. I do not mind for us but the baby and the animals are so unhappy. A rhyme keeps running through my head and I wonder—"

"How does it go?" asked his wife.

"Like this:

There is no room in a little hut
For a lordly rooster to crow and strut,
For chicks and hen, for women and men,
And a nanny goat that likes to butt.

There is no room, alas and alack,
For a lamb to wobble forward and back,
For a donkey to bray, a cow to play,
And a wandering goose going quackety,
  quack.

And for a baby learning to crawl,
There is no room, no room at all.

"If I were not so busy in the fields," he went on, "I would say it to the Wise Man. I think he would help if he knew how miserable they are."

The young wife sighed. "And I cannot go to see him because I have so much to do all day."

They talked together for a little while and then fell asleep.

Now the selfish old peasant had listened carefully to all this and had memorized the little rhyme. It was not easy for him to think of the comfort of others but as time went on and life in the little hut grew more and more unbearable, he decided to call up his courage, take it firmly by the hand and pay the Wise Man a visit. This time he would have something worth while to say.

So one bright morning he set off and soon he stood on the threshold of the

Wise Man's house. He lingered in the doorway, shifting from one foot to the other, twirling his cap. The Wise Man looked up but did not ask him to come in. The peasant took a deep breath and said humbly: "Peace to this house and to all within it."

"As to that," said the Wise Man, "peace is not a commodity to be bought and sold; nor is it to be had for the wishing. Each man must find it for himself."

The peasant was silent. After a moment he said, "Perhaps a man's peace depends a little on the happiness of his fellows? A man—a man might find peace within himself if—if—his fellow creatures were not unhappy."

"Well!" The Wise Man looked up in astonishment. "That is a thought. Come in, my friend."

The peasant entered slowly. "I wish to speak for the baby and for the animals:

There is no room in a little hut
For a lordly rooster to crow and strut,
For chicks and hen, for women and men,
And a nanny goat that likes to butt.

There is no room, alas and alack,
For a lamb to wobble forward and back,
For a donkey to bray, a cow to play,
And a wandering goose going quackety,
* quack.*

And for a baby learning to crawl,
There is no room, no room at all."

The Wise Man laughed. "Oh, ho! So that's how it is? And your concern is chiefly for the baby and the animals?"

The peasant did not answer.

"Well," said the Wise Man dryly, "one must not expect too much at one time. Let me see. Suppose you let the rooster and hens and chicks out of the hut."

"Thank you," cried the peasant and hurried home. And that night, if the hut was as crowded as ever, at least it was quiet as the rooster was not there when he took up his ancient feud with the sun.

This contentment did not last long, for with the other creatures about, life was quite hazardous. The peasant called up his courage again and off he went to see the Wise Man. As before, he approached him humbly, and in behalf of the animals, pointing out that the combined smell of lamb, goat, pig, and donkey, while pleasant out-of-doors, indoors was just as objectionable to the animals as to the people. The Wise Man smiled: "Hm. Yes. Undoubtedly. But one must not hurry a cure. Suppose you let out the goat and pig?"

The peasant went joyfully home. And that night the goat and the pig returned to their own places outdoors. And now what happiness. Beyond any doubt the hut did smell better. Yet—hold on a minute. Something is ailing the lamb. It had struck up a friendship with the goat and protested being separated from it in piteous bleating. All day, all night, the poor lamb begged to be reunited with its friend.

"Do go to the Wise Man," at last said the peasant's wife. So he went and when he had explained the situation, the Wise Man advised him to let the lamb out.

But the peasant did not remember the donkey. *It* had become very fond of the

48

lamb. No sooner was the lamb outside, frisking and happy, when a new ear-splitting sound shook the hut. It was the mournful braying of the donkey. He kept it up without seeming to pause for breath until the old man near lost his senses.

So for the fourth time he went back to the Wise Man and obtained permission to release the donkey. And now, at last, at last, joy. But—hold on—not so fast. With the other creatures out of the way, the cow really took over, while the goose decided this was the time to explore once and for all every nook and cranny in the hut. How those two harried the old man! No sooner did he doze off, than a sharp beak pecked at his nose; no sooner did he fill his pipe and lay down the tobacco than it was all over the floor.

The moo, moo, moo of the cow and the sharp quack, quack, quack of the goose echoed steadily and piercingly through the hut. They were more difficult to bear than the smells and noises of all the other animals had been.

"I cannot stand this," cried the peasant. "A charm if it works once and twice and thrice and still again should gain in power with use." And off he went to the Wise Man. Humbly and respectfully he suggested that perhaps the outdoors was more suitable than the hut for the goose to wander about in.

"You may be right," said the Wise Man. "Yes, try it."

So the peasant went home and put out the goose.

Well, now things were really looking up. There was quiet and there was room.

But—was there room? The cow, seeing no other animal about, turned this way and that and gave full play to her long swishy tail. The baby viewed all this with delight and the cow was nothing loath to entertain him.

Swish! went the tail and off came the old man's cap.

Swish! went the tail again, and there—there went his pipe.

And when she finally settled down to sleep in the middle of the room, a steady thumping of her tail tickled the old man's nose all night long, so that he could not close his eyes for one instant. Yes, the cow was the hardest of all to bear. And she grew bigger and bigger each day.

This went on for some weeks. The grass grew green and the air grew sweet with clover. The cow's tail became swishier and more restless than ever. She sniffed at the open door and window and into her eyes came a longing, sad look. She yearned to be out-of-doors and she became less and less placid. Presently she gave such vent to her feelings that there was hardly an unbroken dish in the hut.

The peasant decided it was time to visit the Wise Man. As before he was respectful and humble when he suggested perhaps with spring so well along the way it was cruel to keep the cow in the hut?

"You may be right," said the Wise Man. "Let her out."

So the cow returned to her home out-of-doors.

And now, at last, at last, what joy, what happiness! And in the hut, what space! Did I say it was the smallest hut the world

49

had ever seen? But I must have been mistaken. For see how many steps the old woman has to take from the stove to the table to serve the soup.

And the baby—room enough for him to crawl and soon to walk and then even to play hide and go seek in and out of the chair and stool legs.

And the blessed, blessed peace. The young husband rose very early and stole softly out of the hut to work in the fields and the old man slept on and on, on his nice warm sweet-smelling bed of straw. When he awoke his wife and daughter had breakfast ready for him and his little grandson filled the hut with smiles like sunlight and chatter gay as birds' songs. And he was so small he hardly ate anything at all and certainly he did not take up much room in this large, spacious, commodious hut.

The peasant thought and thought. He

remembered how dreary and lonely it had been before his daughter came and it occurred to him that it might be lonely and dreary again. And yet he felt he had to make one more visit to the Wise Man—but he decided he would not mention his daughter and her family.

And so, again for the seventh time, he stood in that familiar doorway and again for the seventh time, he said, "Peace to this house and to all within it."

"And may you 'find peace," said the Wise Man.

"I have found it," answered the peasant, "and I have come to thank you for showing me how."

"Well, now," said the Wise Man, "now that all is well and times are better, how about your daughter and her family? Surely there is no room in your little hut for them? Shall they be sent away?"

"Oh no," cried the peasant hastily. "I couldn't think of their going. What would we do, my old woman and I, rattling around alone in that great, big hut? Did I say it was little? I must have been under a spell. You never saw such a roomy hut. Why it takes so long to carry the soup from the stove to the table that it is fairly frozen by the time it is served."

The Wise Man looked at the peasant steadily. "Ah well," he said not unkindly, "truly all things are relative. Go home, my friend; indeed I do think you have found peace."

And the peasant went happily home.

51

The Duck and the Kangaroo

Written and Illustrated by Edward Lear

SAID the Duck to the Kangaroo,
  "Good gracious! how you hop!
Over the fields and water too,
  As if you never would stop!
My life is a bore in this nasty pond,
And I long to go out in the world beyond!
  I wish I could hop like you!"
  Said the Duck to the Kangaroo.

"Please give me a ride on your back!"
  Said the Duck to the Kangaroo.
"I would sit quite still, and say nothing but
    'Quack,'
  The whole of the long day through!
And we'd go to the Dee, and the Jelly Bo
    Lee,
Over the land, and over the sea;—
  Please take me a ride! O do!"
  Said the Duck to the Kangaroo.

Said the Kangaroo to the Duck,
  "This requires some little reflection;
Perhaps on the whole it might bring me
    luck,
  And there seems but one objection,
Which is, if you'll let me speak so bold,
Your feet are unpleasantly wet and cold,
  And would probably give me the roo-
  Matiz!" said the Kangaroo.

Said the Duck, "As I sat on the rocks,
  I have thought over that completely,
And I bought four pairs of worsted socks
  Which fit my web-feet neatly.
And to keep out the cold I've bought a
    cloak,
And every day a cigar I'll smoke,
  All to follow my own dear true
  Love of a Kangaroo!"

Said the Kangaroo, "I'm ready!
  All in the moonlight pale;
But to balance me well, dear Duck, sit
    steady!
  And quite at the end of my tail!"
So away they went with a hop and a bound,
And they hopped the whole world three
    times round;
  And who so happy,—O who,
  As the Duck and the Kangaroo.

Nonsense Limericks

Written and Illustrated by Edward Lear

THERE was an Old Man
                     with a nose,
Who said,
  "If you choose to suppose
That my nose is too long,
You are certainly wrong!"
That remarkable Man
                   with a nose.

There was a Young Lady
                   whose bonnet,
Came untied
   When the birds sat upon it;
But she said, "I don't care!
All the birds in the air
Are welcome to sit
                   on my bonnet!"

There was a Young Lady
               of Bute,
Who played on a silver-gilt flute;
She played several jigs,
To her uncle's white pigs,
That amusing Young Lady
               of Bute.

There was an Old Man
            with a beard
Who said,
  "It is just as I feared—
Two Owls and a Hen,
Four Larks and a Wren,
Have all built their nests
         in my beard!"

There was a Young Lady of Firle,
Whose hair was addicted to curl;
It curled up a tree,
And all over the sea,
That expansive Young Lady of Firle.

There was an Old Man
  of West Dumpet,
Who possessed a large nose
  like a trumpet;
When he blew it aloud
It astonished the crowd,
And was heard through the whole
  of West Dumpet.

There was an Old Person
    whose habits,
Induced him to feed upon rabbits;
When he'd eaten eighteen,
He turned perfectly green,
Upon which he relinquished
    those habits.

There was a Young Person
    of Bantry
Who frequently slept
    in the pantry;
When disturbed by the mice,
She appeased them with rice,
That judicious Young Person
    of Bantry.

There was an Old Person of Bree,
Who frequented the depths
    of the sea;
She nursed the small fishes,
And washed all the dishes,
And swam back again into Bree.

There was an Old Man
     who said, "How
Shall I flee
     from this horrible cow?
I will sit on this stile
And continue to smile,
Which may soften the heart
     of that cow."

There was an Old Man
     on whose nose,
Most birds of the air
     could repose;
But they all flew away
At the closing of day,
Which relieved that Old Man
     and his nose.

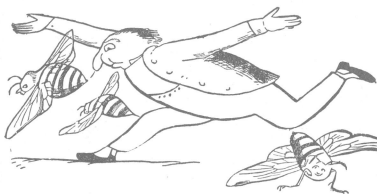

There was an Old Person
     of Dover,
Who rushed through a field
     of blue clover;
But some very large bees,
Stung his nose and his knees,
So he very soon went back
     to Dover.

There was an Old Person of Wilts,
Who constantly walked upon stilts;
He wreathed them with lilies
And daffy-down-dillies,
That elegant person of Wilts.

There was an Old Man of Blackheath,
Whose head was adorned with a wreath
Of lobsters and spice,
Pickled onions and mice,
That uncommon Old Man of Blackheath.

There was an Old Person
    of Ware,
Who rode on the back
    of a bear,
When asked, "Does it trot?"
He said, "Certainly not!
He's a
    Moppsikon Floppsikon bear!"

58

More Limericks

THE SMALL BOY OF QUEBEC

By Rudyard Kipling

THERE was a small boy of Quebec,
Who was buried in snow to his neck;
   When they said, "Are you friz?"
   He replied, "Yes, I is—
But we don't call this cold in Quebec."

THE HEN

By Oliver Wendell Holmes

THE Reverend Henry Ward Beecher
Called a hen a most elegant creature.
   The hen, pleased with that,
   Laid an egg in his hat,
And thus did the hen reward Beecher!

WHY?

THERE was a young maid who said, "Why
Can't I look in my ear with my eye?
   If I give my mind to it,
   I'm sure I can do it—
You never can tell till you try."

YOUNG LADY OF NIGER

THERE was a young lady of Niger
Who smiled as she rode on a tiger;
   They came back from the ride
   With the lady inside,
And the smile on the face of the tiger.

THERE'S NOTHING
IN AFTERNOON TEA

By Gelett Burgess

THERE's nothing in afternoon tea
To appeal to a person like me;
   There is little to eat;
   What there is is too sweet!
And I feel like a cow in a tree!

I'D RATHER
HAVE FINGERS THAN TOES

By Gelett Burgess

I'D RATHER have fingers than toes;
I'd rather have ears than a nose;
   And as for my hair,
   I'm glad it's all there;
I'll be awfully sad when it goes!

The Happy Cure

Retold by Rose Dobbs

A FOOLISH king lay dying. At least, that's what he said. Yes, he said he was at death's door. But the truth of the matter was this: the king was suffering from having nothing to do. He was being bored to death.

Of course, the king would not admit this. He groaned and moaned and complained of sharp stabs in every muscle and sticking pains in every bone in his body. Physicians and surgeons came from far and wide. They looked down the king's throat, they tapped his chest, and they felt his pulse. They hemmed and hawed and stroked their beards. But they could find nothing wrong.

"Physicians and surgeons are dolts," cried the king. "Aren't there any plain ordinary doctors in the kingdom?"

The plain ordinary doctors came from hither and yon. They felt the king's pulse, tapped his chest, and looked down his throat. They hawed and hemmed, took off their spectacles, put them on again. But they could find nothing wrong.

"Plain ordinary doctors are idiots," cried the king in a rage. "The next one who examines me and finds nothing wrong will have his ears cut off and his nose shortened."

Well, you would think that would have put a stop to the coming of the doctors and the surgeons and the physicians. But no. The king kept sending messengers and couriers to bring them in. The people were in despair. Such an epidemic of heads without ears and faces with shortened noses were never seen!

Finally a simple old woman came to see the king. The exhausted prime minister brought her into the royal bedchamber.

The simple old woman peered into the king's face for a long time. Then she said, "Your Majesty, you are suffering from a strange and rare disease. So rare and strange, that no name exists for it."

"There, I knew it," cried the king in glee. "I kept telling all of them, the fools, that I'm a sick man."

"A very sick man," said the old woman.

The king leaned back among his silken

pillows and closed his eyes and wrinkled his brow as if he were in pain.

"And is there no cure for me?" he asked.

"Oh, yes, your Majesty. You need sleep but one night in the shirt of a happy man and you will be cured instantly," said the simple old woman.

The king summoned the captain of his guard and his bravest soldiers; the best couriers in the land; and the swiftest messengers and heralds.

"Start off at once," he commanded them, "and bring me back the shirt of a happy man. And mind you don't return without it," he added darkly.

The soldiers and couriers, messengers and heralds traveled far and wide from east to west, from north to south, across seas and deserts; through cities and over mountains, from one end of the kingdom to the other. But nowhere could they find a happy man. They sent long reports to the king. And this is what they said:

The people in the east might be happy if your Majesty didn't tax them so heavily.

And, the people in the west might be happy if they didn't have to work so long and so hard, so they might have a little time to enjoy singing and dancing.

And, the people in the north might be happy if sometimes they could see you and felt you were interested in them.

And, the people in the south might be happy if your Majesty would notice their industry and faithfulness and would reward them.

The king read the reports hastily and flung them away. But as time went by and none of the messengers returned, and more and more reports came to him of a people that might be happy if their king so chose, he began to read more carefully.

One day a little stableboy, wandering about the palace grounds, came upon a man sitting under a tree in the royal garden. He was singing lustily.

The little stableboy approached him.

"Good afternoon," he said politely. "What makes you sing so merrily?"

"I sing from joy," said the stranger. "I love my fellow man, I own but little and want less. I am a happy man and I sing."

"A happy man," cried the little stableboy. "Oh, do you not know then that the whole kingdom is looking for you? Do you not know that the king is very ill and only if he can sleep one night in the shirt of a happy man can he be cured? Quick, quick, take off your shirt! Quick, quick, give it to me."

The man burst into laughter. "My shirt," he gasped. "Why, you little ragamuffin, I don't possess a shirt." And jumping to his feet, he gathered his tattered coat about him and walked off.

The little stableboy flew to the palace. Past the guards and the prime minister he sped, right into the royal bedchamber.

"What have we here?" cried the king.

The little stableboy had to wait to recover his breath before he could talk.

"Oh, your Majesty," he cried. "The cure was right here all the time—right at hand—right on the palace grounds. I found him—he said he loved his fellow man, owned but little and wanted less. But," and the little boy's lips trembled, "but he didn't possess a shirt."

Then the king hung his head, ashamed.

"Yes, the cure has been here all the time," he murmured. "Only I can cure my own folly."

And he resolved then and there to be a good king, to help his people, to rule wisely and well. He never fancied himself ill again for he became too busy for such folly, and so he lived to a ripe old age.

The Animals' Fair

By Carolyn Wells

Twas long ago, they say, in the Land of
Faraway,
  The beasties clubbed together and they
  held a big bazaar;
Not an animal was slighted, every single
one invited,
  And they all appeared delighted as they
  came from near and far.

The Bear brushed his hair and dressed himself with care;
  With the Lynx and two Minks he started
  to the fair;
The Tapir cut a caper as he read his morning paper,
  And learned about the great bazaar and
  all the wonders there.

The chattering Chinchilla trotted in with
the Gorilla,
  Much elated, so they stated, by the pros-
  pect of the fun;
While the Yak dressed in black, came riding
in a hack,
  And the Buffalo would scuffle, oh,—because he couldn't run.

The Donkey told the Monkey that he had
forgot his trunk key,
  So an Ox took the box, and put it in the
  way
Of a passing Hippopotamus, who angrily
said, "What a muss!"
  As he trod upon the baggage and observed the disarray.

Graceful little Antelope bought a delicious
canteloupe,
  And at table with a Sable sat primly down
  to eat;
While a frisky young Hyena coyly gave a
philopena
  To an Ibex who made shy becks at her
  from across the street.

A Bison was a-pricin' a tea-chest of young
hyson,
  So cheap, said the Sheep, that it nearly
  made her weep;
The lazy Armadillo bought a satin sofa-
pillow,
  Then found a cozy, dozy place and laid
  him down to sleep.

The Baboon and the Loon and the rollick-
ing Raccoon
  Fed an Otter with a blotter, though it
  wasn't good to eat;
The Bunny thought 'twas funny all his
money went for honey,
  But a Rabbit has a habit of liking what
  is sweet.

The Ape left her cape out on the fire-escape,
  The Jerboa lost her boa, which caused
  her much distress;
But the fair was well attended and the
money well expended,
  And financially and socially it was a great
  success.

63

The Monkeys and the Crocodile

By Laura E. Richards

FIVE little monkeys
   Swinging from a tree,
Teasing Uncle Crocodile,
   Merry as can be.

Swinging high, swinging low,
   Swinging left and right:
"Dear Uncle Crocodile,
   Come and take a bite!"

Five little monkeys
   Swinging in the air;
Heads up, tails up,
   Little do they care.

Swinging up, swinging down,
   Swinging far and near:
"Poor Uncle Crocodile,
   Aren't you hungry, dear?"

Four little monkeys
   Sitting in the tree;
Heads down, tails down,
   Dreary as can be.

Weeping loud, weeping low,
   Crying to each other:
"Wicked Uncle Crocodile,
   To gobble up our brother!"

The Skunk in Tante Odette's Oven

By Natalie Savage Carlson

ONCE in another time, my friends, an old woman called Tante Odette lived in Canada. She was a plump little woman with beady, black eyes, a pouf of a moustache and a double chin. She lived at the edge of the village in a neat white-washed house with a sharp roof and two dormer windows.

Tante Odette was all alone except for the beasts in the barn and Chouchou, the big gray cat who lived in the house with her. She worked her own little field and cared for her beasts all by herself because she was too stingy to pay anyone to help her.

For this reason, things did not always go so smoothly for her. The ox broke through the fence or the well froze over or the roof began leaking.

There was that Tuesday morning that she got up very early to start the fire in her outdoor oven. The fat loaves were rising nicely in the pans, the weather was pleasant and there was plenty of dry wood for the fire. It looked like a day in which everything would go right from beginning to end.

Tante Odette gathered a load of wood in her arms and carried it over to the oven. She laid it down in a neat pile and picked up a stick. She noticed that the oven door had been left open, so she poked her stick inside to see that no leaves or twigs had blown in. The stick would not go in very far because something was in the way.

The old woman stooped lower and peered into the dark depths of the oven. The sight that met her eyes caused her to scream and slam the door shut.

She went running out of her yard and down the road as fast as her bunions and old bones would take her.

At Albe Roberge's farm, she saw Albe drawing water from the well.

"Albe, Albe," she cried breathlessly, "come quick! There is a skunk in my oven."

Albe let the bucket sink back into the well. He stared at Tante Odette.

"Are you sure it is a skunk?" he asked. "Perhaps it is your cat."

"Believe me," said Tante Odette, "if that skunk had turned his weapon on me, you would not have to ask such a question. Of course it is a skunk. Is my Chouchou a black cat with a white stripe down his back?"

Then as Albe still stood there as stupidly as François Ecrette's simple son, René, she explained the whole matter.

"I went out early to start the fire in my oven," she began. "I carried a load of wood in my arms, like this. I laid it down, over here. I picked up this stick, see. The oven door was open so I poke, poked the stick inside, but something was in the way. It was a skunk in my oven."

At last Albe seemed to understand.

"I will come right over as soon as I draw a bucket of water," he promised.

Tante Odette turned and hurried back to the road. But she did not go home. She headed for the farm of Jean Labadie. If two heads were better than one, three would be even more dependable.

Jean Labadie was on his way to his henhouse with a pail of chicken feed in his hand. Tante Odette panted up to him.

"Jean, Jean Labadie," she cried. "Come quickly! There is a skunk in my oven."

Jean Labadie regarded her politely.

"Are you sure it is a skunk?" he asked. "Perhaps it is a scrap of old fur coat that you threw away."

Tante Odette was becoming quite exasperated with her neighbors. When faced by an emergency, they seemed even more simple-minded than René Ecrette, who went slap, slapping through the fields, talking to the birds and bushes.

"Of course it is a skunk," she insisted. "Would I throw away a scrap of any-

thing? Am I such a spendthrift?"

Jean had to agree that she was anything but a spendthrift.

"I went out early to start the fire for my baking," she went on. "I carried a load of wood in my arms, like this. I laid it down, over here. I picked up this stick, see. The oven door was open so I poke, poked the stick inside. But something was in the way. It was a skunk—in my oven."

Tante Odette moaned and wrung her plump hands.

"I will come over as soon as I have fed the chickens," promised Jean Labadie.

Then the old woman turned and limped toward André Drouillard's farm. The wits of her neighbors seemed unusually dull on this fresh morning that had turned sour so unexpectedly. She would need all the heads she would like to knock together.

André Drouillard was just coming out of his back door. He looked surprised to see Tante Odette calling at such an hour, for the old woman was not given to neighborliness.

"André Drouillard," she wheezed, "come quickly. There is a skunk in my oven."

"Are you sure it is a skunk?" blinked André. "Perhaps you saw a shadow inside as you opened the door."

Tante Odette was outraged.

"Does a shadow have a bushy tail?" she demanded. "Does it have two shiny black eyes? Does it grit its teeth at me? No! It was this way. I went out early to start the fire in my oven. I carried a load of wood in my arms, like this. I laid it down,

over here. I picked up this stick, see. The oven door was open so I poke, poked my stick inside, but something was in the way. It was a skunk."

André's face brightened.

"Why didn't you tell me that at first?" he asked. "I will come right over."

So as long as her breath came and went, Tante Odette stumbled from farm to farm seeking help. And everyone came quickly, for although a skunk in one's oven is a calamity, a skunk in the oven of one's neighbor is an interesting diversion. Not since the past Sunday had so many people traveled down the dusty road.

Albe Roberge and his family were the first to arrive. Jean Labadie came on their heels. Albe opened the oven door, peered in, then carefully closed it.

"It is a skunk indeed," he said.

Then Jean Labadie opened the door, peered in also, then closed it carefully.

"Yes, you are right," he admitted. "It *is* a skunk."

In pairs and threes and fours, the people of the parish arrived. There were five of the blue-eyed Meloches, making jokes with pretty Eulalie Beneteau to make her dimples wink. Henri Dupuis, the storekeeper, who looked as if he had just eaten one of the pickles out of his own crock, was only two skips behind his gossipy wife, Hortense. There were Delphine Langlois, the old maid, and several others who did not matter and would certainly be of no help.

And each one must look in the oven for himself, close the door and name the uninvited occupant a skunk.

Since everyone who wanted to help had arrived and no one denied that a skunk was in Tante Odette's oven, it was now time to think of some way to get the skunk out.

"I will run home and get my gun," cried Jean Labadie. "I'll put a quick end to that caller."

"No, no," howled Tante Odette, "not in my oven."

"Not in the oven," agreed all the others. "She would not be able to bake bread in it for a month—perhaps never."

"And it would spoil the pelt," added Albe Roberge, who trapped for the trader and knew what he was talking about.

"Perhaps we should get somebody's dog," suggested one of the blue-eyed Meloches. "A dog would bark and frighten him out of the oven."

"No, no," cried Tante Odette, "the skunk must not be frightened while he is in my oven."

Everyone agreed that this was true. A frightened skunk was apt to be a very unpleasant fellow.

"Perhaps we should tie a piece of meat on a string and coax him out," said someone else. "Get a piece of meat, Tante Odette."

"I have no meat," snapped the old woman, "and I wouldn't waste it on a skunk if I had."

So this plan was dropped because no one else cared to use his meat to coax a skunk out of Tante Odette's oven.

"Someone should get the priest," suggested Madame Roberge. "He might know what to do."

But others thought that it was more a matter for Dr. Brisson.

"He could give him a pill that would put him to sleep," said one, "then we could carry the skunk out into the woods."

"No, no," cried Albe Roberge, "do not let such a fine pelt get away. I will take care of the skunk once he is asleep."

Then the youngest Meloche howled with laughter.

"Ha, ha!" he roared, "and that will be one surprised skunk when he wakes up and finds his skin on Albe Roberge's board and Dr. Brisson's bill in his paw."

Then everybody but Tante Odette laughed and a light mood fell upon the crowd. André Drouillard was reminded of the time he had worked in the lumber camps and a porcupine had gotten caught in his boot one night.

"And believe me, my friends," he added, "a porcupine wedged in a boot makes as big a problem as a skunk in an oven."

That promptly set Jean Labadie off on a long tale about a deer that was accidentally shut up in the barn with his cows one winter.

"And when spring came, that doe had twin fawns that I raised with my own calves," he ended.

If old Gabriel Meloche had been there with his fiddle and Tante Odette's bread already baked, the whole thing could have been a gay fete.

Only Tante Odette could not forget the reason that everyone had dropped his work at the start of the morning to hurry to her little farm.

"The skunk!" she reminded them. "The skunk is still in my oven. How can I bake bread today?"

One by one, the neighbors walked over to the oven, opened the door, looked surprised to see the skunk still there, then carefully closed the door again.

"Yes," said each one in turn, "he is still there."

And while this was going on, Samigish the Indian came riding down the road on his sway-backed pony. When he saw all the people in Tante Odette's yard, waiting with the air of those about to sit down to a feast, he dismounted and made his way through the gate.

Tante Odette was overjoyed to see an Indian entering her yard. After all, this was more of a problem for one close to nature.

"Samigish," she cried, "come help us.

There is a skunk in my oven. We need your help."

"You sure him skunk?" asked Samigish, who had never heard of a skunk in a white man's oven. Bread or venison or a ham, yes, but never a skunk.

"Of course it's a skunk," said Albe Roberge with disgust, for by this time everyone could see what a foolish question this made.

Samigish opened the door, looked in, then carefully closed the door again.

"What shall we do?" asked Tante Odette.

Samigish licked his lips.

"Young, tender skunk," he said. "Anybody got match?"

"Oh, no, no," screamed Tante Odette, "not in my oven."

Everyone tried at once to explain to the Indian that the skunk was not to be cooked.

Samigish stared at them in puzzlement. He shrugged his shoulders.

"Then why skunk in oven?" he asked.

But he did not wait for an answer. Answers never really explained the white man's queer ways. He mounted his swaybacked pony and rode away without another word.

By now, all the people were becoming a little bored with the skunk matter, and it did not look as if Tante Odette was going to serve any food or drink.

Jean Labadie remembered that he hadn't milked his cow. André Drouillard spoke of the job of cleaning his barn. Madame Roberge said it was long past time for breakfast.

It was at this stage that René Ecrette, the simple son of Francois, came slap, slapping his feet down the road with his head bobbing about like a loose cork. His dull eyes brightened at sight of the gathering in Tante Odette's yard. Like Samigish, he thought that where there was a crowd of people, there must be food. He turned in.

At the time René entered the yard, Tante Odette was quite at the end of her wits. She made one desperate attempt to do something about the skunk in the oven. This René might be simple-minded, it was true, but it was said that he talked to the birds and the trees. Perhaps he had a way with wild things.

The old woman went running to him, twisting the folds of her apron.

"René," she cried, "René Ecrette. There is a skunk in my oven. Can you get him out without frightening him?"

René nodded his head gravely. And he didn't ask "Are you sure it is a skunk?"

"Then do something," implored Tante Odette.

René nodded again.

"What will you do?"

But René did not answer her. He slap, slapped over to the oven and opened the door. He leaned inside. The people could hear him talking in a low, earnest voice. No one could hear what he said because his head was inside the oven. And no one cared to venture closer to try to hear. There was a tight feeling in the air, and Tante Odette felt it from the knot on top of her head to the bunions on her feet.

At last René stepped back. Everyone stared and stretched his neck. For a few moments nothing happened. Then the sharp face of the skunk appeared in the doorway of the oven. Everyone stepped back a few feet. The skunk clumsily wriggled over the edge and dropped to the ground.

Slowly he started through the yard.

70

Roger Duvoisin

The crowd respectfully parted to make a wide path for him—a very, very wide path.

The skunk marched toward the woods. He walked with majesty, his flag of truce held high, and not even Albe Roberge, the trapper, blocked his way. In awe, all watched him disappear into the bushes.

Tante Odette was delighted. The others were amazed. They gathered around René Ecrette.

"How did you get him to come out?" asked André Drouillard.

"What did you say to him?" asked Jean Labadie.

René Ecrette hung his head and swung his arms back and forth because he was not used to such admiring attention from the people of the parish. At last he was persuaded to tell the secret.

"I just told him that if he stayed in the oven any longer," he said, "he would begin to smell like Tante Odette's bread, and none of the other skunks would come near him."

So you see, my friends, only the simple-minded René Ecrette was wise enough to know that even a skunk, the lowliest of beasts, has his self-respect and values the good opinion of his own kind.

—From *The Talking Cat and Other Stories*

The Pobble Who Has No Toes

By Edward Lear

THE POBBLE who has no toes
  Had once as many as we;
When they said, "Some day you may
    lose them all";
  He replied, "Fish fiddle-de-dee!"
And his Aunt Jobiska made him drink
Lavender water tinged with pink,
For she said, "The World in general knows
There's nothing so good for a Pobble's
    toes!"

The Pobble who has no toes
  Swam across the Bristol Channel;
But before he set out he wrapped his nose
  In a piece of scarlet flannel.
For his Aunt Jobiska said, "No harm
Can come to his toes if his nose is warm;
And it's perfectly known that a Pobble's
    toes
Are safe,—provided he minds his nose."

The Pobble swam fast and well
  And when boats or ships came near him,
He tinkledy-binkledy-winked a bell,
  So that all the world could hear him.
And all the Sailors and Admirals cried,
When they saw him nearing the further
    side,—
"He has gone to fish, for his Aunt Jobiska's
Runcible Cat with crimson whiskers!"

But before he touched the shore,—
  The shore of the Bristol Channel—
A sea-green Porpoise carried away
  His wrapper of scarlet flannel.

And when he came to observe his feet,
Formerly garnished with toes so neat,
His face at once became forlorn
On perceiving that all his toes were gone!

And nobody ever knew,
  From that dark day to the present,
Whoso had taken the Pobble's toes,
  In a manner so far from pleasant.
Whether the shrimps or crawfish gray,
Or crafty Mermaids stole them away—
Nobody knew; and nobody knows
How the Pobble was robbed of his twice
    five toes!

The Pobble who has no toes
  Was placed in a friendly Bark,
And they rowed him back, and carried him
    up
  To his Aunt Jobiska's Park.
And she made him a feast, at his earnest
    wish,
Of eggs and buttercups fried with fish;
And she said, "It's a fact the whole world
    knows
That Pobbles are happier without their
    toes."

How Many Donkeys?

A TURKISH FOLK TALE

Retold by Alice Geer Kelsey

THERE was the tinkle of tiny bells, the sharp click of small hoofs, the throaty drone of a solitary singer. Nasr-ed-din Hodja was bringing the donkeys back from the mill, their saddle bags filled with freshly ground wheat. The hot Turkish sun beat down on his turbaned head. The brown dust from the donkeys' feet puffed about him. The staccato trot of his donkey jiggled him back and forth. But Nasr-ed-din Hodja was too pleased to be uncomfortable.

"I'll show them," he chuckled. "They gave me plenty of advice about taking care of their donkeys and their wheat. As though I did not know more about donkeys than any man in the village of Ak Shehir!"

His eyes rested lazily on the narrow road ahead. At first it followed the brook running from Mill Valley, the brook that turned the heavy stones to grind the wheat. Then the road disappeared.

"Just over that hill," he mused contentedly, "is Shehir where they are waiting for their donkeys. There is not a scratch nor a bruise on one of the little creatures. No donkeys in all Turkey have had better treatment today than these nine." Idly he began counting them.

"What?" he gasped. "Eight donkeys?"

He jumped from his donkey and ran hither and yon, looking behind rocks and over hilltops but no stray donkey could he see. At last he stood beside the donkeys and counted again. This time there were nine. With a sigh of relief he climbed onto his own donkey and went singing along the road. His long legs in their baggy trousers swung easily back and forth in time to the donkey's trot.

Passing through a cluster of trees, he thought it time to count the donkeys again. "One—two—three—" up to eight he counted but no ninth donkey was to be seen. Down from his donkey's back he came. Behind all the trees he peered. Not a hair of a donkey could he find.

Again he counted, standing beside his donkeys. There they all were—nine mild little donkeys waiting for orders to move on. Nasr-ed-din scratched his poor head in bewilderment. Was he losing his mind or were the donkeys bewitched? Again he counted. Yes, surely there were nine.

"Brrrr." Nasr-ed-din Hodja gave the low guttural Turkish for "Giddap."

As he rode on, he looked about him for the evil spirits which must be playing tricks on him. Each donkey wore the blue beads which should drive away the evil spirits. Were there evil spirits abroad stronger even than the blue beads?

He was glad to see a friend coming down the road.

"Oh, Mustapha," he cried, "have you

seen one of these donkeys? I have lost a donkey and yet I have not lost it."

"What can you mean, Hodja?" asked Mustapha.

"I left the mill with nine donkeys," explained Hodja. "Part of the way home there have been nine and part of the way there have been eight. Oh, I am bewitched! Help me!"

Mustapha was used to the queer ways of Hodja but was surprised at such a wailing. He counted the donkeys silently.

"Let me see you count the donkeys," he asked Hodja.

"One—two—three—" began Hodja, pointing at each one as he counted up to eight.

As he said the last number, he stopped and looked at his friend with a face full of helplessness and terror. His terror turned to amazement as Mustapha slapped his knee and laughed until he almost fell from his own donkey.

"What is so funny?" asked Hodja.

"Oh, Nasr-ed-din Hodja," laughed Mustapha. "When you are counting your brothers, why, oh why, do you not count the brother on whom you are riding?"

Nasr-ed-din was silent for a moment to think through this discovery. Then he kissed the hand of his deliverer, and thanked him a thousand times for his help. He rode whistling on to Ak Shehir to deliver the donkeys to their owners.

Never Worked and Never Will

By Margaret Wise Brown

Once upon a time, in the time we are now living, there was an old man who made things out of wood. He had a shop on a street in a small town where all day long he carved wooden ducks and wild geese for weather vanes and hunters' decoys and, also, for people to buy and hang up in their houses like pictures— flocks of wild, black geese flying across a white wall. All his life the old man had loved to carve wood. And so that was what he did. All his life he had sat in his shop with a knife in one hand and a block of wood in the other hand, carving wild birds. He would paint them the green and black colors of wild ducks and the wonderful colors of wild geese and hang them in the windows of his shop where people passing by could see them.

People from all over would come to his shop to buy the things he made and to talk to the old man, because he was a happy old man.

But there was one thing people from all over the world could not understand. Over the woodcarver's door was a large sign which said: NEVER WORKED AND NEVER WILL.

"How," said the people from all over, "can Jim Bailey carve wood all day and paint it and sell it and then say he 'NEVER WORKED AND NEVER WILL'?"

"Why," said the people from all over, "he works all day, and he has worked all his life carving wood, and he will work tomorrow. What does he mean?"

"It means," said Jim Bailey, "that I never worked a day in my life and I never will."

"But you work from eight in the morning until eight at night, every day, carving the wild geese out of wood. What do you mean?"

"If you don't know, I can't tell you," said the old man. "I never worked and I never will."

And then the old man laughed because the people were so puzzled and he laughed some more because he was a happy man.

Then the people from all over the world went away with the wooden ducks and the weather vanes they had bought, shaking their heads. "We don't know what he means. He works harder than any of us, yet he says, 'I never worked a day in my life and I never will.'"

Then the lazy children from all around came to the old man's shop to watch him carve the wooden ducks out of blocks of wood. When they saw his sign, NEVER WORKED AND NEVER WILL, they thought, "Here is a man like us. He doesn't work either."

But when the lazy children saw him carving wild geese out of wood from eight in the morning till eight at night, they said, "Jim Bailey, you do work. You make things. And you work all day. You work harder than we do."

But the old man shook his head and said, "Go away, lazy children. You don't know what I mean, but still I say, 'I never worked a day in my life and I never will.' And you wouldn't have to work, either, if you knew my secret."

But the lazy children from all around were too lazy to guess his secret, so they went off shaking their heads. They said, "The old man is crazy. We don't know what he means. The old man is crazy, he works all day."

Then the other children from all around came to the old man and watched him carve the wild geese out of wood and paint them the wonderful wild bird colors. It made them happy to see what the old man was doing, and sometimes he let them help him paint.

But they never asked the old man what his sign meant, because they were so delighted with what he was doing that they never thought of it as work. And that was how they knew the old man's secret.

Mrs. Snipkin and Mrs. Wobblechin

By Laura E. Richards

1. SKINNY Mrs. Snipkin,
   With her little pipkin,
Sat by the fireside a-warming of her toes.

2. Fat Mrs. Wobblechin,
   With her little doublechin,
Sat by the window a-cooling of her nose.

3. Says this one to that one,
   "Oh! you silly fat one,
Will you shut the window down? You're freezing me to death!"

4. Says that one to t'other one,
   "Good gracious, how you bother one!
There isn't air enough for me to draw my precious breath!"

5. Skinny Mrs. Snipkin
   Took her little pipkin,
Threw it straight across the room as hard as she could throw;

6. Hit Mrs. Wobblechin
   On her little doublechin,
And out of the window a-tumble she did go.

Poems for Pleasure

Poetry

By Eleanor Farjeon

WHAT is poetry? Who knows?
Not the rose, but the scent of the rose;
Not the sky, but the light of the sky;
Not the fly, but the gleam of the fly;
Not the sea, but the sound of the sea;
Not myself, but something that makes me
See, hear and feel something that prose
Cannot. What is it? Who knows?

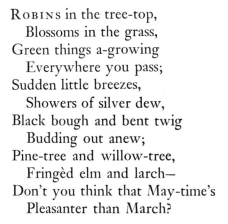

Marjorie's Almanac

By *Thomas Bailey Aldrich*

ROBINS in the tree-top,
  Blossoms in the grass,
Green things a-growing
  Everywhere you pass;
Sudden little breezes,
  Showers of silver dew,
Black bough and bent twig
  Budding out anew;
Pine-tree and willow-tree,
  Fringèd elm and larch—
Don't you think that May-time's
  Pleasanter than March?

Apples in the orchard
  Mellowing one by one;
Strawberries upturning
  Soft cheeks to the sun;
Roses faint with sweetness,
  Lilies fair of face,
Drowsy scents and murmurs
  Haunting every place;
Lengths of golden sunshine,
  Moonlight bright as day—
Don't you think that summer's
  Pleasanter than May?

Roger in the corn-patch
  Whistling Negro songs,
Pussy by the hearth-side
  Romping with the tongs;
Chestnuts in the ashes
  Bursting through the rind;
Red leaf and gold leaf
  Rustling down the wind;
Mother "doin' peaches"
  All the afternoon—
Don't you think that autumn's
  Pleasanter than June?

Little fairy snow-flakes
  Dancing in the flue;
Old Mr. Santa Claus,
  What is keeping you?
Twilight and firelight
  Shadows come and go;
Merry chime of sleigh-bells
  Tinkling through the snow;
Mother knitting stockings
  (Pussy's got the ball)—
Don't you think that winter's
  Pleasanter than all?

DEWDROPS

By *Mary Frances Butts*

A MILLION little diamonds
  Sparkled on the trees;
And all the little maidens cried:
  "A diamond, if you please!"

But while they held their hands out far,
  To catch the diamonds gay,
A million little sunbeams came,
  And stole them all away.

AROUND THE YEAR

By George Cooper

OH, BEAUTIFUL world of green!
When blue-birds carol clear
    And rills outleap
    And new buds peep
And the soft sky seems more near,
With billowy green and leaves—what then?
How soon we greet the red again!

Oh, radiant world of red!
When roses blush so fair
    And winds blow sweet
    And lambkins bleat
And the bees hum here and there,
With thrill of bobolinks—ah, then,
Before we know, the gold again!

Oh, beautiful world of gold!
When waving grain is ripe
    And apples beam
    Through the hazy gleam
And quails on the fence rails pipe,
With pattering nuts and winds, why then
How softly falls the white again!

Oh, wonderful world of white!
When trees are hung with lace
    And the rough winds chide
    And snowflakes hide
Each bleak unsheltered place;
When birds and brooks are dumb, what
    then,
Oh, 'round we go to the green again!

The Months

By Sara Coleridge

JANUARY brings the snow;
Makes the feet and fingers glow.

FEBRUARY brings the rain;
Thaws the frozen pond again.

MARCH brings wind so cold and chill;
Drives the cattle from the hill.

APRIL brings us sun and showers,
And the pretty wildwood flowers.

MAY brings grass and leafy trees,
Waving in each gentle breeze.

JUNE brings roses, fresh and fair,
And the cherries, ripe and rare.

JULY brings the greatest heat,
Cloudless skies and dusty street.

AUGUST brings the golden grain;
Harvest time begins again.

Mild SEPTEMBER brings us more
Fruit and grain, for winter store.

Brown OCTOBER brings the last
Of ripening gifts, from summer past.

Dull NOVEMBER brings the blast;
Down from the trees the leaves fall fast.

Cold DECEMBER ends the rhyme
With blazing fires and Christmas time.

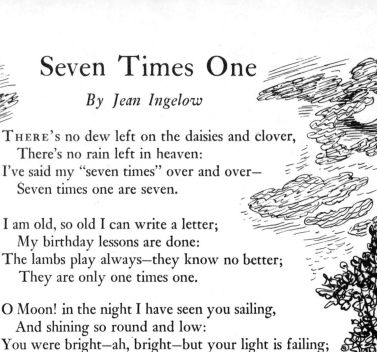

Seven Times One

By Jean Ingelow

THERE's no dew left on the daisies and clover,
　There's no rain left in heaven:
I've said my "seven times" over and over—
　Seven times one are seven.

I am old, so old I can write a letter;
　My birthday lessons are done:
The lambs play always—they know no better;
　They are only one times one.

O Moon! in the night I have seen you sailing,
　And shining so round and low:
You were bright—ah, bright—but your light is failing;
　You are nothing now but a bow.

You Moon! have you done something wrong in heaven,
　That God has hidden your face?
I hope, if you have, you will soon be forgiven,
　And shine again in your place.

　O velvet Bee! you're a dusty fellow—
　　You've powdered your legs with gold.
　O brave marsh Mary-buds, rich and yellow,
　　Give me your money to hold!

　O Columbine! open your folded wrapper,
　　Where two twin turtle doves dwell.
　O Cuckoo-pint! toll me the purple clapper
　　That hangs in your clear green bell:

And show me your nest with the young ones in it;
　I will not steal them away.
I am old! you may trust me, Linnet, Linnet!
　I am seven times one to-day.

84

What Do We Plant When We Plant a Tree?

By Henry Abbey

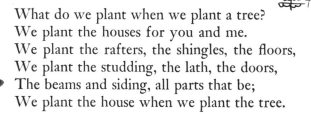

WHAT do we plant when we plant a tree?
We plant the ship which will cross the sea.
We plant the mast to carry the sails;
We plant the planks to withstand the gales—
The keel, the keelson, the beam, the knee;
We plant the ship when we plant the tree.

What do we plant when we plant a tree?
We plant the houses for you and me.
We plant the rafters, the shingles, the floors,
We plant the studding, the lath, the doors,
The beams and siding, all parts that be;
We plant the house when we plant the tree.

What do we plant when we plant a tree?
A thousand things that we daily see;
We plant the spire that out-towers the crag,
We plant the staff for our country's flag,
We plant the shade, from the hot sun free;
We plant all these when we plant the tree.

AN ARBOR DAY TREE

DEAR little tree that we plant today,
What will you be when we're old and gray?
"The savings bank of the squirrel and mouse;
For robin and wren an apartment house,
The dressing room of the butterfly's ball,
The locust's and katydid's concert hall.

The schoolboy's ladder in pleasant June,
The schoolgirl's tent in July at noon,
And my leaves shall whisper them merrily
A tale of the children who planted me."

85

HURT NO LIVING THING

By Christina Rossetti

HURT no living thing,
  Ladybird nor butterfly,
Nor moth with dusty wing,
  Nor cricket chirping cheerily,
Nor grasshopper so light of leap,
  Nor dancing gnat, nor beetle fat,
Nor harmless worms that creep.

QUEEN ANNE'S LACE

By Mary Leslie Newton

QUEEN Anne, Queen Anne has washed her
    lace,
  The dainty lace she'd spun,
And hung it in a grassy place
  To whiten in the sun.

Queen Anne, Queen Anne has left it there,
  And slept the dewy night;
Then waked to find the sunshine fair
  And all the meadows white.

Queen Anne, Queen Anne is dead, alas,
  (She died a summer's day)
But left her lace out on the grass
  In summer-long display.

86

The Sandpiper

By Celia Thaxter

Across the narrow beach we flit,
  One little sandpiper and I;
And fast I gather, bit by bit,
  The scattered driftwood bleached and dry.
The wild waves reach their hands for it,
  The wild wind raves, the tide runs high,
As up and down the beach we flit—
  One little sandpiper and I.

Above our heads the sullen clouds
  Scud black and swift across the sky:
Like silent ghosts in misty shrouds
  Stand out the white lighthouses high.
Almost as far as eye can reach
  I see the close-reefed vessels fly,
As fast we flit along the beach—
  One little sandpiper and I.

I watch him as he skims along,
  Uttering his sweet and mournful cry;
He starts not at my fitful song,
  Or flash of fluttering drapery;
He has no thought of any wrong,
  He scans me with a fearless eye.
Stanch friends are we, well tried and strong,
  The little sandpiper and I.

Comrade, where wilt thou be tonight
  When the loosed storm breaks furiously?
My driftwood fire will burn so bright!
  To what warm shelter canst thou fly?
I do not fear for thee, though wroth
  The tempest rushes through the sky:
For are we not God's children both,
  Thou, little sandpiper, and I?

87

Little Rain

By Elizabeth Madox Roberts

When I was making myself a game
Up in the garden, a little rain came.

It fell down quick in a sort of rush,
And I crawled back under the snowball
    bush.

I could hear the big drops hit the ground
And see little puddles of dust fly round.

A chicken came till the rain was gone;
He had just a very few feathers on.

He shivered a little under his skin,
And then he shut his eyeballs in.

Even after the rain had begun to hush
It kept on raining up in the bush.

One big flat drop came sliding down,
And a ladybug that was red and brown

Was up on a little stem waiting there,
And I got some rain in my hair.

Hildegard
Woodward

88

THE MOUNTAIN AND THE SQUIRREL

By Ralph Waldo Emerson

THE mountain and the squirrel
Had a quarrel,
And the former called the latter
  "Little Prig."
Bun replied,
"You are doubtless very big;
But all sorts of things and weather
Must be taken in together
To make up a year
And a sphere.
And I think it no disgrace
To occupy my place.
If I'm not so large as you,
You are not so small as I,
And not half so spry.
I'll not deny you make
A very pretty squirrel track;
Talents differ; all is well and
  wisely put;
If I cannot carry forests on my back,
Neither can you crack a nut."

AUTUMN

By Emily Dickinson

THE morns are meeker than they were,
The nuts are getting brown;
The berry's cheek is plumper,
The rose is out of town.

The maple wears a gayer scarf,
The field a scarlet gown.
Lest I should be old-fashioned,
I'll put a trinket on.

89

Song

By William Blake

WHEN the voices of children are heard
   on the green
  And laughing is heard on the hill,
My heart is at rest within my breast,
  And everything is still.

"Then come home, my children, the sun
   is gone down,
  And the dews of night arise;
Come, come, leave off play, and let us
   away
  Till the morning appears in the skies."

"No, no, let us play, for it is yet day,
  And we cannot go to sleep;
Besides, in the sky the little birds fly,
  And the hills are all covered with sheep."

"Well, well, go and play till the light
   fades away,
  And then go home to bed."
The little ones leaped and shouted and
   laughed;
  And all the hills echoèd.

Little Fox Lost

By Frances Frost

"IT is dark in the world," wept the little
  fox,
"And I don't know where I am!
There are three big sheep in that uphill
  field
And a great big black-faced ram!"

"It is dark in the wood," said the little fox,
"And I've lost the starmoss way!
The trees are tall and my fur is wet—
What will my mother say?

"My fur is wet with the starlit dew,
A cobweb tickles my nose,
And my heart is a grasshopper wild in my
  chest—
Where *am* I, do you suppose?"

"It is dark in the world!" sobbed the little
  fox.
"This path must be wrong! Here's another—"
"*You're safe at my side! You're right at
  the door!
Big foxes don't cry!*" said his mother.

91

The Lamb

By William Blake

LITTLE lamb, who made thee?
Dost thou know who made thee,
Gave thee life and bade thee feed
By the stream and o'er the mead;
Gave thee clothing of delight,
Softest clothing, woolly, bright;
Gave thee such a tender voice
Making all the vales rejoice?
Little lamb, who made thee?
Dost thou know who made thee?

Little lamb I'll tell thee;
Little lamb, I'll tell thee:
He is called by thy name,
For he calls Himself a Lamb
He is meek and He is mild,
He became a little Child.
I a child and thou a lamb,
We are called by His name.
Little lamb, God bless thee!
Little lamb, God bless thee!

Ring
Around the World

By Annette Wynne

Ring around the world
Taking hands together
All across the temperate
And the torrid weather.
Past the royal palm-trees
By the ocean sand
Make a ring around the world
Taking each other's hand;
In the valleys, on the hill,
Over the prairie spaces,
There's a ring around the world
Made of children's friendly faces.

MORNING

By Emily Dickinson

Will there really be a morning?
Is there such a thing as day?
Could I see it from the mountains
If I were as tall as they?

Has it feet like water-lilies?
Has it feathers like a bird?
Is it brought from famous countries
Of which I have never heard?

Oh, some scholar! Oh, some sailor!
Oh, some wise man from the skies!
Please to tell a little pilgrim
Where the place called morning lies!

COLOR

By Christina Rossetti

What is pink? A rose is pink
By a fountain's brink.

What is red? A poppy's red
In its barley bed.

What is blue? The sky is blue
Where the clouds float through.

What is white? A swan is white
Sailing in the light.

What is yellow? Pears are yellow,
Rich and ripe and mellow.

What is green? The grass is green,
With small flowers between.

What is violet? Clouds are violet
In the summer twilight.

What is orange? Why, an orange,
Just an orange!

Stopping by Woods on a Snowy Evening

By Robert Frost

Whose woods these are I think I know.
His house is in the village though;
He will not see me stopping here
To watch his woods fill up with snow.

The little horse must think it queer
To stop without a farmhouse near
Between the woods and frozen lake
The darkest evening of the year.

He gives his harness bells a shake
To ask if there is some mistake.
The only other sound's the sweep
Of easy wind and downy flake.

The woods are lovely, dark and deep.
But I have promises to keep,
And miles to go before I sleep,
And miles to go before I sleep.

Barbara Cooney

The Sugar-Plum Tree

By *Eugene Field*

Have you ever heard of the Sugar-Plum Tree?
　　'Tis a marvel of great renown!
It blooms on the shore of the Lollipop sea
　　In the garden of Shut-Eye Town;
The fruit that it bears is so wondrously sweet
　　(As those who have tasted it say)
That good little children have only to eat
　　Of that fruit to be happy next day.

When you've got to the tree, you would have a hard time
　　To capture the fruit which I sing;
The tree is so tall that no person could climb
　　To the boughs where the sugar-plums swing!
But up in that tree sits a chocolate cat,
　　And a gingerbread dog prowls below—
And this is the way you contrive to get at
　　Those sugar-plums tempting you so.

You say but the word to that gingerbread dog
　　And he barks with such terrible zest
That the chocolate cat is at once all agog
　　As her swelling proportions attest.
And the chocolate cat goes cavorting around
　　From this leafy limb unto that,
And the sugar-plums tumble, of course, to the ground.
　　Hurrah for that chocolate cat!

There are marshmallows, gumdrops, and peppermint canes
　　With stripings of scarlet or gold,
And you carry away of the treasure that rains
　　As much as your apron can hold!
So come, little child, cuddle closer to me
　　In your bed-time pajamas or gown,
And I'll rock you away to that Sugar-Plum Tree
　　In the garden of Shut-Eye Town.

Kentucky Birthday: February 12, 1816

By Frances Frost

Leaning his chin in his small hard
    hands,
Abraham thought and thought
About adventures in distant lands:
His breath came fast and caught

In his throat as he dreamed on the cabin
    floor.
The firelight danced on his book
In a gust from the suddenly opened door,
And he twisted around to look.

His father stamped the snow from his
    feet;
The steaming stew on the crane
Smelled tender-rabbity, spiced and sweet;
The sharp snow knocked at the pane.

Abraham smiled at the alphabet,
Tall on the firelit page:
He guessed he'd remember the dark floor
    wet
With snow, till he came of age.

He thought of wide American lands,
But this warm room was heaven.
He cupped his chin in his small hard
    hands—
Abraham Lincoln, seven.

Theme in Yellow

By Carl Sandburg

I spot the hills
With yellow balls in autumn.
I light the prairie cornfields
Orange and tawny gold clusters
And I am called pumpkins.

On the last of October
When dusk is fallen
Children join hands
And circle round me
Singing ghost songs
And love to the harvest moon:

I am a jack-o'-lantern
With terrible teeth
And the children know
I am fooling.

Silver

By Walter de la Mare

Slowly, silently, now the moon
Walks the night in her silver shoon;
This way, and that, she peers, and sees
Silver fruit upon silver trees;
One by one the casements catch
Her beams beneath the silvery thatch;
Couched in his kennel, like a log,
With paws of silver sleeps the dog;
From their shadowy cot the white breasts
    peep
Of doves in a silver-feathered sleep;
A harvest mouse goes scampering by,
With silver claws, and silver eye;
And moveless fish in the water gleam,
By silver reeds in a silver stream.

ANSWER TO A CHILD'S
QUESTION

By Samuel Taylor Coleridge

Do you ask what the birds say? The sparrow, the dove,
The linnet, and the thrush say, "I love and I love!"
In the winter they're silent—the wind is so strong;
What it says I don't know, but it sings a loud song.
But green leaves and blossoms and sunny warm weather
And singing and loving—all come back together.
But the lark is so brimful of gladness and love,
The green fields below him, the blue sky above,
That he sings and he sings and forever sings he—
"I love my love and my love loves me!"

Animal Stories

The Animal Store

By Rachel Field

If I had a hundred dollars to spend,
  Or maybe a little more,
I'd hurry as fast as my legs would go
  Straight to the animal store.

I wouldn't say, "How much for this or
    that?"— "What kind of a dog is he?"
I'd buy as many as rolled an eye,
  Or wagged a tail at me!

I'd take the hound with the drooping ears
  That sits by himself alone;
Cockers and Cairns and wobbly pups
  To be my very own.

I might buy a parrot all red and green,
  And the monkey I saw before,
If I had a hundred dollars to spend,
  Or maybe a little more.

The Seventh Pup

By Doris Gates

IN SOME ways Billy Bent was a very lucky boy, and he knew it. But in other ways he wasn't so lucky. That's the way it is with nearly everybody, only it was more so with Billy.

First of all Billy loved dogs. What boy doesn't? But Billy loved dogs in a special way. All he really cared about was dogs. He had already decided that when he grew up, he was going to earn his living training them. That wouldn't happen for quite a while, though, because Billy was only nine years old.

But already he had a way with dogs, and an eye for them, too. At least that's what Mr. Riggs said, and he should have known. For Mr. Riggs raised fox terriers and sold them to people who came from miles around to buy them. And Billy lived next door to Mr. Riggs.

The people he lived with were paid by the county to take care of Billy because he was an orphan. That was not lucky. But living next door to Mr. Riggs

was. Billy spent most of his time there.

Now one day, Queenie, the best dog at the Riggs kennel, presented her owner with a litter of puppies. Billy happened to be right at Mr. Riggs' side when he discovered Queenie's new family.

"Well, old lady," Mr. Riggs said kindly, and Queenie wagged her stump of a tail and looked at him with adoring eyes. "How many babies this time?"

He moved Queenie out of her box and there, in a black and white heap, were seven puppies cuddled closely together. They were beautiful puppies, with strong, healthy bodies and perfect markings. All but one. He was little and all his markings were in the wrong places. The black spot that should have fitted neatly over his back had slid down on one side. One half of his face was black and the other white. And on the white side he had a black ear, and on the black side a white ear. In short, he couldn't have been more sadly mixed up.

"Well," said Mr. Riggs again, "it won't be hard to decide what to do with that seventh pup." He had put the six good puppies in the box and the seventh was sitting all by himself on the floor of Queenie's pen.

"What do you mean?" asked Billy, but in his heart he knew exactly what Mr. Riggs was going to say.

"Queenie won't have milk for more than six puppies, and that seventh one isn't any good anyway. I'll just have to kill him."

Billy looked at the seventh pup, and all at once he knew that he loved him better than all the rest of Queenie's litter put together. Perhaps it was because the puppy wasn't wanted that made Billy love him so. He could understand how the pup might feel about that, because nobody cared much about him, either.

There is a great difference between having a home of your own and being cared for by people who are paid to do so. Billy always had enough to eat and a good bed to sleep in. Just the same, he knew what it was not to be wanted. So now he wanted the seventh pup. He wanted him more than anything in all the world.

"Yep, I'll have to kill him," Mr. Riggs repeated. "But he's so homely, it won't be much of a loss."

Then Billy spoke. "Don't kill him," he begged. "Give him to me."

Mr. Riggs looked at Billy in surprise. "He's too little to take away from his mother," he said. "You couldn't feed him, son."

"Yes, I could," Billy insisted. "I'll feed him with a baby's bottle. And if he doesn't keep well and strong, then—then, why then I guess you'll have to kill him."

Mr. Riggs could think of nothing to say against Billy's plan, so he gave him the pup. Billy lifted it from the floor while Mr. Riggs held on to Queenie. She didn't care if the puppy was homely, either. Then Mr. Riggs gave Billy one of the nursing bottles which he kept at the kennel for emergencies, and Billy went proudly home, the seventh pup cuddled close in his arms. This was his first dog, and it was the dog among all dogs which he had most wanted for his very own.

The man the county paid for keeping Billy was sitting on the front porch when Billy reached the house. He lowered the paper he was reading to glance at Billy as he came into sight. He started to raise the paper again when his eyes fell upon the seventh pup.

"Where on earth did you find that?" he demanded, in a voice which said as plain as day he didn't think much of it.

This was the moment Billy had been waiting for. "How do you like my dog?" he asked.

"What do you mean, *your* dog?" The man's voice had a sharp edge to it now.

"Mr. Riggs just gave him to me for keeps," explained Billy.

"Well, you can just take him right back," said the man. "What made you think you could have a dog?" He gave the paper an angry shake. "Besides, he's about the homeliest mutt I ever saw."

"I'll keep him out of sight," begged

Billy. "I'll feed him and take care of him and he won't bother anybody."

"Yeah?" said the man. "And who'll pay for his grub? You eat more than your keep right now. There isn't any extra for a dog."

Billy swallowed hard. "He's not a very big dog," he insisted. "He wouldn't eat much and I'll share what's coming to me with him."

"Talk's cheap," said the man, going

him. He won't let me have the food for him and I couldn't let the puppy starve." Billy spoke the words in a shaky voice.

"I haven't said he would starve," said Mr. Riggs. "I only said he was still your dog. How would you like to have him board and room over here?"

"I haven't any money to pay for his keep," explained Billy hopelessly.

"I haven't asked for money," said Mr. Riggs and smiled. "How would you like

WM. MOYERS

back to his paper. "You do as I say and take him back to Mr. Riggs."

So Billy turned right around and walked sadly back to the Riggs place with the pup. But Mr. Riggs wouldn't take him back.

"He's your dog," he told Billy, who was trying to wipe the tear stains off his cheeks. "When I give a dog, I give him for good."

"But he," Billy nodded toward the house next door, "he won't let me keep

to earn the pup's keep?"

Billy looked with surprised eyes at Mr. Riggs. "How?" he asked.

"I've noticed for some time now, that you have a way with dogs," Mr. Riggs explained. "I need a little extra help now and then, especially since this new litter arrived. Suppose you come over whenever you get the chance and mix feed and clean kennels, and I'll board the pup for your pay."

Billy's face broke into a smile so bright

that Mr. Riggs couldn't face it and had to look down at the ground for a minute. Would he work for the pup's board! Would he! Why he'd rather be fussing around dogs than doing anything else in the world anyway. And just by fussing around dogs, he could keep the pup.

"Gee, Mr. Riggs," he said with a long happy sigh. "Gee, thanks."

In a couple of days, Mr. Riggs cut off the puppies' tails because people expected fox terriers to have short tails. But Billy wouldn't let him touch the seventh pup.

"He's so homely anyway it won't matter a bit if his tail is too long," he explained. "I don't want him hurt."

"He'll be a funny-looking fox terrier with a too-long tail, all right," said Mr. Riggs. Then he added with a chuckle, "But then, he's funny-looking anyway."

Billy hadn't listened to a word since Mr. Riggs had said "Too-long tail." For the past two days, ever since he had had him, in fact, Billy had been trying to think of a name for his pup. Nothing seemed good enough. Spot, Trixy, Pal. They were all ordinary and none of them seemed to fit. But now, suddenly, Mr. Riggs had given him a name.

"That's it," Billy shouted. "That's his name."

"What is?" demanded Mr. Riggs.

"Why, Too-long. It's perfect. He's a dog with a too-long tail, and so Too-long is his own special name."

Mr. Riggs grinned and walked away. And from that day, the seventh pup was known as Too-long.

The weeks passed and then the months. Too-long grew, and his tail grew with him. From the first he thrived on Billy's care. And it seemed as if his too-long tail had been one reason for his good start in life. For while the other puppies were licking their sore stumps and waiting for their shortened tails to heal, Too-long frisked gaily at his master's heels as Billy went faithfully about his kennel chores.

It turned out to be lucky after all that the people he lived with didn't care much about Billy. If they had, they might not have wanted him to spend so much time away from home.

As it was, Billy spent more time at the Riggs place than he did at his own. As soon as school was over, he dashed next door, where Too-long fell upon him with sharp barks of welcome. And whenever Billy had a chance he worked with the pup, teaching him the things a well-trained dog should know. By the time Too-long was six months old, he had learned to follow at Billy's heels, to lie down when told to do so, and to bring a ball right to his master's feet. Even Mr. Riggs had to admit that Too-long, for all his bad looks, was as sharp as a needle.

By the time he was a year old and Billy ten, Too-long stayed wherever you told him to, jumped over a broomstick to bring the ball, spoke, shook hands, and rolled over. Billy thought he was the most wonderful dog in the world.

"You've done a good job with him," Mr. Riggs told Billy. "It's too bad you've taken all that trouble with a dog that can't ever go into the show ring. He could be a champion with what he knows if he just had the looks."

Then, one day just a week before the dog show, bad luck decided to pay a visit to Mr. Riggs. The only dog that he had planned to enter in the show that year took a bad cold. How it happened nobody knew. Mr. Riggs' face looked as long as Too-long's tail.

That's the way it is with the people who own kennels. If they don't have a dog to put in the show, they feel as if the whole year had been lived in vain. Never before, since he had been raising fox terriers, had Mr. Riggs failed to bring home a blue ribbon, which means first prize. And this year, he would have no ribbon at all. Not even a second or a third, which, though they are only yellow and white, are better than no ribbon.

Billy, noticing how sad Mr. Riggs looked, began to put his brain to work. He knew a thing or two about dog shows.

That very day, with Too-long at his heels, he went downtown to the dog-show office. He didn't say a word about it to Mr. Riggs. But the evening before the show day, he bathed and brushed Too-long within an inch of his life. Then he went over with him again all the things he had taught him. Then he went home, still without saying a word of his plan to anyone.

The next morning, Billy borrowed a collar and rope from the kennel office, and started for the dog show.

Two hours later, Mr. Riggs, wandering about among the barking dogs and crowding people, came at last to the ring where the Obedience Trials were being held. A large crowd was gathered there, for this event was for boys and girls who handled their own dogs, and he had a little trouble at first in seeing what was going on. When at last he could get a view of things, his jaw dropped in astonishment. For there, going through his

107

trials as easily and perfectly as he did in his own back yard, was Too-long. And with him was Billy.

In the ring were other dogs, held a little to one side by their masters while Too-long was having his turn. All kinds of dogs, big and little, fine and homely. But the homeliest of them all was Too-long. Mr. Riggs remembered then that there was one part of every dog show where looks didn't count. That was the Obedience Trials. Just so a dog carried out his master's orders perfectly, nobody cared what he looked like. And if he were perfect enough, he might win the blue.

Mr. Riggs felt his eyes grow misty as he watched the little dog, his spots all wrong and his tail held out straight and long behind him. There was such an eagerness in the way he tried to do just what Billy wanted that it seemed as if he knew he had a chance of bringing home a prize ribbon today.

Billy was as eager as the dog. He never once looked at the crowd. He never even heard the applause when Too-long jumped the hurdle and brought Billy the make-believe bone. He was too busy trying to send a thought message to Too-long saying that the hurdle was only a broomstick.

Too-long obeyed every command. Each time this happened, his too-long tail beat his sides in joyful thanks for the attention. The homely little dog had cap-tured the hearts of the audience, as had the boy with the patched jeans.

At last it was over and, after a check-up, a man approached Billy and handed him a blue ribbon. Too-long had won the blue!

Mr. Riggs caught up with Billy outside. "I saw you in there," he said. "I was proud of you."

Billy held out the blue ribbon. "You can put it in the glass box with the others," he said. "The kennel will have a ribbon to show for this year, too. Too-long's blue," he added.

Mr. Riggs took the ribbon. "Thank you, Billy," he said. "I appreciate what you've just done. Another thing. Too-long is big enough to earn his own keep. He's worth his weight in rats and is every inch a terrier. How would you like to work for wages instead of his board?"

"For you?" asked Billy, a light coming into his face.

"For me," said Mr. Riggs.

"You bet," said Billy. "I'd like that."

"Then you're hired as my right-hand man," said Mr. Riggs, and laid his hand on Billy's shoulder. Under it, he could feel Billy straighten his shoulders.

Ahead of them, Too-long frisked and galloped, his too-long tail wagging happily. It is doubtful if he knew any more than did Billy that seven is really a very, very lucky number!

Pino and Paint

By Dan Noonan

IF YOU had seen Pino riding along behind his father on the big paint horse that day, you would have thought he was just like any other Indian boy in that part of the Southwest, and you would have been right—almost.

Pino was much like all the other boys. Like them, he lived in a house of sun-dried brick, called adobe; like them, he spent much of his time helping his father and mother. Pino's parents made pottery painted with bright designs he was learning to copy. When he was not busy working with the fine red clay, he played and ate and slept and grew, just like all the other boys.

the settlement whose eyes were brighter, whose ears were keener, whose feet could run more swiftly or whose hands were more deft and sure.

There were many things Pino liked to do, but best of all he liked to go to the Indian agency with his father when he went to sell the pottery and buy supplies.

Pino liked everything about those days. He liked the trip over the twisting trail to the settlement. He liked the wide empty stretches of desert on all sides. Better still, he liked scrambling up behind his father and jogging along with the solid feeling of a horse between his legs.

How Pino wished that he might some

Pino was like them in every way but one. He could not talk.

"Do not be concerned," Pino's father said often to his mother. "Some day our son will talk. And meanwhile, see how fast he learns."

It was true; there was not a boy around

day have a horse of his own! When they reached the agency, there were other things to think of and wish for.

All the men lounging in the scant shade in front of the building called, "Hello there, Ata," to Pino's father and "Hello, Pino!" to Pino himself.

Pino's father called back, "Hello there!" and Pino smiled and waved his hand. All the men knew that this was Pino's way of saying Hello.

Then they unloaded the pottery and carried it inside and, while Ata bargained, Pino rambled around the dim, fragrant room, soberly eyeing the bolts of calico, the piles of moccasins, the shelves of bright-labeled tins, the knives and tools and sacks and cartons and boxes of goods. But in all the store nothing brought a gleam to Pino's eyes today. There was nothing he wanted but a horse.

Just as he was considering going out to sit on the step with the men, his father put a firm hand on his shoulder.

"This has been a good day," his father said, and Pino could see that he looked happy. "We have sold all but that cracked pitcher."

Pino smiled his approval and took the cracked pitcher from his father's hands as they walked out together.

Now there was time to visit with the men. They used few words but there was friendliness in their voices. A good trading day, they agreed. Good weather. Everything felt fine.

As they waited quietly between speeches, up came Tall Hat, the horse trader.

"How went everything with you, Tall Hat?" Pino's father asked his friend, while Pino stood by listening.

"Pretty good, thanks," Tall Hat replied, taking off his hat to pull out a cigar from inside the crown, "except for that pinto pony." He paused to light the cigar.

"That horse is loco. He lets no one ride him. I guess he is good for nothing. Every time I am left with him on my hands." He sighed as he looked toward the pony, standing alone in the corral. "I'd trade him for that cracked water pitcher; I am that tired of him."

As he finished, all the men chuckled at Tall Hat's joke. But Pino did not know that it was a joke, and he wanted that pony very much, so he silently held up the cracked water pitcher to Tall Hat.

Again everyone laughed, except Tall Hat. Without a word he took the pitcher and stood looking down at Pino. Then he turned to the boy's father and said, "The pony is traded to Pino."

Pino was not half a step behind as Tall Hat strode over to the corral. He was hanging over the topmost rail as Tall Hat swung a loop and lassoed the pinto pony. Then Tall Hat put a halter on the pinto and led him over to the boy. Putting the lead rope into Pino's hand he said, "Now he is yours, my friend."

Pino beamed his thanks, and when he and his father rode out of the settlement on their way home, the lead rope was still in Pino's hand, and the pony was following behind.

Pino was very happy. He kept looking back at his pony and thinking what a handsome animal he was and how splendidly he held his head. "I shall call him Paint to myself," Pino thought happily, "for he is a paint pony, and such a fine one, too. I wonder why Tall Hat thought he was loco."

As they drew near Pino's home, he

found out. The pony suddenly decided, with a toss of his head, to stop—and he did! Pino's father's horse, of course, kept right on going. Pino, with the lead rope looped snugly around his waist, sailed through the air and landed kerflop! right in the dusty road.

Pino picked himself up and sat there in the dust looking sadly at the horse.

"Now why did you do that, Paint?" he wondered silently.

At that the pony pricked up his ears and stared at Pino. "Why," the pony thought in surprise, "you can talk!"

Then they both stared at each other, for without either of them uttering a sound, they both could understand every word the other thought!

"Imagine a horse being able to talk," thought Pino.

"Well," thought the pony, "imagine a boy talking like a horse!"

At that moment Pino's father, who by now had reached home and dismounted, came out to the road and called back, "Come on, Pino!"

"Get on my back," said the pony, "for if anyone is to ride me it shall be you."

So to the amazement of his father and mother, Pino rode into the yard sitting

WM. MOYERS

easily on the back of the "loco" pony.

"You see," said his father to his mother, "although the boy cannot speak, he is a natural horseman."

"Your father is right," said the pony, when Pino repeated his father's words to Paint, "for what horseman can talk to his horse as you can?"

From that day on Pino and Paint were great friends, and always together.

Of course Pino still had work to do. But every afternoon when he had finished helping his mother with pottery, he could hear Paint calling to him.

"Come on, Pino, let's go! I'm tired of standing in the corral all day. Let's go for a ride," Paint would say, though Pino's mother never heard a word.

Then Pino would take a running jump onto his friend's back and away they would go. Sometimes they explored the Painted Mountain country with its vast stretches of bright-colored rocks and its great bowl of bright blue sky overhead.

They visited with prairie dogs on guard at the doorways to their underground cities; they drank together from small, clear, hidden springs. They told each other their thoughts as they jogged homeward in the gold and purple twilight. And always they were not just horse and rider, but good friends who spoke the same silent language.

On market days they rode into the settlement, where all the men were amazed at the way Pino had tamed down Tall Hat's loco pony.

And of course when Rodeo Day came and his father and mother rumbled off in the wagon, Pino, mounted proudly on Paint, went trotting along behind them.

Pino and Paint saw everything there was to see that wonderful day, and when the big event, the pony race, came along, they were beside the track, watching.

"What is this?" Paint asked as the horses formed up at the starting line.

"It's a race," Pino told him, "the big pony race."

"Why aren't we in it then?" asked Paint. "Why aren't we racing? Hey, move over there!" Paint whinnied to the other ponies. "Make room for us."

To the amazement of everyone, especially the riders, all the horses moved over and made room for Pino and Paint.

When Pino and Paint had joined them, the gun barked and off they all went!

Down the track they pelted, with dust clouds flying. Pino and Paint were far in the rear, but Paint was getting the feel of the track.

What a thunder of hoofs as the dust clouds swirled! And through it all Pino and Paint edged forward past more and more of the flying feet.

Coming around the last turn, Paint put on a desperate burst of speed. With Pino, breathless from excitement, crouching close to his neck, Paint thundered past the lead horses and up the home stretch.

One last frenzied effort, and Paint had crossed the finish line—Pino and his pony had won the race!

"Paint! We've won!" Pino cried out loud as Paint slowed down to a walk, his sides heaving. "We've won!" Pino screamed, beside himself with joy. But

Paint said nothing.

"Paint!" cried Pino again. "Can't you hear me?"

Now his father came running alongside, open-mouthed with surprise, for he had heard Pino's shouts.

"My son!" he cried. "You can speak!"

Pino, too, was surprised. "Yes," he said, after he had tried again, "I can speak."

But Paint said not a word. He could no longer understand what Pino was saying, now that he talked like other boys.

Or perhaps the trouble was that Pino could not understand Paint any more.

At first, when he realized this, Pino felt very sad. But he could see how fine it would be to be able to talk to the other boys and to the men at the agency house.

"And we shall always be friends," Pino whispered to Paint in boy talk as he led the pony back to the judge's stand.

And they are friends to this day, for there is one thing they both still understand—that they like each other.

WM. MOYERS

The Dog Who Chose a Prince

By Catherine Cate Coblentz

Long, long ago a small black spaniel howled mournfully through the night, as he shivered outside the high walls guarding the Dutch city of Delft. He was wet and cold and his feet hurt. He had traveled all day. He had swum ditches and canals, crossed fields and followed dusty roads. But always he had gone toward the sweet sound of the Delft bells. Something besides the sound of the bells had drawn him toward the city. Something seemed to tell him that here at last he would find the master he had been seeking.

When morning came, the spaniel howled no longer. He was too tired. But when the crowds of people gathered in one place, he slipped in among them. There were peddlers and vagabonds and honest countryfolk bringing their vegetables and chickens, and even their little fat pigs to market.

The little dog's eyes wandered from face to face and his ears listened to the voices. But if he saw a face he liked, he did not like the voice. Not a man nor a woman, nor a boy did he see and hear, whom he would choose for his master.

He sighed a little, for it was clear he had not undertaken an easy task. And then he heard the sound of many horses coming down the road.

The horses held their heads proudly, even though they had journeyed a long way. The men wore uniforms of blue and gold. One of them carried a banner of orange with these words written on it: "I shall carry on."

Then the little dog heard a voice which was deep and at the same time gentle and filled with beauty. It was like the sound of the bells which had led the dog through the night.

"The city is gold and silver in the sun," said the voice. "It is a good city and a good land. I shall strive to keep the rights which these cities have gained and give this land the freedom it deserves."

The little dog looked into the face of the speaker. The face was thin and lined, as though the man had suffered much. But his brown eyes had a marvelously kind expression. This man, he decided, should be his master.

Just then someone cried, "See, the drawbridge falls."

The drawbridge had indeed fallen over the moat, and the great door of the city gate was opened. The horses bearing the blue-and-gold-dressed riders dashed over the bridge.

The spaniel leaped quickly from the crowd. He must follow them. He must follow the man whom he had chosen for his master!

But the people who had been waiting

for the city gate to open surged forward and made a wall of legs between the spaniel and the horsemen. The spaniel dashed to one side and the other, but he could not get through. Finally he dashed underneath an ox-cart. And in this fashion he entered the city.

There were boats slipping along the canals, and there were many people and much laughter. There was a great market where all the country folk were gathering. And here and there was a horse. But the spaniel found no trace of the crowd of horsemen with the man whom he had chosen in their midst.

Up one canal and down another, the little dog wandered. Through this narrow street and that he went, sniffing and listening and watching. At last he came to the saddler's house, and the saddler, who was fond of animals, invited the dog to come in. He gave the spaniel a good breakfast. Then he opened the door to a little courtyard, where there was a fountain and pigeons, and said, "Come out and rest in the sun, for I must finish this saddle. It is for an Important Person."

The dog was not the least bit interested in an Important Person. So, with a full stomach he lay down in the sun on the warm bricks of the courtyard and put his nose in his paws. Soon he was fast asleep. He dreamed, and when he awoke, he thought he was still dreaming. For he could hear the voice of the man whom he had chosen for his master.

"It is a fine saddle," said the voice. "Clearly you are a Master Workman, for I have never had a better."

The dog hurled himself at the door, barking sharply. "Let me in," said the bark. "Let me in. This is an important matter! A most important matter!"

But the door to the courtyard remained closed. And when at last it did open, the Important Person had gone. The dog leaped to a little chest beside the window

115

and looked out. Yes, it was the same. His ears, his nose had not deceived him. Now he filled his eyes with the sight of his chosen master.

"The Prince of Orange knows good work," said the saddler.

The dog barked once more. But it was useless. Down the narrow street the man went and turned a corner. The dog started to whine. Then he stifled the whine, for he saw that the saddler had forgotten him. The man threw wide the door and stepped briskly down the street. He must tell his friend, the weaver, how the Prince of Orange had praised the saddle he had made.

But the spaniel did not wait. Even as the saddler opened the door, the dog was out of the saddler's house and headed for the corner where his chosen master had disappeared.

It was easy enough, he found, to trail the Important Person, if he kept his head low and sniffed along the ground. Finally he came to a house under some linden and willow trees. Here the trail ended.

So the spaniel sat down on the white-scrubbed walk and waited. He had learned that if one only waited long enough, closed doors would open.

This time it happened as it had before. A man came with a letter in his hand, and the door was opened. The spaniel fairly flew through the air, and he managed to get inside beside the messenger before the door closed. As luck would have it, he dashed straight into the open room where the Prince was sitting before a great table.

"What . . . ?" came the voice.

"Only a dog, sire," said the servant, banging his head as he reached under the table to haul forth the spaniel. Before the Prince had even seen him, the dog found himself outside.

"Be off," said the servant sharply.

But the spaniel did not go far. The moment the door was closed, he crept back and sat down on the white-scrubbed walk once more.

A second time he managed to slip in, and again a servant drove him out.

When for a third time the dog succeeded in entering the house, he jumped straight into the lap of his chosen master.

"Let me look at this persistent one," laughed the Prince. The spaniel wiggled with delight at the sound of that laugh, for it was free and deep.

The Prince turned the little dog's head upward, and the kind eyes of the man looked deep into the eyes of the dog. The spaniel tried to put all that he felt in the look which he gave back to the man. He tried to say how he had set forth to choose a master and how he had chosen the Prince from the moment he had seen him. He tried to explain how he had hunted for him all through the city.

Strangely enough, the Prince of Orange understood. For after a silence he asked, "Would you like to remain with me, then?"

The spaniel barked and his tongue darted toward the man's fingers.

"A nuisance, your highness," protested the servant.

"Perhaps . . . perhaps a friend!" The voice had a strange hushed tone in it. And the dog understood that the man needed him as much as he needed the man.

"Will you serve me faithfully?" asked the voice, very softly. And the man added slowly, "It may not be easy."

The dog's bark was sharp and eager. Again the Prince seemed to understand. He turned and said, "The spaniel is mine. His name—well, it must be imposing. Let me think." Then he laughed aloud. "He looks somehow like my favorite Roman general. His name was Pompey."

The dog barked. It was a good name.

So that is how a little Dutch dog chose his master. And wherever the Prince of Orange went, the spaniel went, too, even into battle. Pompey proved himself a good companion. For, when the day was over and cares were heavy on the man's shoulders, the spaniel cheered and comforted the Prince. Those who bear the burden of freedom for others are often lonely themselves. So it was with William of Orange.

Now the Spaniards were determined to put an end to the Prince. For, under his leadership, the Dutch were united in their struggle for freedom. But always the Prince escaped the soldiers of Spain. Always he remained to lead his people.

So it went until the year 1568, when the Prince of Orange pitched his tent near the city of Mons. There he rested, with Pompey on guard, and his own men near in tents close by. Meanwhile, in the camp of the Spaniards, an officer named Romero plotted against the life of Prince William. He planned to do by a trick what the Spaniards had not yet been able to do on the field of battle.

Through a traitor, Romero arranged that the men who guarded the Prince of Orange should be drugged. So, while the Prince worked late in his tent, one by one those about him who should have been watching fell asleep.

Meanwhile through the night came the Spanish soldiers with their leader, Romero. Over their armor they wore long white shirts, so that they seemed like a horde of ghosts in the dark. Like so many snowflakes they slipped across the countryside. Their swords flashed and the sleeping soldiers of the Prince were killed.

Nearer and nearer they came to the tent of the Prince. The Spaniards were triumphant. Let them but kill the Prince, and the King of Spain could do thereafter just as he pleased with his Dutch subjects.

But they had not counted on Pompey, who spent each night by his master's bed. Something in the strangeness of the silence, it may be, wakened him. Perhaps he heard a stifled groan or the sound of a sword clinking on a stone.

At any rate, inside the tent of the Prince of Orange, the spaniel Pompey burst into a sudden torrent of barks. At first, the Prince, who had thrown himself upon his camp cot without undressing, did not waken. Perhaps he, too, had partaken of the drugged food. Perhaps he was simply too weary.

Pompey was certain now that evil things were afoot. He caught new, unknown scents. He heard strange voices. He ceased barking and leaped to his master's bed. His pink tongue licked fever-

ishly at his master's face. His paws tugged at the man's shoulders.

The Prince sat up. He shook his head and he, too, heard strange sounds. He called to the guard outside, but no one answered. He heard a thud and then someone was fumbling at the entrance to the tent.

The Prince waited not a second. He jerked up the tent behind him and crawled underneath. Pompey flattened himself and was at his heels. There was a riderless horse, standing uncertainly in the darkness.

The Prince leaped into the saddle, and the spaniel followed. In one arm the Prince cradled the dog, and the horse, as though understanding the precious bur-

den he bore, moved quietly away from the empty tent. Crouching low, the Prince escaped.

"Only a riderless horse," whispered one Spanish soldier to another.

But another Spaniard came angrily from the tent. "This is the tent. And the bed is warm. But there is no one here. The dog is gone, too."

"That dog . . ." swore Romero, tearing his white shirt in his anger.

But freedom was saved, for the Prince of Orange was saved. The spaniel had served the Prince faithfully. And to this day you will see that the statues of the Prince of Orange—whom the Dutch called the Father of his Country—always have a little spaniel at the man's feet.

Karoo, the Kangaroo

By Kurt Wiese

KAROO, the Kangaroo was born in a land where it rains but once a year. The sands there are so thirsty that they drink up all the water, and there are few rivers that run between green banks down to the sea. Australia is a pleasant place, in spite of that, for the sun is warm.

When little Karoo was born, there was no fur at all on his smooth little body, no bigger than a squirrel's, and he was glad about the warm sun, and glad there was no rain, as he curled on the ground waiting for his mother.

Presently she came jumping through the tall grass. She picked him up tenderly with her strong soft lips. Then she dropped him in a pocket inside herself. That is what mother kangaroos are famous for!

Inside his mother, in her warm, dark, deep, soft pocket, Karoo went sound asleep as children do in bed. It was cosy.

And after a while, velvety brown fur began to grow on his bare little body. And his hind legs grew longer and longer. But his front legs stayed short. And his tail grew even faster than his hind legs, and it grew strong enough to use as a brace. He could sit upon his tail almost as if it were a stool, when his mother was standing still. When she hopped about, that was different. But when she was listening, or sunning herself, or quietly eating, Karoo practiced mightily with his short front legs, and his long hind legs, and his fine strong tail.

By and by he could sit up, and he thought "Maybe I can hop." So he pulled himself up by his front paws, and poked his head out of his mother's pocket to have a look at the world.

What he saw was one of the great rolling grassy plains of Central Australia. Hundreds of beautiful Kangaroos were nibbling the tender green grass. It was a most exciting luncheon.

Not far away, well balanced on his stout and useful tail sat an old, old Kangaroo, Captain Kango Kangaroo.

Suddenly Captain Kango wiggled his ears and waggled them and whistled through his nose. And when he whistled, all the hundreds of Kangaroos went plop and hop, hoppity hop. They went in a herd. They went in a rush. Hop. Hop.

Ploppity hop.

Karoo's mother pushed him inside her, plop, fast quick into her pocket, and hop, hop, off she went as fast as the rest. She didn't want to be left behind.

Hop, hop! Little Karoo wondered what it was all about. But nobody stopped to tell him what the hurry was for.

By and by there came a day when Karoo's mother let him out of her pocket and began to teach him the ways of a proper kangaroo.

He learned to jump. Just at first he often tumbled on his velvet nose.

Then he learned to leap and land in elegant curves like Captain Kango's.

He nibbled at the sweet green grass, that grew higher than his head, and he watched all the others out of the corner of his eye.

"I am growing up," he said to himself, "and I am a part of this great big wonderful herd." It was very fine to be a kangaroo in the spring of the year on the wide plains of Australia.

Karoo's mother gave him rules to keep him safe.

"Karoo, my little Kangaroo," she said, admiring his bonny little velvet coat, "eat plenty of fine, green, tender grass, but never, never wander out of your mother's sight. Between nibbles look and see just where I am, and at any strange sight, or any strange sound, steer with your tail, and jump for my pocket.

"And most particularly, ever and always, beware the barking Dingo. The Dingos are wild dogs. They are fierce and always hungry, and they eat Kangaroos. Never waste a second when you hear a Dingo bark. Fly for my pocket. And all your life, when you hear the bark of a Dingo, make haste. The Dingos run so fast themselves that Kangaroos must always hurry out of their sight. Dingos are dreadful. Every Kangaroo knows that!"

Little Karoo was much impressed. And every day he watched his mother out of the corner of his eye.

But one day, when the sun was very bright, and the wind played tunes among the grasses, he forgot

He was practicing with his stout tail, and jumping more and more like Captain Kango, when he heard a warning whistle, and far across the plain the terrifying bark and yelp of the Dingos.

He looked for his mother. She was nowhere to be seen.

"Mother! Mother!" cried Karoo, but there was no answer, and the whole herd came through the grasses with a sound like thunder and the big flying feet of Captain Kango, leaping, leaping, knocked poor little Karoo into the sand under the grass.

The bristling, barking, snarling Dingos in a great pack came bounding after. The noise was terrible. The dust was, too.

By and by, Karoo stopped trembling and sat up. Far away in the distance all the Kangaroos and all the Dingos were vanishing.

Little Karoo was alone.

Karoo was sad. He did not wish to be all alone in the world. So he decided to follow the footprints of the Dingos and the Kangaroos. As he hopped along over the plain, the grasses seemed to grow taller and taller.

"I think this must be the forest," he said, when he came to a eucalyptus tree.

He was very tired so he sat down under the tree and went to sleep.

When he woke up it was dark. The white trunks of the gum trees frightened him. The loose bark on the trees scratched in the wind and made flapping sounds. All sorts of noises that he did not know the why of, worried him.

All night he shivered, and his little heart ached whenever he thought of how kind his mother was and how warm and soft her body used to be when he slept in her pocket.

Long before the sun was golden, when the day was still gray, Karoo made up his mind to go back to the grassy plain. The forest was too strange and different.

Out on the plain, even being lonely was not so bad. The sun was warm. The dew dried.

He was nibbling at his breakfast in a most contented way, when he heard a sly slither in the grass.

It was a snake! A coiled black snake with wicked eyes and darting tongue.

With all the strength of his whole young life in his sturdy little tail, Karoo pushed off and leaped into the air. Over the snake and away like hopping lightning, Little Karoo made for the forest.

When he reached the shady woods his heart began to beat more slowly. He caught his breath and hopped to a clearing in the forest.

Karoo looked around, and lo, climbing a young gum tree was his mother's friend, Koala, the chunky Australian bear, with a baby bear on her back.

"Koala, Good One," shouted Karoo. "Help me. I lost my mother when the Dingos came barking upon us. Where has the herd gone?"

"That I cannot say," said Koala, kindly, "but Ant-eater will know. Look for him in his cave beyond the three eucalyptus trees. He comes out in the open to feed. I stay hidden in the leaves, and see no one pass. But Ant-eater knows everything that goes on in the grass and on the plain."

So Karoo hopped off toward the three trees. Sure enough, there was a cave door in the sunny patch beyond the trees.

"Ant-eater, Good One," shouted Karoo, "come out and help me. Show me the way to the herd. I lost my mother when the Dingos came barking upon us."

Then Karoo became very frightened for the Ant-eater seemed to him more ugly than any other creature, with his back like a stubby bobbed porcupine, skin as thick and tough as shoe soles, and a nose as long as a policeman's club.

"That I cannot say," said the Ant-eater kindly, "but the Duck's Bill will know. She spends her days swimming up and down the little river which is the only one for hundreds of miles around. All the animals come to the river; she can hear under water and she will tell you where the Kangaroos spoke of going. Go west until you come to the river, Karoo, and then shout."

So Karoo hopped west. By and by, he smelled water. A few more jumps and he came to a flowing river with gum trees green along the bank.

"Duck's Bill, Good One," he shouted.

Bubbles came up from the water. Karoo's mother had told him many things about Duck's Bill—how she laid eggs like a bird, and had a mouth like a beak. Yet she was an animal and fed her babies with her own milk. Duck's Bill rose from the water and looked out of small cross eyes at Karoo.

"Duck's Bill," said Karoo politely, "where has the herd gone? I lost my mother yesterday when the Dingos came barking upon us."

But Duck's Bill said, "Only the Dingos have drunk of the river since yesterday. When they come all creatures stay away."

And she started to slip under the water again. But Karoo looked so tired that she added, "Go deep into the jungle and call the Kiwi—an old wise bird who knows all things without seeing or hearing any of them."

So Karoo hopped straight into the forest, and the trees grew thicker and thicker and the path very dark.

"Kiwi," he shouted. "Kiwi," and by and by, suddenly right in front of him was Kiwi—a portly fellow with a very long beak, with a thin mustache all around it. His legs were strong and his feet were like a giant's rake and very good for scratching.

"Kiwi, Good One, you who know all things, which is the way to the herd? Yesterday I lost my mother when the Dingos came barking."

"The herd is very far away," said Kiwi slowly. "You must go and ask the birds who live in the tops of the trees. The Kookaburra will know for he lives on the edge of the forest and he has very big eyes."

Then Karoo began to cry. "That is where the snake lives. I cannot go there to ask."

"Don't be silly," said the Kiwi. "Don't you know that Kookaburra is the great Snakekiller? Clever snakes never come near the nest of the Kookaburra."

So Karoo turned around and hopped back through the forest toward the plain.

He was growing tired, and feeling very blue when he came to the Red Gum tree. He sat down sadly and waited for the sun to set. Soon the light faded and the Kookaburra and his wife arrived.

When Kookaburra saw the little Kangaroo, he began to laugh. "HaHaaHa-Haa! Haw Haw Hoo Hoo Hoo!"

It was the most terrible and cruel noise Karoo had ever heard.

Karoo stopped trembling long enough to shout, "Kookaburra, Good One, where has the herd gone? Yesterday I lost my mother."

"Haw Haw Hoo Hoo Ha Ha!" crowed Kookaburra. "The Dingos almost got your mother, but she is where the herd is now. Due East across the desert."

Karoo pushed hard on his strong tail and started off Due East.

He had not leaped very far when he saw that it was night so he hopped straight back to the Red Gum tree, where he could see the Kookaburra up in the tree. Safe from the snakes, he slept all night, and early in the morning when the stars were still in the sky he started off again, after a mouthful of delicious grass, Due East across the desert.

He hopped all morning, and he did not stop at noon. There was not a single leaf to munch nor any blade of grass. All around him was the desert. So he hopped Due East all night long, and in the morning licked a little dew from the rock for his breakfast and hopped Due East, as if he were running away from the little black shadow that was the only company he had.

When the sun was red in the sky and just going down, he caught sight of something green and knew that the rim of the desert was just ahead.

Karoo was too tired to jump any further, so he lay down in the cold sand and did not open his eyes until daybreak.

Karoo woke with a start and there all around him was the herd. Karoo leaped high in the air. He was surprised himself that he could jump so high.

Old Captain Kango caught sight of him and made a most familiar toot.

Karoo heard a sound like rushing and thunder. The herd jumped toward him, and there was his mother, looking lovelier and kinder than all the rest.

She snatched him up and dropped him in her soft warm pocket. It was almost too small for him. He knew then that he was almost grown up. But it was very nice to be there, cosy and safe, with their two hearts throbbing like two parts of the same tune. He could hear her voice: "I think it will never happen again!"

"Absolutely," said Karoo to himself as he snuggled down to rest from his trip across the desert.

The Horse That Came From Heaven

By Catherine C. Coblentz

THE Black Horse hoped something important was going to happen to him. There was expectation in each high-stepping foot, in the way he arched his neck, in the tilt of his nose.

Proudly and happily he led all the other Spanish horses. Forgotten was the ocean journey of several weeks from the Island of Cuba to Mexico. Forgotten, too, were the battles with the Indians when he had carried first one master and then another on his back.

Now his rider was Cortez himself, that Spanish Conquistador who had conquered the Aztecs and all Mexico for Spain. The Black Horse had heard him say that he was going southward next to Honduras.

It didn't matter much to the Black where they went. He liked to glimpse from the corners of his slanting eyes that black silken banner with a scarlet cross in its centre waving over the Spanish soldiers. He liked to hear the bugle playing, and didn't mind at all the high shrill shrieks from the herd of pigs taken along to provide food for the soldiers in case game should be scarce.

But gradually the pace of the Black slowed a little. Cortez was not a light person to carry, and besides he was dressed in heavy armor. The Black remembered that he had no idea how long the way might be to Honduras.

He was glad later that he had saved his strength. He had never dreamed there would be such high chains of mountains to be crossed, such rivers that must be conquered. Sometimes he swam across them. Sometimes he was carried across by Indians in canoes.

Good grass was often scarce. Flies settled on the Black's coat by day and mosquitoes by night, even though he switched his tail or twitched his skin constantly to shake them off.

Sometimes in the dusk horrible bats would descend upon him and plague him almost as much as did the insects and flies, and the bats were not so easily dislodged.

Day after day went by, and the Black still led the way southward. After all, he once thought, this was probably the most important thing that could happen to him.

One morning he came to a wide river. It flowed fast in places, but along the shores it seemed hardly to move at all, and it was filled with alligators. The Black had heard it said that alligators were fond of eating horses. So he waited eagerly for the bridle rein to tighten. If Cortez urged him into the water, he knew he would obey.

But after he had cantered up and down the river-bank for a little, Cortez patted his neck and said, "No, my Black, that

125

river is not for *you* to swim." And the man slipped from the horse's back and led him over to the shadow of some ceiba trees.

There for four days the horse of Cortez rested with the other horses, watching while the Spaniards cut down trees and built a narrow bridge. When it was done Cortez led the Black across the bridge, while the other Spaniards followed, leading their steeds. The Black switched his tail triumphantly at the hungry alligators. Surely now the worst of his troubles were over.

Even as that idea passed through his mind his left fore foot sank under him.

Quickly he placed the other front foot on what appeared to be solid ground. It, too, sank out of sight.

Then the third and fourth foot plunged into black mud and ooze. All the horses that had followed after him were sinking also. He could hear their frightened breathing; somewhere one of them screamed. What had looked like solid earth was a terrible marsh.

He glimpsed Cortez jumping from grassy hummock to grassy hummock. Then he heard the voice of his master calling his horse to follow him.

Vainly the Black tried to obey. But the more he struggled the deeper he sank

into the muck. His two front legs were in the mire to his knees, his hind quarters to his body.

Desperately he lunged, and succeeded in raising his front feet for a moment on what seemed to be firm ground. But as he attempted to free his hind quarters even this ground failed him, and the front feet sank down once more, until he felt the mire along his whole body. The morass was filled with struggling, snorting, and neighing horses.

Taking another quick glimpse, the Black saw that all the *men* had crossed, and he was glad of that. He heard Cortez shout an order and caught the answering voices of the men, who were coming back again toward their horses. They had picked up anything on which they could lay their hands, and brought armfuls of long reed-like grasses and fallen tree branches, and threw them down in front of the animals, urging them to attempt to use even this frail support. Some of the horses succeeded in partially raising themselves in this way.

But the Black, after getting one foot upon the armful of stuff Cortez thrust before him, saw both foot and the green grass disappear again in the dark slipperiness.

Deeper and deeper he sank. The mud was cool against his sides, but he did not appreciate the coolness. He was afraid, desperately afraid.

Then the mud closed over his spine with a sucking sound. He flung his head up and back as far as he could. But it seemed useless. The black stuff drew him down, down. Now it was at his mouth, his nostrils. Taking one last, long breath of air, he sank out of sight. Only his ears were to be seen, little points above the black mud.

And then, "Swim, my Black One, swim," came the voice of his master. "Swim, swim! I tell you, *you can swim.* Black One, come, *come! Swim!*"

Was the master out of his mind? What horse could swim in *mud?* But the horse of Cortez obeyed the voice. He thrust his feet out in the swimming motion. And he moved. Slowly but surely he moved forward.

The sucking mire seemed to leave his nose. He felt men's hands pushing down through the mud to his hind quarters, propelling him forward. He heard the voice of Cortez calling, coaxing. Valiantly he struggled.

Suddenly he was freed. He was swimming quite easily. He shook the mud from his eyes and opened them. A few feet ahead of him some Spaniards were standing and calling. Others were jumping frantically from grass spot to grass spot at one side of the horses. Horses were swimming to the right and to the left of the Black. Ahead of him he saw one scrambling out of the mire and standing erect with four feet securely on firm ground. The Black made for that spot.

Afterward as he lay panting on the ground he listened to the men explaining how the struggling of the many horses in the mud had caused a middle lane of water to gather, and by this narrow waterway the steeds had finally been able

to swim to safety.

The Black looked around him happily. He was a ridiculous sight, covered from his eyes to the end of his tail with drying mud. But he did not mind. The sky had never seemed so blue, or the trees so green.

He struggled to his knees. Suddenly Cortez was beside him and all the Spaniards likewise fell on their knees. There in the sunlight, under the gray moss that swayed from dead tree branches, the men gave thanks for the saving of their horses.

The Black, too, felt very thankful.

All Mutt

By Helen Train Hilles

TONY woke up with a gulping feeling
of something going-to-happen. He
lay flat on his back in bed, his heart
thumping almost straight through him to
the mattress. It was a little like the breathless feeling you got just before Christmas
—except that at Christmas you were sure
something *nice* was going to happen.

Today was the day of the Pet Show.

Tony kept his eyes closed. Then he
slowly stretched out one arm in the
candy-striped pajama sleeve till it hung
over the edge of the bed. He heard a little
thump and then a sniff. Then he could
feel warm breath on his knuckles, and a
wet cold nose. He waited. In a moment
he felt a rough sandpapery tongue covering his fingers with short timid licks.

Tony sighed, and some of the hard
lump went out of his throat. Then, forgetting, he moved his hand. There was a
gentle yelp, and something heavy scuttled
under the bed.

"Doggone it!" sighed Tony. "Now I've
gone and scared him and he was getting
so good!"

He rolled out of his bed and crawled
under it.

"Come, Handsome, nice doggie," he
coaxed, a little breathlessly, because of his
cramped position. Nothing happened.
Tony came out from under the bed, sat
down in a resigned sort of way on the

floor, and waited patiently.

By degrees Handsome inched himself
forward until the heavy head that Father
said reminded him of a bulldog stuck out
from under the box spring. Next came

two forepaws, on either side of the head. The paws didn't look as though they belonged to Handsome at all. They had a sort of delicate curly French-poodley look that went oddly with his heavy head and ferocious jaw.

Tony coaxed him farther out. Even he couldn't help being surprised all over again at the black and white fox-terrier thinness of Handsome's middle. A laugh started inside of Tony. But he was very careful not to let it come out, because the last thing he wanted to do was hurt Handsome's feelings, particularly to-day.

Handsome was all the way out from under the bed now, his long feathery tail brushing the floor like a mop. Mother was sure there was some setter in him.

"How could I have entered him in the Pet Show?" thought Tony in despair.

Of course it was all the fault of Tom Green who had started all the teasing that Tony had to stand, and who'd given Handsome the name that made Tony hurt inside every time he heard it.

Tony'd never thought of entering Handsome till he'd met Tom whistling along the street only two days ago.

"Hi!" said Tom loudly. "I got some raw meat here for my alligator." Tony set his jaw.

"Hi!" he said. Tom Green needn't be so cocky about his darned alligator. He knew it was the only alligator in town. So he'd be bound to win with the alligator entry.

"Too bad," said Tom with a smirk, starting to walk on, "*you* haven't got anything to enter."

Tony's mouth opened of its own accord and, before he had time to shut it, he heard his voice saying, "I'm going to show H-Handsome." (The name had stuck.)

"W-what!" Tom's jaw dropped, and he looked so funny that it helped take away the unexpected feeling that Tony's own words had given him. Tony gulped.

"Sure," he made himself say airily, and walked on. Tom recovered himself enough to yell at Tony.

"Ya!" he jeered. "I'd like to know where that will get you! Handsome isn't handsome—he isn't even *anything!*" The words cut into Tony's back. He quickened his steps. As he rounded the corner he heard Tom's last words.

"He doesn't even wag his tail!"

Once around the corner a dreadful weight sank on Tony. What had made him say that to Tom? He didn't want to show Handsome! And Tom was right. Handsome wasn't handsome—he wasn't anything *yet!*

You couldn't explain to Tom Green or anyone else how you felt about Handsome. When you found a pathetic looking dog on your lawn, and you were the only person he'd ever let come near, you just *had* to take him in. And because he was so scared of everybody, and ran with his tail between his legs at the slightest sound, it made you even sorrier for him. Somebody must have been horrid to him —somebody probably like Tom Green.

Tony had worked gently and patiently with Handsome and the dog really had improved. He wasn't very scared with

Tony alone, now—only if Tony forgot and raised his hand or dropped something. Yesterday Handsome's tail had given a thump on the floor that might be called almost a wag. But with other people, Handsome hadn't improved much.

And in an hour or two now Tony and Handsome would be at the Pet Show.

Tony looked down at Handsome. The dog's head was on his knee and he was looking up at Tony with big bulldog eyes. Tony felt his own eyes water a little.

"If *they* could only see you now—just your head, I mean, without the rest of you!" he whispered huskily. "You look almost h-handsome!"

Tony got to his feet and started dressing. Dressing didn't usually take Tony very long, but this morning he brushed his tow head even in the back, and put on a bright tie and tied it carefully.

Ready! Tony opened the door and called to Handsome, still hopeful that some day Handsome would follow. He didn't. Tony's patience cracked.

"Oh, all right, *stay* there!" he yelled. "*I* don't care if you want to be so dumb!" Then he ran back. "I'm sorry, I didn't mean to hurt your feelings," he whispered. Tony's bluff slipped over him again as he walked into the hall. He whistled as he slid down the bannisters, and bounced into the dining room. Father and Mother and Jane were having breakfast. There was a ring of puffed rice around Jane's place.

"Hello, Son," called Father in a hearty hollow voice that didn't fool anybody, least of all Tony..

"We've got wheat cakes, dear," said Mother in a sweet anxious voice.

"Hello," said Tony. He poured himself a glass of milk.

"It's a beautiful day—" began Mother.

"For the Pet Show!" burst out Jane, emerging suddenly from her mug, a white milk moustache on her upper lip.

Mother and Father looked at each other, then started talking very quickly, both at once.

"Jane thought she'd show the baby mouse," said Mother, "the one that got caught on the flypaper and we washed off."

"In a saucepan, so's he can't crawl up the sides," said Jane, her face anxious under the thick black bang that covered her forehead.

"Not a bad idea," said Tony.

"Of course there will be ever so many dog entries," said Father, much too casually. "That's the biggest class and no one can expect to win with so much competition."

"Better be going," said Tony, gruffly. He knew Father was being kind and he could not bear to have anyone be kind to him just now. He rose from the table.

"We'll get ready," said Mother.

"You all going?" asked Tony.

"Certainly," exclaimed Father. "Promised Mr. Green we'd see him judge."

When Tony reached his room he opened his top bureau drawer and took out something carefully wrapped in tissue paper. It had taken all his allowance for weeks, and it exactly matched the color of his tie.

He looked down at Handsome.

"If you don't like this—well, you're just crazy," he said firmly. He leaned down and gently fastened the shiny green patent leather collar round Handsome's neck and snapped the leash to it.

Handsome sniffed but didn't scratch.

Suddenly the window shade flapped. Handsome tried to scuttle under the bed, but Tony had the leash tight in his hand. Handsome almost, but not quite, pulled Tony over. Tony set his teeth.

"You just *got* to come now," he said desperately.

Without looking back Tony pulled Handsome along with all his strength. By the time he reached the stairs Tony's nose was beaded with perspiration, between the freckles. Handsome, he thought, weighed a ton.

Down the stairs they went, Handsome sitting, his fox-terrier body landing with a thump at each step.

It was easier to pull Handsome along the slippery floor at the bottom of the steps to where Father and Mother and Jane were waiting.

"My mouse is in here!" said Jane, holding out her saucepan, covered by a clean dish towel. Father and Mother looked at Handsome and his new leash.

"Why!" exclaimed Father in his hollow, this morning's voice. "Doesn't he look—unusual!"

The whole family were on the street now. The street was usually quiet, but this morning it was alive with children, parents, and animals, and strange yelps and noises were in the air. All the action on the street was surging in one direction, towards the Bakers' large Field.

The noise was too much for Handsome. He shivered, turned, and tried desperately to claw his way back.

"You can't!" Tony whispered between gritted teeth. He turned and scooped up the heavy dog in his arms. It was a much warmer day than he had realized.

Tony struggled along for a few steps without Father and Mother noticing him, because Father and Mother were calling greetings to friends and trying to restrain Jane, who was jumping up and down, sing-songing "I've got a teeny mouse! I've got a teeny mouse!" Then Father saw and flashed a quick look at Mother.

"Here, I'll take him," he offered.

"No—you—won't," panted Tony. He could stand it if he just looked straight ahead and didn't listen to the cheery sounds and squeals around him. Handsome weighed a lot, but he looked quite well as he lay there, confidently, his big head hanging over Tony's right arm, which was beginning to go to sleep. He could see the Field now—only a few more steps.

Walking ahead of him was the broad back of Mr. Green, the Judge. Next was Tom, carrying a cigar box with holes punched in the lid. For a fleeting moment Tony envied him. How light that tiny alligator in a cigar box must be!

The Bakers' Field was already trampled all around the temporary platform that Mr. Baker had laid down specially for the show. For quite a circle around it parents, children, and pets were surging.

Tony sat down on the grass a little way off from the platform. Handsome was still trembling, but there were so many people that no one noticed. Tony saw that some of the other pets were frightened, too. He felt a little better, and he could rest his arms.

There was a hush of human voices as Mr. Green got on the platform and clapped his hands. The animal voices, of course, went right on. Mr. Green cleared his throat.

"The first class," he announced, "seems to be birds. Will all the entries please step to the platform?"

The crowd murmured with interest as a long line of assorted children filtered through the mob to the platform, bird-cages held on high, then stood giggling before Mr. Green, who looked a little uncertain as to what to do.

"Put all those—all those things down on the floor," he directed, looking at the frame of bird cages which encircled him.

All the bird cages were set down—small wooden traveling ones, gold-colored wire canary ones, the Travis' green painted one that had a stand that made it loom high above the others, even though there was only a rather forlorn pair of love-birds in it; and the Cullens' parrot protesting loudly over being placed on the draughty floor of the platform.

The twittering of the disturbed birds started the other animals off. Dogs strained at their leashes and there were loud yelps and low snuffling noises.

"Hold your pets tight!" directed Judge Green through cupped hands.

Tony was watching everything with interest. No one had noticed either him or Handsome, and the dog was resting quietly on his knee, making only a few whuffly, soothing noises in his throat, because he had a touch of asthma.

Luck was with Mr. Green. It might have been hard to judge the birds—but a hush descended on the whole audience, even stilling the animals, when pale little Joe Malloy got down on his knees and opening the door of his shabby little wooden cage whistled softly to his bird. There was a gentle fluttery little noise that even Tony could hear and a flash of something tiny and primrose-colored; then Joe stood up, holding out his arm. A little yellow canary was perched on the boy's scrawny wrist, not at all scared. Amid the friendly roar of the audience you could hear a tiny clear trill.

No one was sorry when Joe got the first blue ribbon of the day.

Next came the alligator class. Tom Green was the only entry. Mr. Green must have known it, thought Tony, but he slipped his spectacles up on his forehead and boomed,

"Any other entries?"

There was a polite silence while Tom waited confidently for his prize. And just enough applause when he got his ribbon so Mr. Green's feelings wouldn't be hurt.

Mr. Green disposed of all the rabbits next. And then a tiny little girl got a ribbon for a chipmunk she had rescued from a cat.

Then Mr. Green called the mouse class. Tony stiffened. Jane's class. He hadn't

133

realized how many mice there were in town. Almost as many children filed up to the platform as in the bird class! There was a very swell-looking cage held above the heads of the Maloney twins. Tony's heart sank as Jane stumbled through the crowd carefully holding her saucepan at arm's length. All the others were *white* mice! Mr. Green adjusted his spectacles and looked over the squealing mice carefully. Then he looked at Jane.

"Let's see yours, Jane."

"Mine's just a *regular* mouse," said Jane. Everyone laughed. She put down the saucepan. Suddenly Tony saw the Reynolds' cat. It flashed towards the saucepan. "Look out!" he shrieked. "Oh, Janey, look out!" Jane whirled, bewildered. Then quick as a flash she sat down on her saucepan. Ned Reynolds came forward sheepishly and collected his cat. There were yells from the crowd:

"Good work, Janey!" "You take good care of your mouse!"

Mr. Green selected the finest white mouse and awarded it the ribbon. Then he turned to Jane.

"You win the field mouse ribbon," he announced kindly. Jane looked pleased but perplexed.

"He isn't a *field* mouse," she protested. "He's a *fly-paper* mouse!" The audience looked at one another. Mr. Green's face grew quite red, but Tony could tell it was a pleasant red.

"What do you mean, Janey?"

" 'Cause Mother and I found him on a fly-paper and washed him off!" piped Jane. Mr. Green cleared his throat.

"We'll change the award!" he said impressively. "Miss Jane Fiske gets a ribbon for the most original way of acquiring a mouse."

Tony beamed. He felt almost as though he'd gotten a prize.

"Anything else to clear up before we start on the dogs?" asked Mr. Green. The old weight hurled itself down on Tony's chest. He'd almost forgotten the dog class. He gulped. There was no reply to Mr. Green's question. Mr. Green took a drink of water.

"All right, bring up the dogs, and we'll get this thing over," he said genially.

There was a scramble as the dog owners made their way to the platform. Tony, heart thumping so loudly he was afraid Handsome might feel it, waited till almost everyone was at the platform. The less rustling around there was, the less scaring to Handsome. Handsome didn't need to be pulled. With a terrified look around him, Handsome stuck close to Tony's legs, almost tripping him. And with a final heave Tony got Handsome up on the platform, where he sat, on the very edge, pushed against Tony. Mr. Green was looking at a small brown Pomeranian-seeming dog, who was yapping at him.

"Take him over there—" he began, then he caught sight of Handsome, and Tony, unhappily, could feel his eyes freeze to him. "Upon my word!" exclaimed Mr. Green. "What's that?" Tony could feel the flush that seeped up from his collar to his forehead. "That's—that's my dog," he said defiantly.

Mr. Green turned his attention to the others. The big Airedale-looking dog of the Maloneys' was straining to get at the Booths' Pomeranian-like one, an old backyard enemy. The platform was crowded with assorted pets, all dogs, if not all unmistakable varieties of dog. Mr. Green was frankly bewildered. But he knew so many dogs from outside contacts that it wasn't so hard after all. He walked around the platform, looking intently at each. And every few minutes his eyes returned, as if fascinated, to Handsome. Tony was getting more and more uncomfortable.

"A most—most amazing dog," he heard Mr. Green murmur.

Tony flushed even redder. Was he making fun of Handsome?

"You can get down, and you, and you," said Mr. Green, and three dogs, held by their leashes in disappointed children's hands, climbed down off the platform.

Each time Mr. Green sent another dog down, and the platform grew less crowded, and the dogs left on it were plainly visible. Tony grew unhappier. Why put it off? Why couldn't he tell them to get down and get it over with?

One more dog out. Another—another —only five dogs left! It got more and more strained. It was like a bewildering game of "going to Jerusalem," one chair going at a time, leaving so few.

Four dogs left! Tony twisted Handsome's green patent-leather leash around his knuckles so tightly his knuckles grew white. What was happening, Tony asked himself.

The yappy Pomeranian was left—a pretty little dog with a horrid disposition. The Barrows' sort of poodle, the trick dog of the community, a teeny pup—and Handsome.

There was a breathless pause, then the teeny puppy was sent down. Three dogs left!

Then Mr. Green walked around the platform, pausing to look intently at each of the three dogs. He stopped at the poodle.

"Put him through his tricks!" he said to the poodle's master. The boy made him play dead dog and shake hands.

Mr. Green nodded. Then he looked at Handsome, with that same perplexed, strange look in his eye.

Mr. Green walked to the edge of the platform. "Folks!" he said, "This is the biggest class and the most difficult to judge. However, I feel sure you will agree with my decision when I award the first prize to the Hodgins' Pomeranian. He has by far the best points, technically,

of any dog here!"

The applause was loud, and Tony nodded. Mr. Green had done right. But why, why had he kept the rest on the platform? Mr. Green raised his hand.

"But we are giving other ribbons in this, the biggest class," he said. "The next goes to this near-poodle, the most intelligent and best trained dog in the show!"

This time the applause was even louder. It roared in Tony's ears. The dreadful feeling of something going to happen came over him again. He didn't breathe as Mr. Green raised his hand for the last time.

"The next prize," he said, "goes to Tony Fiske's dog, Handsome—for having more different kinds of dog in him than any other dog at the show!"

The wave of noise was deafening. Loud clapping filling the field, clapping for Handsome! Tony felt weak. He looked at Mr. Green with eyes that suddenly felt wet. He tried to speak when Mr. Green handed him the ribbon, but no words would go up his throat. He got down on his knees to pin the ribbon on Handsome, burying his face against Handsome's big head.

Then suddenly he straightened up and stared. Handsome was wagging his tail!

Such a Kind World

By *Mabel Leigh Hunt*

OLD gray Nellie was not a handsome horse. But in a kind world one does not need to be handsome in order to be loved. And the orphans who lived at the Children's Home dearly loved Nellie. Being too old and stiff to work, Nellie's time was theirs. Being slow, she was safe for even the littlest ones to ride. And on that elderly sagging back as many as six children could squeeze themselves in a merry row.

Privately, Nellie thought six riders were too many. Three, now—she wouldn't have minded at all. "But, by crickey, six squirming, kicking, screeching little orphans! Of course," added Nellie, kindly, "they're too young and lively to know how it feels to be old."

And, Nellie reminded herself, she had a great deal to be thankful for. Wasn't she spending her declining years in comfort? "An easy, idle life, with plenty of hay in my feed-box and plenty of love from the best sort of people, and that's kids," reflected Nellie. "Of course not a *lavish* amount of hay. It could be more, if you

URSULA KOERING

come right down to it and state the facts plainly. But no one has any extras in a County Children's Home, so you're really a lucky old nag," Nellie told herself.

Imagine, then, what a shock it was to her, one cold December day, to look into her box and find it empty! And oh, the children felt almost as mournful as Nellie! For Mom Pickett, the matron, said, "It's too, too bad, but the time has come when we shall have to get rid of Nellie. There's never any extra money, you know, and none to buy grain for an old horse that can no longer work for her board and keep. So," added the matron, before she thought how terribly shocking it sounded, "I'm afraid we shall have to sell Nellie for fertilizer."

"Sold down the river to the fertilizer plant!" ran the horrified whisper through the Children's Home.

The littlest orphans didn't understand, fortunately, but they heard that Nellie was doomed to go *away* because there was no food to be spared for her. They saved bits of crusts and apple-cores, prunes, scraps of carrots, potato-peel, cabbage leaves, and turnips and spinach, cooked and uncooked. Secretly and openly they carried these tidbits to Nellie, shivering in the damp December fields, where she had been turned to nibble what little grass she could find. The poor old nag, growing more bony every day, was in no condition to turn up her nose and be choosey, though she found prunes hard to get down; and the cheese offered her in the sticky small palm of four-year-old Ruby McGlish made Nellie's mouth feel queer and gummy for hours afterward. Oh yes, it was a dismal time for all!

To make it worse, Mom Pickett said, "No more rides on Nellie! A horse needs strength for that. Besides, the youngest ones must get used to doing without her."

"Maybe if you just mentioned Nellie —an' everything—to the Board," suggested Susan Spitznagle. Susan was thirteen, and had been in the Home a long time—long enough to know that in the hands of the Board of Directors rested the fate of orphans.

"I have the feeling that the Board would decide, without a moment's prittle-prattle, that Nellie must go," said Mom.

"Maybe if we'd drop hints around—to folks in town—and around," ventured Corky Trotter, uncertainly.

"We could send an article to the Bakersville *Tattler!*" cried Mickey Malone, who was as smart as they come. "In the article we'd tell how hard Nellie used to work for the Home, how we hate to see her go to the . . . oh, you know . . . how the little kids will cry! It ought to make folks awful sorry. They'd do something—maybe."

Mom Pickett smiled at Mickey. "It is a good idea," she murmured. "But there again I'm afraid the Board would think we were behaving in a way not expected of a Children's Home."

But Mickey and Corky and Susan and all the other older children thought an item in the Bakersville *Tattler* ought to work magic. They couldn't give up such a promising idea.

"I could write the article myself," de-

clared Susan, who was good in English composition. "I just know I could make it so sorrowful that people would bring hay to Nellie *hurry-scurry!*"

And when Susan was not at school, or minding babies, or peeling potatoes, or wiping dishes, or dusting, or mending socks, she composed feverishly, the tears rolling off her small, freckled nose as she described with many vivid adjectives the plight of poor Nellie. When she read it aloud to the other children, her voice shaking, she could hear long-drawn sighs, sniffles, and choked sobs.

Even Mom Pickett was touched. "I declare," she said, "it seems a pity not to see such a fine article published."

"Well?" queried the children, eagerly.

"I'll call Mr. Cox, the president of the Board, and explain," promised Mom, seeing the hope in all the upturned faces. "If Mr. Cox says *Yes*, then the next time I go into Bakersville you may go along. You may take Susan's composition to the *Tattler* office and present it to the editor. But—if Mr. Cox says *No*, then that will be quite another matter, you understand," warned Mom.

"Please, God, let Mr. Cox see how important Nellie is to us," prayed the orphans that night. So it was perfectly right and natural to them when Mr. Cox said *Yes*. Mom Pickett made an excuse to go to Bakersville the very next day, and with her, as Nellie's champions, went Susan and Mickey and Corky.

With thumping hearts the children entered the newspaper office. The editor, his hat on the back of his head and his pipe hanging on his lower lip, read Susan's composition, while the three orphans sat tense and solemn-eyed. When the editor looked up, they could see twinkles in his eyes. He asked several questions, and with a thick blue pencil wrote across Susan's pages.

"By gravy, kids, this will make a spanking good story!" he said at last, with a grin. "Watch for Thursday's *Tattler*."

"DO RIGHT BY OUR NELL,"
SAY KIDS AT COUNTY HOME.
CAMPAIGN NOW ON TO
PROVIDE OLD-AGE PENSION
FOR BELOVED OLD NAG.

So ran the headlines in Thursday's *Tattler*. Oh, how the eyes of the orphans lighted up when they read these words and the article that followed! They could talk of nothing else. Happy as she was, Susan couldn't help feeling a bit disappointed that the editor had told Nellie's story in his own words, not in hers.

"Never mind, child," comforted Mom Pickett. "Editors are like that."

Susan forgot her disappointment in the flurry of events that followed. On the very next day the editor telephoned that citizens of Bakersville had begun to contribute money for Nellie's groceries.

"I now have four dollars from the Women's Book Club, a dollar and ten cents from some town kids, and eight dollars from the Chamber of Commerce," said the editor. He sounded as excited as any gleeful orphan.

"That's thirteen dollars and ten cents

for Nellie," cried Mickey, doing the sum rapidly in his head.

"Boy, oh boy!" exclaimed all the children, full of breathless admiration for everyone. For Mickey, because of his lightning mental arithmetic; for the editor because he was so definitely on their side; for Mom Pickett because she was their only mother; for Nellie, *of course;* and for the Bakersville folk because of their kind hearts and giving hands.

The next day an animal doctor came for the sole purpose of making a profes-

years," he assured the children. "What she needs most is rest, plenty of nourishing food, and at least three loving pats a day. I'll be around now and then to take her pulse and look at her tongue."

He gave Nellie a pill to show that he meant every word he said. It was huge. Corky Trotter and Mickey Malone promptly went into fits of laughter.

The children were still gazing fondly after the obliging veterinarian when the

sional call on Nellie. Mom called him a veterinarian, a word nobody could spell except Susan, and she got it wrong the first time. The doctor promised to give Nellie the best of medical care, *free of charge!*

"The old girl's pretty sound, for all her

postman drove up, chuckling. Among the letters he left was one from New York, addressed to Nellie the Nag, County Children's Home, Rural Route 3. When it was opened by Mom, two twenty-dollar bills dropped out! The card that came with them bore these words, *From an orphan who knew Nellie when she and I were young.*

Gracious! How perfectly thrilling to know that an orphan could go to New York and become prosperous enough to help out an old friend in need!

"Such things do happen to boys and girls who are good, hard-working, and ambitious," said Mom. "In fact," she went on, as if it were quite an ordinary, everyday thought, "there's nothing to hinder an orphan from becoming President. Or a great writer."

At that, the Home was so full-blown with large, intense, round *Oh's* and *Ah's*, it was a wonder it didn't float off its foundations and soar skyward like an inflated balloon!

Smiling farmers from at least three adjoining counties drove into the barnyard of the Home with corn and hay for Nellie. While these gifts were piling up, there came a photographer from one of the newspapers in the big city, thirty miles distant. He took Nellie's picture, munching from a nose-bag, with six orphans astride her. The photograph, which appeared in the newspaper's Sunday issue, was explained in large type:

ORPHANS SAVE AGED PET FROM FERTILIZER PLANT

It was the best thing in the paper, of course. There was Ruby McGlish sitting in the middle, squeezed, but adorable. Susan Spitznagle perched proudly on Nellie's bony rump. Corky, a little blurry from having wiggled just as the camera's shutter snapped, clutched the mare's scraggly mane. The other three riders were grinning from ear to ear. And to the rueful surprise of Mickey Malone, only half of him showed, standing just inside the margin of the picture.

As for Nellie herself, crunching happily in her warm stall, the best moment of all came when Mom Pickett said, "Nellie is fattening up and getting strong again, but the doctor said she must take life easy. So, from now on, children, only three-at-a-time may ride her."

"Okay!" cried every little orphan.

"Okay, indeed!" exclaimed Nellie, under her breath. "Why, it's a dream come true!" And she reached for such a large mouthful of hay that it stuck out from her lips like a cat's whiskers. "By crickey, I'm the luckiest old nag in the world, even if I did look every day my age and not at all handsome in that newspaper picture!"

Nellie stopped chewing, and dropped her head humbly, for she was feeling very sentimental and deeply, deeply thankful. "In such a kind world as this," said Nellie, blowing softly through her nose, "one doesn't need to be handsome to be loved. And in my own case at least, it all goes back to being loved by the best sort of people—and that's kids."

Champion Fire 'n Feather

By Lavinia R. Davis

THE Coventry dog show was a great success. As usual, old Mrs. Tatham's Great Danes won most of the ribbons. Her big Champion Bally MacClough won best dog of the show and her brindle pup led the novice class.

Jimmy Harris hadn't been taken to the show, but his family had gone and told him all about it. In the cool of the evening Jimmy ambled over toward the Tatham place. He didn't exactly set out for there, but his feet seemed automatically to move down the soft dirt road in that direction. Queer old Mrs. Tatham didn't relish visitors, but surely she'd show off her new litter of puppies. Jimmy's feet moved faster as he approached the square white house.

The place was very quiet except for the occasional barking of a dog. Jimmy walked up the overgrown front drive with his hands in his pockets. No well-brought-up dog would go after you if you went squarely and openly up the front drive.

The old Ford that carried Mrs. Tatham and her dogs to the show was in the front yard but the house seemed deserted. Jimmy walked around to the low white kennels and there he found Mrs. Tatham. The old lady was dressed in an old tweed jacket and boots up to her knees. She was feeding one of the yearlings and she didn't seem glad to be interrupted. She looked up as Jimmy came in and her blue eyes were as cold as deep ice.

"Goo—good evening," Jimmy said, but Mrs. Tatham never softened.

"What are you doing here?" she asked, and Jimmy knew that he was trespassing.

"I—I just came to see the dogs," he said lamely.

Mrs. Tatham finished feeding one of her dogs and stalked back to her quiet house. She was a little woman, as short as Jimmy, but she held herself like a queen.

"When I want visitors, I invite them," she said. "The rest of the time my dogs can be seen at dog shows."

Jimmy felt as though he'd been slapped in the face. He wanted to talk, to explain that he couldn't very often get to the shows, and that he was more interested in dogs than anything in the world. Old Mrs. Tatham wasn't interested. She opened the door of her kitchen and Jimmy saw the big face of one of the Great Danes. The dog barked once and Jimmy felt sure it was Champion Bally MacClough. As Mrs. Tatham went in the dog subsided. The door shut and Jimmy was left alone.

There was nothing to do but turn around and go home. Jimmy started down the road, thought better of it, and headed cross country behind the house and over

the fields. Perhaps all the stories he'd heard about Grandma Tatham were true and the sooner he got off her land the better. Grandma liked dogs better than humans, and plenty of the people in Coventry thought she was a bit touched in the head. She lived alone and except for Jeb Green who did her chores, few people called on her. She kept herself to herself, and it was only when she drove out in the rusty sedan with the huge dogs filling the back seat that people saw her.

Jimmy slowed up as he neared the orchard. Two robins picked for worms on the grass ahead of him and overhead a bird sang. No matter what people thought about Mrs. Tatham, birds and animals recognized her as their friend. A calf bleated as Jimmy reached the trees and Jimmy jumped. Perhaps some of the Danes were left loose to keep out intruders. Perhaps old Mrs. Tatham herself had her eye on him from the house. Jimmy remembered the story he'd heard

about her scaring Bill Blaine on Halloween when he'd come to lift her gate off its hinges. Jimmy tried to hurry through the deep grass.

He'd gotten about as far as the woodpile when he heard a twittering in front of him. He looked around and for a moment he couldn't see anything. There was the woodpile, and a scrawny overgrown plum tree, and just beyond was the incinerator. Jimmy began to go ahead and, then, he saw the little bird in front of him. It lay quite still like a brown, crumpled leaf.

Jimmy stooped down and picked it up and the little thing peeped desperately and beat its tiny wings against his hand. It had a downy orange breast and barred wing feathers. It might be an oriole, Jimmy decided, and wondered if he could find its nest. He didn't dare take it home. Bill Blaine said Grandma Tatham knew every kitten that was born in her stable. The chances were good that if there were birds nesting in her orchard she'd know them, too.

Finally, Jimmy saw the nest in the plum tree. He climbed up and put the little thing inside. There was nothing else he could do. He hoped that the parent birds would come and care for it, and stood for a moment watching the nest. As he stood there he heard the sharp snap of a window being shut. He looked at the Tatham house but the empty windows stared back at him blankly. Jimmy felt uncomfortable and hurried on.

Jimmy headed southward through the meadow toward the Blaines' farm. Bill Blaine had plenty of stories about Grandma Tatham. Jimmy didn't especially like Bill Blaine and he'd never paid much attention to the stories, but now his interest was thoroughly aroused. He wanted to hear everything the Blaines had to say.

Bill was in the barn watering the overworked team. Jimmy couldn't help noticing the collar galls on both of the horses. Jimmy's father would have had a fit if any horse on his farm had looked like that, but the Blaines didn't seem to mind. They had a big radio and two shiny new cars, but the livestock on the place was down at the heel. A yellow mongrel barked furiously as Jimmy appeared but Bill cuffed him into silence.

"Hi, Jim." he said. "How's things?"

Jimmy said that he had been over at the Tathams' to look at the dogs. Bill laughed before he finished his sentence. "Bet you didn't get to first base. The old woman's crazy."

Bill turned his horses into the paddock and gave the old mare a swift crack with his hand as she passed. "Sure she's crazy," he said. "Babies them dogs as though they was people."

Bill settled down into the haymow to talk and Jimmy seated himself nearby to listen. It was an hour and a half later before he realized that he ought to go home. By that time Jimmy was half certain that Grandma Tatham was crazy and a witch.

When Jimmy finally said good-by and started for home, the early summer twilight was nearly over and it was quite dusky. Something stirred under a quince bush on the Blaines' place and Jimmy jumped. It was nothing but a mangy looking cat and Jimmy laughed to himself. Bill's stories had made him creepy.

Jimmy skirted the Tatham place and then he saw the fire. It was just at the edge of the property and Jimmy knew that it must be the incinerator. For a minute Jimmy hesitated. If you had your incinerator right by your woodpile you deserved a fire. There was nothing else nearby to catch and the grass was drenched with dew. Suddenly Jimmy thought of the bird and he started to run. He stumbled through the daisies and hawkweed. It was silly to care, but when he'd saved that bird once he couldn't let it die now.

By the time Jimmy reached the fire the flames lapped at the edge of the woodpile. Jimmy's heart pounded. There was no water near by. There was not even time to get help.

Jimmy lunged forward and began to separate the long logs. They had not been

144

sawed yet. That was in his favor. The smoke caught his throat, stung his eyes. His hands ached as he hauled the hot logs. He danced up and down on the flames, scattered the wood with bare hands. Once he felt the searing of fire on his forearm, but it was no time to stop. The flames were still near the plum tree, too near for the bird's safety.

"Help!" Jimmy shouted. "Help!" The sound was empty on the quiet air. He kept on fighting until he knew that the fire was no longer gaining. He stopped for one moment to suck the fresh air into his lungs. Then he shoved forward blindly, his arm in front of his face. He was beating, yanking, tearing the fire when there was the sudden spurt of steam. He looked up. Old Mrs. Tatham threw another bucket of water at the fire. One of her big dogs barked at her side.

Jimmy gasped, "Give me those pails," and ran toward the kennel. By the time he was back again, the fire was nearly out. With the last swish of water the wood was black and charred, but there wasn't a spark left. Jimmy glanced at the incinerator and saw the wire basket blown over on its side. So that had started it. He looked past it at the plum tree and saw the nest still safe and untouched. He breathed deeply and for the first time he was really aware of old Mrs. Tatham.

She did look like a witch in the soft darkness. Her long white hair streamed untidily down her neck and she had an old dark cloak thrown over her shoulders. She had her hand on her dog's collar and the big dog seemed turned to stone.

"You did a good job," she told Jimmy.

WM. MOYERS

"Come back tomorrow and see me."

Jimmy got out a hurried "Yes, ma'am." Then he ran for home.

The next morning when he woke up he remembered that he had something ahead of him. For a minute he couldn't think; then he knew that he was going to see Grandma Tatham. After Bill's stories, Jimmy didn't relish another visit, but he had said he would go.

In the broad daylight the house was less spooky. Jeb Harris was cutting grass near the house. Three big Great Danes thumped their tails on the wooden porch as Jimmy approached. Mrs. Tatham was waiting for him at the kitchen door.

"You're a good boy," she said when she saw him. "You saved that woodpile. Come and I'll show you my new litter."

Jimmy's heart lifted. He wanted to see those puppies more than anything in the world. He felt he was sailing under false colors. He'd wanted to save the bird, not the woodpile, but what could he say without being rude. Mrs. Tatham led the way to the big whitewashed kennel and went in. The mother dog wagged her tail and, when Mrs. Tatham spoke, allowed Jimmy to go close to her puppies.

They were wonderful puppies, brindle and brown and gray. They had long soft ears and the biggest, floppiest feet Jimmy had ever seen.

"Golly," Jimmy breathed. "Golly."

"Which one would you pick if you were judging a show?" Mrs. Tatham asked briskly. "Which one's worth a blue ribbon?"

Jimmy studied them carefully. They were all good, and to a boy who had always longed for a dog they seemed perfect. How could any one choose a best among such perfection? Finally, one by one, he discarded the biggest, the smallest, one with bent legs, and picked on a brindle with a round face.

"I'd give that the blue," he said and Grandma Tatham picked it up.

"He's yours," she said shortly. "I owe you that for the wood."

For a second Jimmy fought with himself. She need never know about the bird. Suddenly he squared his shoulders and told her. "It wasn't the wood, Ma'am," he got out. "There was a bird in that plum tree—"

Mrs. Tatham nodded at him and her old eyes were soft now and gentle. "I know, son," she said. "I saw you from the house."

Jimmy remembered the click of the window that had sent him scampering, and grinned. Dad was right, as usual, about old Mrs. Tatham. She might be queer, she might like dogs better than people, but she was quicker and fairer than most people. More than that she was generous. He turned back to the pup.

"You call for him in another week," she said. "I'll have him weaned by then."

Jimmy stroked the puppy wondering if it could be true. This little dog, the son of champions, really his?

"What are you going to call it?" old Mrs. Tatham asked, and Jimmy shook his head. He was beyond speech, beyond thanks. He could do nothing but hold the soft, marvelous creature and hope he was not dreaming that this beautiful dog was truly his.

Mrs. Tatham lifted the pup gently away from Jimmy and handed it back to its mother. "Call it Fire and Feather," she said crisply. "That's how you won him."

Jimmy nodded. "Champion Fire 'n Feather," he said slowly. "It sounds swell."

NEXT DOOR DOG

By Dixie Willson

SOME people say the next door dog
And mine are just the same.
They say the only difference is
Mine has a different name.
But for a million dollars down
And fifty million more
I wouldn't trade my little dog
For the little dog next door.
He may look just the same to you
He may be just as fine
But the next door dog is the next door dog
And mine is—mine.

How Bambi Found the Meadow

By Felix Salten

IN the earliest days of Bambi's life, he would walk behind his mother on a narrow track that ran through the midst of the bushes. The thick foliage stroked his flanks softly and bent aside. There were tracks like this everywhere, running criss-cross through the whole woods. His mother knew them all, and if Bambi sometimes stopped before a bush as if it were a green wall, she always found where the path went through, without hesitation or searching.

Bambi loved to ask his mother questions. It was very delightful, too, to wait expectantly till the answer came. If it turned out the way he wanted, he was satisfied. Sometimes, of course, he did not understand, but that was pleasant also because he was kept busy picturing in his own way what he had not understood.

Sometimes he felt very sure that his mother was not telling him all she knew. And, at first, that was very pleasant, too. For then there would remain in him such a lively curiosity that he would become anxious and happy at the same time.

Once he asked, "Whom does this trail belong to, Mother?"

His mother answered, "To us."

Bambi asked again, "To you and me?"

"Yes."

"Only to us two?"

"No," said his mother, "to us deer."

"What are deer?" Bambi laughed.

His mother looked at him from head to foot and laughed too. "You are a deer and I am a deer. We're both deer," she said. "Do you understand?"

Bambi sprang into the air for joy. "Yes, I understand," he said. "I'm a little deer

148

and you're a big deer, aren't you?"

His mother nodded and said, "Now you see."

But Bambi grew serious again. "Are there other deer besides you and me?"

"Certainly," his mother said.

"Where are they?" cried Bambi.

"Here, everywhere."

"But I don't see them."

"You will soon," she said.

The mother walked on quietly. Bambi followed her. He kept silent for he was wondering what "soon" might mean. He came to the conclusion that "soon" was certainly not "now." But he wasn't sure at what time "soon" stopped being "soon" and began to be a "long while." Suddenly he asked, "Who made this trail?"

"We," his mother answered.

Bambi was amazed. "We? You and I?"

The mother said, "We, we deer."

Bambi asked, "Which deer?"

"All of us," his mother said sharply.

They walked on. Bambi felt like leaping off the path, but he stayed close to his mother. Something rustled in front of them, close to the ground. The fern fronds and wood-lettuce hid something that advanced in violent motion. A thread-like little cry shrilled out piteously; then all was still. Only the leaves and the blades of grass shivered back into place. A ferret had caught a mouse. He came slinking by, slid sideways, and prepared to enjoy his meal.

"What was that?" asked Bambi.

"Nothing," his mother soothed him.

"But," Bambi trembled, "but I saw it."

"Yes, yes," said his mother. "Don't be frightened. The ferret has killed a mouse." But Bambi was dreadfully frightened. A vast, unknown horror clutched at his heart. It was long before he could speak again. Then he asked, "Why did he kill the mouse?"

"Because," his mother hesitated. "Let us walk faster," she said as though something had just occurred to her and as though she had forgotten the question. She began to hurry. Bambi sprang after.

Finally Bambi asked anxiously, "Shall we kill a mouse, too, sometime?"

"No," replied his mother.

"Never?" asked Bambi.

"Never," came the answer.

"Why not?" asked Bambi, relieved.

"Because we never kill anything," said his mother simply.

Bambi grew happy again.

Loud cries were coming from a young ash tree which stood near their path. The mother went along without noticing them, but Bambi stopped inquisitively. Overhead two jays were quarreling about a nest they had plundered.

"Get away, you murderer!" cried one.

"Keep cool, you fool," the other answered, "I'm not afraid of you."

"Look for your own nests," the first one shouted, "or I'll break your head for you." He was beside himself with rage. "What vulgarity!" he chattered.

The other jay had spied Bambi and fluttered down a few branches to shout at him. "What are you gawking at, you freak?" he screamed.

Bambi sprang away terrified. He reached his mother and walked behind

149

her again, frightened and obedient, thinking she had not noticed his absence.

After a pause he asked, "Mother, what is vulgarity?"

"I don't know," said his mother.

Bambi thought a while; then he began again. "Why were they both so angry with each other, Mother?" he asked.

"They were fighting over food," his mother answered.

"Will we fight over food, too, sometime?" Bambi asked.

"No," said his mother.

Bambi asked, "Why not?"

"Because there is enough for all of us," his mother replied.

They walked along again. Presently it grew light ahead of them. The trail ended with the tangle of vines and bushes. A few steps more and they would be in the bright open space that spread out before them. Bambi wanted to bound forward, but his mother had stopped.

"What is it?" he asked impatiently, already delighted.

"It's the meadow," his mother said.

"What is a meadow?" asked Bambi.

His mother cut him short. "You'll soon find out for yourself," she said. She stood motionless, holding her head high and listening intently.

Bambi leaped forward, but his mother barred the way.

"Wait till I call you," she said. Bambi obeyed at once and stood still. "That's right," said his mother, to encourage him, "and now listen to what I am saying to you." Bambi heard how seriously his mother spoke and felt terribly excited.

"Walking on the meadow is not so simple," his mother went on. "It's a difficult and dangerous business. Don't ask me why. You'll find that out later on. Now do exactly as I tell you to. Will you?"

"Yes," Bambi promised.

"Good," said his mother, "I'm going out alone first. Stay here and wait. And don't take your eyes off me for a minute. If you see me run back here, then turn round and run as fast as you can. I'll catch up with you soon." She grew silent and seemed to be thinking. Then she went on earnestly, "Run even if something should happen . . . even if you should see me fall to the ground. . . . Don't think of me, do you understand? No matter what you see or hear, start·running right away and just as fast as you possibly can. Do you promise me to do that?"

"Yes," said Bambi softly. His mother spoke so seriously.

"Out there if I should call you," she said, "there must be no looking around and no questions, but you must get behind me instantly. If I begin to run, that means for you to run too, and no stopping until we are back here again. You won't forget, will you?"

"No," said Bambi in a troubled voice.

"Now I'm going ahead," said his mother.

She walked out. Bambi, who never took his eyes off her, saw how she moved forward with slow, cautious steps. He stood there full of expectancy, full of fear and curiosity. He saw how his mother listened in all directions, saw her shrink together, and shrank together himself, ready to leap back into the thickets. Then his mother looked around satisfied and called, "Come!"

Bambi bounded out. Joy seized him with such tremendous force that he forgot his worries in a flash. Through the thicket he could see only the green tree-tops overhead. Once in a while he caught a glimpse of the blue sky.

dren do. So he rejoiced with his legs and with his whole body as he flung himself into the air.

His mother stood by and was glad. She stretched out her forefeet and bent laughingly towards Bambi for a moment. Then she was off with one bound, racing around in a circle so that the tall grass stems swished.

Now he saw the whole heaven stretching far and wide and he rejoiced without knowing why. In the forest he had seen only a stray sunbeam now and then, or the tender, dappled light that played through the branches. Suddenly he was standing in the blinding sunlight, in the splendid warmth that made him shut his eyes but which opened his heart.

Bambi was as though bewitched. He leaped into the air three, four, five times. He stretched his young limbs joyfully. His breath came deeply and easily. He drank in the air. The sweet smell of the meadow made him wildly happy.

Bambi was a child. If he had been a human child he would have shouted. But he was a young deer, and deer cannot shout, at least not the way human chil-

Bambi was frightened and stood motionless. Was that a sign for him to run back to the thicket? His mother had said to him, "Don't worry about me no matter what you see or hear. Just run as fast as you can." He was going to turn around and run as she had commanded him to, but his mother came galloping up with a wonderful swishing sound and stopped two steps from him. She bent towards him, laughing as she had at first and cried, "Catch me." And in a flash she was gone.

Bambi started after her. He took a few steps. Then his steps became short bounds.

He felt as if he were flying without any effort on his part.

The swishing grass was soft and fine as silk where it brushed against him. He turned and flew off in a circle, turned around again and kept running.

His mother was standing still, getting her breath again. She kept following Bambi with her eyes.

Suddenly the race was over. He stopped and came up to his mother, lifting his hoofs elegantly. He looked joyfully at her. Then they strolled contentedly side by side.

Since he had been in the open, Bambi had felt the sky and the sun and the green meadow with his whole body. Presently he began to enjoy the meadow with his eyes also. Its wonders amazed him at every step. You could not see the tiniest speck of earth the way you could in the forest. Blade after blade of grass covered every inch of the ground. It bent softly aside under every footstep, only to rise up unharmed again. The broad green meadow was starred with white daisies, with the thick, round red and purple clover blossoms and bright, golden dandelion heads.

"Look, look, Mother!" Bambi exclaimed. "There's a flower flying."

"That's not a flower," said his mother, "that's a butterfly."

Bambi stared at the butterfly. It had darted lightly from a blade of grass and was fluttering about in its giddy way. Then Bambi saw that there were many butterflies flying in the air above the meadow. They seemed to be in a hurry and yet moved slowly, fluttering up and down in a sort of game that delighted him. They really did look like gay flying flowers that would not stay on their stems but had unfastened themselves in order to dance a little. They looked, too, like flowers that come to rest at sundown but have no fixed places and have to hunt for them, dropping down and vanishing as if they really had settled somewhere, yet always flying up again, a little way at first, then higher and higher, and always searching farther and farther because all the good places have already been taken.

Bambi would have loved to see one close by, but he was not able to. They sailed in and out continually. The air was aflutter with them.

When he looked down at the ground again he was delighted with the thousands of living things he saw stirring under his hoofs. They ran and jumped in all directions. He would see a wild swarm of them, and the next moment they had disappeared in the grass again.

"Who are they, Mother?" he asked.

"Those are ants," his mother answered.

"Look," cried Bambi, "see that piece of grass jumping. Look how high it can jump!"

"That's not grass," his mother explained, "that's a nice grasshopper."

"Why does he jump that way?"

"Because we're walking here," his mother answered, "he's afraid we'll step on him."

"O," said Bambi, turning to the grasshopper who was sitting on a daisy; "O," he said again politely, "you don't have to be afraid; we won't hurt you."

"I'm not afraid," the grasshopper replied in a quavering voice; "I was only frightened for a moment when I was talking to my wife."

"Excuse us for disturbing you," said Bambi shyly.

"Not at all," the grasshopper quavered. "Since it's you, it's perfectly all right. But you never know who's coming and you have to be careful."

"This is the first time in my life that I've ever been on the meadow," Bambi explained. "My mother brought me. . . ."

The grasshopper murmured, "That doesn't interest me. I have to look for my wife. Hopp!" And he gave a jump.

"Hopp!" said Bambi in surprise at the high jump with which the grasshopper vanished.

Bambi ran to his mother. "Mother, I spoke to him," he cried.

"To whom?" his mother asked.

"To the grasshopper," Bambi said. "He's so wonderful and green and you can see through his sides. They look like leaves, but you can't see through a leaf."

"Those are his wings," said his mother.

"O," Bambi went on, "and his face is so wise. And how he can jump!"

They walked on. The conversation with the grasshopper had excited Bambi and tired him a little, for it was the first time he had ever spoken to a stranger. He felt hungry and pressed close to his mother to be nursed.

Then he stood quietly and gazed dreamily into space for a little while with

a sort of joy that came over him every time he was nursed by his mother. He noticed a bright flower moving in the tangled grasses. Bambi looked more closely at it. No, it wasn't a flower, but a butterfly. Bambi crept closer.

"O, please sit still, just for a minute," Bambi pleaded, "I've wanted so much to see you close to. Please."

"Well," said the butterfly, "for your sake I will, but not for long."

Bambi stood in front of him. "How beautiful you are," he cried fascinated, "like a flower!"

"What?" cried the butterfly, fanning his wings, "did you say like a flower? In my circle it's generally supposed that we're handsomer than flowers."

Bambi was embarrassed. "O, yes," he stammered, "much handsomer, excuse me, I only meant . . ."

"Whatever you meant is all one to me," the butterfly replied. He arched his thin body affectedly and played with his delicate feelers.

Bambi looked at him enchanted. "How elegant you are!" he said. "And how splendid and white your wings are!"

The butterfly spread his wings wide apart, then raised them till they folded together like an upright sail.

"O," cried Bambi, "I know that you are handsomer than the flowers. Besides, you can fly and the flowers can't because they grow on stems."

The butterfly spread his wings. "It's enough," he said, "that I can fly." He soared so lightly that Bambi could hardly see him or follow his flight. His wings moved gently and gracefully. Then he fluttered into the sunny air.

"I only sat still that long on your account," he said balancing in the air in front of Bambi. "Now I'm going."

That was how Bambi found the meadow.

His First Bronc

By Will James

WM. MOYERS

BILLY was a born cowboy; the only kind that ever makes the real cowboy. One day Lem told him he could have a certain black horse if he could break him. It was a little black horse, pretty as a picture. Billy went wild at the sight of him, and ran into the corral to get as close a view of the horse as he could.

"By golly!" he said. "I've always wanted to break in a horse. That'll be fun."

The next morning Lem found Billy in the corral with the new horse.

"Well, I see you're busy right early, Billy."

"You bet you," he said. "He's some horse, ain't he?"

"He sure is," agreed Lem. "And your first bronc, too."

An hour or so later Billy had his saddle on the black horse, and cinched to stay. By this time quite a crowd had gathered around. The foreman, the cowboys, all the ranch hands were watching. All was set but taking the hobbles off the horse's front feet and climbing on. Some of the men offered to do that for Billy but that young cowboy refused. He wanted to do it all himself; it was his bronc.

Billy gathered his hackamore rope and a hunk of mane to go with it, grabbed the saddle horn with his right hand and, sticking his foot in the stirrup, eased himself into the saddle. He squirmed around until he was well set like an old bronc fighter, saw that the length of reins between his hands and the pony's head was just right,

155

then he reached over and pulled off the blindfold.

Billy's lips closed tight; he was ready for whatever happened. The pony blinked at seeing daylight again, looked back at the boy sitting on him, snorted, and trotted off.

A laugh went up from all around. Billy turned a blank face toward his father and hollered, "Hey, Dad, he won't buck!"

Another laugh was heard and when it quieted down Lem spoke up.

"Never mind, Son," he said trying to keep a straight face, "he might buck yet."

The words were no more than out of his mouth, when the little black lit into bucking. Billy was loosened the first jump for he'd been paying more attention to what his dad was saying than to what he was sitting on. The little pony crow-hopped around the corral and bucked just enough to keep the kid from getting back in the saddle. Billy was hanging on to all he could find, but pretty soon the little old pony happened to make the right kind of a jump for the kid and he straightened up again.

Billy rode pretty fair the next few jumps and managed to keep his seat pretty well under him, but he wasn't satisfied with just sitting there; he grabbed his hat and began fanning. All went fine for a few more jumps and then trouble broke loose. Billy dropped his hat and made a wild grab for the saddle horn.

But the hold on the saddle horn didn't help him any; he kept going, up and up he went, a little higher every jump, and pretty soon he started coming down.

When he did that he was by his lonesome. The horse had gone in another direction.

"Where is he?" said Billy, trying to get some of the earth out of his eyes.

"Right here, Son," said his father, who'd caught the horse.

He handed the kid the hackamore reins and touched him on the hand.

"And listen here, young feller, if I catch you grabbing the horn with that paw of yours again, I'll tie it and the other right back where you can't use 'em."

Those few words hit the kid pretty hard. There was a frown on his face and his lips were quivering at the same time. He was both ashamed and peeved.

His father held the horse while Billy climbed on again.

"Are you ready, cowboy?" Lem looked up at his son and smiled.

After some efforts the kid smiled back and answered.

"Yes, Dad, let him go."

The pony lit into bucking the minute he was loose this time and seemed to mean business from the start. Time and again Billy's hand reached down as if to grab the saddle horn, but he kept away from it.

The little horse was bucking pretty good, and for a kid Billy was doing mighty fine, but the horse still proved too much for him. Billy kept getting further and further away from the saddle till finally he slid along the pony's shoulder and to the ground once again.

The kid was up before his dad could get to him and began looking for his horse right away.

"I don't think you'd better ride him

any more today, Sonny," Lem said as he brushed some of the dust off the kid's clothes. "Maybe tomorrow you can ride him easy."

But Billy turned and saw the horse challenging him, it seemed, and he crossed the corral, caught the black, blindfolded him and climbed on again.

Then Lem walked up to Billy and said the blind off the pony's eyes. "I'm a wolf!"

Billy was a wolf; he'd turned challenger and was pawing the black from ears to rump. Daylight showed plenty between him and the saddle but somehow he managed to stick on and stay right side up. The horse, surprised at the change of events, finally let up on his

so nobody else could hear,

"You go after him this time, Billy, and just make this pony think you're the wolf of the world. Paw him the same as you did that last calf you rode."

"Y-e-e-ep!" Billy hollered as he jerked

bucking, he was getting scared and had found a hankering to start running.

After that it was easy for Billy; he rode him around the corral a couple of times and then, all smiles and proud as a peacock, he climbed off.

Billy had ridden his first bronc.

Almost an Ambush

By Le Grand

TOM PERKINS and his army were holding a council of war in a thick grove of the young pines that covered Eagle Hill. Pinned to each shoulder of Tom's shirt, four silver-paper stars gleamed in the sunlight, indicating that he was a full general.

One of the other two boys also wore silver stars on his shoulders. That was Herb Wilks who had the three stars of a lieutenant general, and so was next in rank to Tom.

Only Peewee Davis had no stars at all. Peewee had no marks of rank of any kind. As the youngest and smallest boy in Tom's army, he was naturally a private. Peewee didn't mind, because he was more than just one. He was all the privates.

There was one other member of the army who, like Peewee, had no marks of rank. This was Tom's small, bright-eyed, black-and-white dog, Floppy.

Tom thought Floppy was stationed a little way off as a sentinel, to bark a warning if Stubby Johnson's enemy army appeared while the council of war was in session. Floppy thought he was out there to look for a rabbit.

"Now, look," Tom said to the council. "Stubby's army is over there on the other side of the hill." He pointed out a position on a smudged, roughly penciled map.

The others nodded in agreement, and Tom went on, "Now what I say is, we have to surprise 'em."

Peewee said, "Yep," and crawled around on his hands and knees to show how he thought it should be done.

Tom scowled and shook his head warningly. "The idea is, we have to be quiet about it. Anybody that makes a noise is just the same as a traitor."

Unfortunately, at that moment, Floppy found the rabbit he had been looking for and started out after it, barking shrilly.

Herb snorted at Tom and said, "What did I tell you? Didn't I say we shouldn't bring him? How we going to surprise any one with him yapping like that?"

Tom didn't answer. He set out after his dog and soon came back with Floppy under his arm. The little dog's eyes sparkled from behind the shaggy hair that nearly hid them. He wriggled and pushed against Tom with all four feet as he tried to get back to the fine new game of chasing a rabbit and being chased by Tom at the same time.

Herb looked at Floppy sourly.

Tom said, "Just you wait. Floppy'll be a big help yet. Just wait, you'll see."

Noticing that Herb's expression didn't change, Tom went on, "Listen. All armies have dogs, don't they? Didn't the gov'ment say that our army needs lots of dogs to train for sentries an' for—well, for sentries an' for uh—well—things?"

Herb couldn't deny that, but he could and did say, "Yeh, but not little noisy dogs like that."

Floppy suddenly raised his ears and looked as if he understood what Herb had said and his feelings were hurt. When Floppy raised his long ears, the ends drooped over and hung nearly to his eyes. That gave him a sad expression. He let his tongue hang out of the side of his mouth and that made him look so mournful that Herb shuffled his feet and looked away. Although Herb liked big dogs best, he and Floppy were old friends and his objections to the little dog now were purely for military reasons.

Tom decided it was a good time to change the subject.

"Look," he said, "we don't have time to stand here and talk. The enemy's coming up over the hill. They'll be here in a little while. Now here's my plan. We'll retreat down this path, toward the old quarry . . ."

Herb broke in, "The old quarry? Huh, that's just where they'll expect us to go."

Tom grinned. "Yeh—only we'll fool them. We'll stop before we get to the quarry and dig in beside the path. Then, when they come running after us, they'll run right into an ambush."

To make sure the enemy would follow, Tom dropped his hat beside the path and, a little farther, Herb his handkerchief.

At a place where the path curved in a bend, Tom said, "This is a good spot for our ambush. Now the best way is to dig foxholes. They'll never see us if we do that."

Without any tools but bare hands and one dull knife, the foxholes were hard to dig. Tom, Herb, and Peewee studied their bruised hands when the shallow holes were done.

Tom licked a brier scratch. "Well, that was a tough job, but it'll be worth it when the enemy comes along. Boy, they'll never know what hit them." He reached into a bag at his side and drew out a pine cone. "Get your ammunition ready."

Herb and Peewee opened their bags of pine-cone ammunition.

Herb looked hopeful. "Uh-huh," he said. "They'll be along any time now. We'd better get in those good ol' foxholes right away—" He stopped suddenly and looked around as a curious expression crossed his face. "Say, where's that noisy little dog of yours?"

Tom looked around quickly. Floppy was not in sight.

"Aw, *now* what's he up to?" Herb asked bitterly.

They didn't have to wait long for the answer to that question. Back up the path Floppy's shrill, eager bark broke out and was followed immediately by the voice of Stubby Johnson. "Hey, here's Tom's dog. The enemy's right around here somewhere. Make a big circle and we'll surround 'em."

There was no chance for an ambush now. A retreat was the only way to avoid being surrounded.

Herb looked bitterly at his foxhole.

"All that work for nothing," he grunted. "And it's all that dog's fault."

That was not a good time for Floppy to come back but he did, bouncing merrily up to Tom, his eyes shining and his tail paddling the air happily. The look Tom gave him stopped him in his tracks. His tail stopped waving. It drooped, and so did his ears. His expression said, "I don't know what I did wrong, but I'm sorry. Please stop looking at me like that."

Herb and Peewee had already started down the path. Tom started after them and Floppy brought up the rear, jogging along in a slow and subdued manner. There was no bounce in his gait. Sometimes he looked up at Tom with a puzzled, sorrowful expression. Clearly, he knew he was in disgrace, but if he was not a good soldier, Floppy was no deserter. Soberly, but steadily, he followed, keeping just behind Tom's heels.

Tom's spirits were as low and troubled as Floppy's. He knew that the only way he could redeem himself was to think up some brilliant plan that would turn defeat into a spectacular victory. The trouble was that he couldn't think of any plan at all. The only thing that seemed possible was to continue down the path which led to the abandoned quarry. In the quarry there would be good hiding places behind the scattered blocks of stone and maybe a plan would come.

The path slanted downward and grew rocky. The quarry was just ahead, at the bottom of the slope.

Scattered over the quarry floor were the big blocks of rock that had been blasted away from the cliffs. Tom sprinted ahead of Herb and Peewee and peered behind one of the rocks. Right there would be a good place to make a defensive stand. The trouble was that Tom didn't want to make a defensive stand. He wanted some bold surprise move that would win the battle brilliantly, and would leave no doubt as to who deserved the credit for winning it!

His glance went past the big rock to the hillside beyond it. He started to run on, stopped and came back, his eyes squinting with the beginning of an idea.

He stopped Herb and Peewee. "Look," he said. "The tunnel's dry."

They all stared at the hole that led into the hillside. Always before, the five-foot opening had been half full of water brought from a stream on the other side of the hill. They knew that, when the quarry was worked, the tunnel had been dug especially to bring that water here to wash the crushed rock.

"Hey," Tom said, "With no water in the tunnel, we could go through it and come out back of the hill."

Herb saw what he had in mind. "Yeh, then we could get back to the path and we'd be back of Stubby's army."

"That's it." Tom's face glowed with the joy of a great idea. "We'd be back of them and they wouldn't know it 'till we attacked them. Boy, that'd be the end of this battle."

He pushed Peewee toward the tunnel saying, "Get in there quick. Say, this is the best war-plan ever, I bet!"

Herb was following Peewee into the

tunnel when a sudden thought struck him and he looked around warily.

"Where's that Floppy?" he asked. "We don't want him hanging around here showing them where we went and spoiling *this* plan."

"Here he is." Tom lifted Floppy and carried him into the tunnel behind Herb. "Now," he said. "This time nothing can go wrong with our plan."

It was black dark in the tunnel. Tom looked back toward the entrance and noticed something.

"Look," he said. "See that big rock? It's just balanced there, and I bet we could push it down so's it would nearly cover the entrance."

"Yeh," Herb agreed. "And then nobody would ever think we came in here.

That would fool 'em all right."

Tom was right. The big rock was delicately balanced, and after the second push it began to roll. The tunnel sloped down toward the entrance and, after the rock began to move, it rolled faster than Tom had expected. It lurched sideways and hit the wall, knocking loose another rock. A clod of earth fell into the place where the other rock had been. A small stone fell from the top of the tunnel, and several lumps of earth followed it. A rumbling, grinding sound echoed through the tunnel. Stones and clods of earth were falling like a dark snowstorm. Near the entrance, the whole top of the tunnel shifted, swayed, and collapsed with a thump like a heavy explosion.

The noise died away. It was very quiet

URSULA KOERING

in the tunnel. Floppy whined a little. The air was thick with dust and Tom sneezed. Suddenly Peewee sniffled.

"How we going to get out of here?"

Tom's attempt to laugh sounded queer. "Huh," he said uneasily. "We'll go on out the other end the way we planned."

"Yeh," Herb said. "C-come on, let's go. It—it might get late, or something."

Tom found himself in the lead. As he couldn't see, he had to feel his way along. Sometimes he bumped into the sides and had to grope around until he could find his direction again.

He had done this several times when Herb heard him mutter excitedly, "Blame ol' tunnel must bend here. I can't find it—keep bumping into the side."

Herb came up to him and they both groped along the wall. They could feel the bend in the wall, but when they followed it they came back to where they had started from. They knew that, because finally they bumped into Peewee who was standing still and so must be where they had left him.

Even Peewee knew what had happened. The tunnel was blocked ahead of them just as it was blocked behind.

No one said anything until Peewee wailed, "I want to go home."

Tom had a horrible feeling that he might say something like that himself. To avoid that he tried to find something else to say, anything at all that would sound steady and unafraid.

His voice didn't quiver *very* much. "I guess that's why the tunnel is dry. That cave-in is damming up the water so it can't come through."

Peewee's sniffles grew louder. "What we going to do?"

Neither Herb nor Tom answered that question. They were both afraid they knew what they were going to do. It looked as if they were going to stay there, buried alive in the tunnel.

"Come on," Tom blurted out desperately. "Let's go back to the other end. Maybe there's some way out there. We didn't stop to look."

Tom found himself thinking about the bright, sunny world above; how the birds were singing up there in the warm sweet air, so different from the damp, moldy underground smell.

It seemed miles back to the other end of the tunnel, but when he reached the blocked entrance Tom could see the wall of earth and stones ahead.

He could *see* again, very dimly, but well enough to make out the caved-in mass ahead. That meant there was light here and light could only come from a hole that led to the outside world.

Now he saw it. A little patch of sky shone gloriously blue at the far end of a slanting crack in the roof. The crack was about ten feet long and it was narrow.

He scrambled up the sloping wall of caved-in dirt and tried to force himself into the opening. His shoulders stuck and no matter how hard he pushed he could not wedge himself up any farther.

He dropped back and watched Herb and then Peewee try to wriggle into the hole. Even Peewee was too big to make it.

They shouted and their voices boomed back at them and died away in rustling echoes along the length of the tunnel.

"Prob'ly no one could hear us no matter how loud we holler," Herb said despairingly. He scrambled toward the opening again and tripped over something soft, something that yelped. The sound startled all of them. They had forgotten Floppy.

"Blame ol' dog," Herb said bitterly. "It's all his fault we're in here. I told you all along not to bring him today."

Tom hardly heard him. "Floppy!" he said to himself. "That's it—Floppy—he's small enough." He turned to Herb. "So Floppy's no good, huh?" he asked. "Well, let me tell you something. Floppy's going to get us out of this."

Herb snorted scornfully. "That dog! How's he going to do anything? He's too small to—" Herb stopped suddenly, then went on, "Yeh, Floppy can get out maybe, but that won't help us."

Tom fished in his pockets and located a stub of a pencil and his map. He turned the map over and wrote on the blank side of the paper. "We are stuck in the tunnel at the old quarry, the one the water comes through. Come to the quarry end of the tunnel and holler. There is a small hole and we can hear you, I guess. We will holler back. Faithfully yours, Tom Perkins, Herb Jenkins, and Peewee Davis. P. S. Holler good and loud."

Tom thought for a minute and then took off his shirt. It was a bright blue shirt. He tied one sleeve to Floppy's collar and knotted the other sleeve around the note.

"There," he said. "I guess some one will wonder what a dog is doing with a shirt, and then they'll see the note."

He picked the little dog up and pushed him into the narrow opening, spanked him once and shouted, "Go home. You hear me, Floppy? You go home."

Floppy wriggled and his paws made a scraping, clawing sound. Loose bits of dirt showered down behind him. For awhile the light in the opening was blotted out, and then the little patch of blue sky appeared again. A high, thin bark sounded faintly in the tunnel.

Floppy was gone. Would he come back? And more important, would he bring someone back with him?

The minutes dragged by and grew into what seemed like years.

Tom was conscious that he was very thirsty. He wondered if it would rain before it was too late and if enough rain water would trickle down through the hole to do any good. He looked up to see if he could tell by the way the hole sloped. And there at the other end of the opening was Floppy's shaggy face staring down at him.

"He's come back alone," was Tom's first thought. "Maybe he's just been standing around up there all the time."

Then Floppy's face disappeared and a man's voice shouted down the hole. It was Tom's father's voice. A shovel thudded into the ground, and the boys took a deep breath.

After that Tom didn't remember anything that happened until he dragged himself up the enlarged hole and stood sighing and blinking at a little dog that seemed more beautiful than any dog possibly could be.

Floppy, however, was not through redeeming himself. When Tom had finished explaining to his father how they had been trapped in the tunnel, he noticed that Floppy had pricked up his ears and was staring excitedly down into the quarry. Tom looked where the little dog's nose was pointing.

Stubby Johnson and his army were marching by at the base of the hill.

Tom motioned to Herb and Peewee. They all drew pine-cone ammunition out of the bags they had forgotten about until that minute.

"Fire," Tom yelled, and for a little while the air was thick with whizzing cones that thudded into the enemy.

Mr. Perkins blinked in amazement as the three boys, apparently forgetting what they had been through, whooped and jeered at Stubby Johnson and his defeated army.

"You're dead, you're dead, you're dead," they yelled. "We win the battle."

Tom picked up Floppy. "Boy, oh boy, what a dog!"

Herb and Peewee very respectfully shook Floppy's paw and repeated, "Boy, what a dog!"

URSULA KOERING

The Black Stallion and the Red Mare

By Gladys Francis Lewis

AT FIRST Donald lay still. Scarcely a muscle moved. The boulders and the low shrubs screened him from view. Excitement held him motionless. His hands gripped the short grass and his toes dug into the dry earth. Cautiously he raised himself on his elbows and gazed at the scene below him.

There, in his father's unfenced hay flats, was the outlaw band of wild horses. They were grazing quietly on the rich grass. Some drank from the small hillside stream. Donald tried to count them, but they suddenly began moving about and he could not get beyond twenty. He thought there might be two hundred.

Donald knew a good deal about that band of horses, but he had never had the good luck to see them. They were known over many hundreds of square miles. They had roamed at will over the grain fields and they had led away many a domestic horse to the wild life. Once in that band, a horse was lost to the farm.

There in the flats was the great black stallion, the hero or the villain of a hundred tales. Over the far-flung prairie and grass lands there was scarcely a boy who had not dreamed of wild rides, with the great body of the stallion beneath him, bearing him clean through the air with the sharp speed of lightning.

There was the stallion now, moving among the horses with the sureness and ease of a master. As he moved about, teasingly kicking here and nipping there, a restlessness, as of a danger sensed, stirred through the band. The stallion cut to the outside of the group. At a full gallop he snaked around the wide circle, roughly bunching the mares and colts into the smaller circle of an invisible corral.

He was a magnificent creature, huge and proudly built. Donald saw the gloss of the black coat and the great curving muscles of the strong legs, the massive hoofs, the powerful arch of the neck, the proud crest of the head. Donald imagined he could see the flash of black, intelligent eyes. Surely a nobler creature never roamed the plains!

Off-wind from the herd, a red mare came out from the fold of the low hills opposite. She stood motionless a moment, her graceful head held high. Then she nickered. The black stallion drew up short in his herding, nickered eagerly, then bolted off in the direction of the mare. She stood waiting until he had almost reached her; then they galloped back to the herd together.

The shadows crept across the hay flats and the evening stillness settled down. A bird sang sleepily on one note. Donald suddenly became aware of the monotonous song, and stirred from his intent watching. He must tell his father and help send news around the countryside. He was still intensely excited as he crept back from the brow of the hill and hurried home. All the time his mind was busy and his heart was bursting.

Donald knew that three hundred years ago the Spaniards had brought horses to Mexico. Descendants of these horses had wandered into the Great Plains. These horses he now was watching were of that Spanish strain. Thousands of them roamed the cattle lands north to the American boundary. This band now grazed wild over these park lands here in Canada— four hundred miles north of the boundary.

His father and the farmers for many miles around had determined to round up the horses and make an end of the roving band. As a farmer's son, Donald knew that this was necessary and right. But a certain respect for the band and the fierce loyalty that he felt toward all wild, free creatures made him wish in his heart that they might never be caught, never be broken and tamed. He, who was so full of sympathy for the horses, must be traitor to them!

There had been conflicts in his heart before, but never had there been such a warring of two strong loyalties. He saw himself for the first time as a person of importance because he, Donald Turner, had the power to affect the lives of others. This power, because it could help or harm others, he knew he must use wisely.

When he stood before his father half an hour later, he did not blurt out his news. It was too important for that. But his voice and his eyes were tense with excitement. "That band of wild horses is in the hay hollow, west of the homestead quarter," he said. "There must be close to two hundred."

His father was aware of the boy's deep excitement. At Donald's first words he stopped his milking, his hands resting on the rim of the pail as he looked up.

"Good lad, Donald!" he said, quietly enough. "Get your supper and we'll ride to Smith's and Duncan's to start the word around. Tell Mother to pack lunches for tomorrow. We'll start at sunup." He turned to his milking again.

The other men were in the yard shortly after daylight.

Donald afterward wondered how long it would have taken ranch hands to round

up the band of horses. These farmers knew horses, but not how to round up large numbers of them as the men of the ranch country knew so well. The farmers learned a good deal in the next two weeks.

Twenty men started out after the band as it thundered out of the hay flats, through the hills and over the country. The dust rose in clouds as their pounding hoofs dug the dry earth. The herd sped before the pursuers with the effortless speed of the wind. The black stallion led or drove his band, and kept them well together. That first day only the young colts were taken.

At sunset the riders unsaddled and staked their horses by a poplar thicket, ate their stale lunches and lay down to sleep under the stars. Their horses cropped the short grass and drank from the stream. Some slept standing; others lay down.

At dawn the herd was spied moving westward. With the coming of night, they, too, had rested. For a mile or more they now sped along the rim of a knoll, swift as bronchos pulled in off the range after a winter out. The black stallion was a hundred feet ahead, running with a tireless, easy swing, his mane and tail streaming and his body stretched level as it cut through the morning mists. Close at his side, but half a length behind him, ran the red mare. The band streamed after.

After that first day's chase and the night under the stars, Donald had ridden back home. Not that he had wanted to go back. He would have given everything that he owned to have gone on with the men. But there were horses and cattle and chores to attend to at home, and there was school.

The roundup continued. Each day saw the capture of more and more horses. As the men doubled back on their course, they began to see that the wild horses traveled in a great circle, coming back again and again over the same ground, stopping at the same watering holes and feeding in the same rich grass flats. Once this course became clear, fresh riders and mounts in relays were posted along the way, while others drove on from behind. The wild band had still to press on with little chance for rest and feeding. The strain of the pursuit took away their desire for food, but they had a burning thirst and the black stallion would never let them drink their fill before he drove them on. Fatigue grew on them.

As the roundup continued, the whole countryside stirred with excitement. At every town where there was a grain elevator along the railroad, people repeated the latest news of the chase. On the farms the hay went unmown or unraked, and the plows rested still in the last furrow of the summer fallow. At school the children played roundup at recess. Donald, at his desk, saw the printed pages of his books, but his mind was miles away, running with the exhausted wild horses.

Near the end of the second week of the chase, Donald's father rode into the yard. Donald dropped the wood he was carrying and ran to meet his father.

"Dad, they haven't got the black stallion and the red mare, have they?" Don-ald could scarcely wait for his father's slow reply.

"No, Donald, lad," he said. "Though those two are the only horses still free. They're back in the flats. We'll get them tomorrow."

Donald felt both relief and fear.

In the yellow lamplight of the supper table his father told of the long days of riding, of the farms where he had eaten and of the adventures of each day.

"That was a gallant band, lad!" he said. "Never shall we see their equal! Those two that are left are a pair of great horses. Most wild horses show a weakening in the strain and grow up with little wind or muscle. But these two are sound of wind and their muscles are like steel. Besides that, they have intelligence. They would have been taken long ago but for that."

No one spoke. Donald felt that his father was on his side, the side of the horses. After a long pause, Mr. Turner continued.

"With his brains and his strength, that stallion could have got away in the very beginning. He could have got away a dozen times and would now be free south of the border. But that was his band. He stayed by them, and he tried to get them to safety. This week, when his band had been rounded up, he stuck by that red mare. She is swift but she can't match his speed. It's curious the way they keep together! He stops and nickers. She nickers in reply and comes close to him, her nose touching his flank. They stand a moment. Then they are away again, she running beside him but not quite neck to neck. Day after day it is the same. They are no ordinary horseflesh, lad!"

There was a lump in Donald's throat. He knew what his father meant. Those horses seemed to stand for something bigger and greater than himself. There were other things that made him feel the same—the first full-throated song of the meadow lark in the spring; ripe golden fields of wheat with the breeze rippling it in waves; the sun setting over the rim of the world in a blaze of rose and gold; the sun rising again in the quiet east; the smile in the blue depths of his mother's eyes; the still whiteness of the snow-bound plains; the story of Columbus dauntlessly sailing off into unknown seas.

These things were part of a hidden, exciting world. The boy belonged to these things in some strange way. He caught only glimpses of that hidden world, but those glimpses were tantalizing. Something deep within him leaped up in joy.

That night Donald dreamed of horses nickering to him but, when he tried to find them, they were no longer there. Then he dreamed that he was riding the great, black stallion, riding over a far-flung range, riding along a hilltop road with the world spread below him on every side. He felt the powerful body of the horse beneath him. He felt the smooth curves of the mighty muscles. Horse and rider seemed as one.

A cold dawn shattered his glorious dream ride. With his father he joined the other horsemen. From the crest of the slope from which Donald had first seen them, the pair of horses was sighted. They were dark moving shadows in the gray mists of the morning.

They had just finished drinking deep from the stream. Not for two weeks had the men seen the horses drink like that. Thirsty as they were, they had taken but one drink at each water hole. This last morning they were jaded and spent; they had thrown caution to the winds.

At the first suspicion of close danger, they stood still, heads and tails erect. Then they dashed toward the protecting hills. There the way forked.

It was then Donald saw happen the strange thing his father had described. At the fork the stallion halted and nickered. The mare answered and came close. She touched his flank with her head. Then they bounded off and disappeared in the path that led northwest to the rougher country where the chase had not led before.

Along the way the horses had been expected to take, grain-fed horses had been stationed. These had now to move over northwest. But the men were in no hurry today. They were sure of the take before nightfall. The sun was low in the west when two riders spurred their mounts for the close in. The stallion and the mare were not a hundred yards ahead. They were dead spent. Their glossy coats were flecked with dark foam. Fatigue showed in every line of their bodies. Their gallant spirits no longer could drive their spent bodies. The stallion called to the mare. He heard her answer behind him. He slowed down, turning wildly in every direction. She came up to him, her head drooped on his flank and rested there. In a last wild defiance, the stallion tossed his magnificent head and drew strength for a last mighty effort. Too late!

The smooth coils of a rope tightened around his feet. He was down, down and helpless. He saw the mare fall as the rope slipped over her body and drew tight around her legs. It maddened him. He struggled wildly to be free. The taut rope held. The stallion was conquered. In that last struggle something went out of him.

Broken was his body and broken was his spirit. Never again would he roam the plains, proud and free, the monarch of his herd.

Donald saw it all. He felt it all. His hands gripped the pommel of the saddle and his knees pressed hard against his pony's sides. Tears blinded his eyes and from his throat came the sound of a single sob. It was as if he himself were being broken and tied.

The sun dipped below the rim of the plains. The day was gone; the chase was ended. The men stood about smoking and talking in groups of twos and threes, examining the two roped horses. Donald's father knelt close to the mare, watching her intently. Donald watched him. His father remained quiet for a moment, one knee still resting on the ground, in his hand his unsmoked pipe. Donald waited for his father to speak.

"Boys," he said, without looking up, and with measured words, "do you know, this mare is blind—stone blind!"

A week later, Donald and his father stood watching those two horses in the Turner corral. They were not the same spirited creatures, but they were still magnificent horses.

"I figured," his father said, turning to the boy, "that they had won the right to stay together. I've brought them home for you, Donald. They are yours, lad. I know you will be good to them."

Pony Penning Day

By Marguerite Henry

PONY PENNING DAY always comes on the last Thursday in July. For weeks before, every member of the Volunteer Fire Department is busy getting the grounds in readiness, and the boys are allowed to help.

"I'll do your chores at home, Paul," offered Maureen, "so's you can see that the pony pens are good and stout."

Paul spent long days at the pony penning grounds. The pens for the wild ponies must be made safe. Once the Phantom was captured, she must not escape. Nothing else mattered.

Paul and Maureen Beebe lived on their grandfather's pony ranch on the island of Chincoteague, just off the Virginia shore. Across a narrow channel lay another island, Assateague, which was the home of the wild herds. They were said to be the descendants of a bunch of Spanish horses off a Spanish galleon which had been shipwrecked there several hundred years ago. Once every July the men of Chincoteague crossed the channel to Assateague and rounded up the wild ponies. They swam them across the channel to Chincoteague to be sold on Pony Penning Day.

Paul and Maureen had gentled many a wild colt. But just as the colt was learning that they were his friends, Grandpa Beebe would sell it and the children would never

see him again. They had earned a hundred dollars to buy a horse of their own—and the horse they wanted was the Phantom. This was the mysterious wild mare about whom so many stories were told. None of the roundup men had ever been able to capture her. But this year Paul was old enough to go with the men, and he was determined to get her.

"When I do," he said, "I'll tie a rope around her neck to show she's already sold. To us."

The night before the roundup, he and Maureen made last-minute plans in Phantom's stall. "First thing in the morning," Paul told Maureen, "you lay a clean bed of dried sea grass. Then fill the manger with plenty of marsh grass to make Phantom feel at home."

"Oh, I will, Paul. And I've got some ear corn and some 'lasses to coax her appetite, and Grandma gave me a bunch of tiny new carrots and some rutabagas, and I've been saving up sugar until I have a little sackful."

It was dark and still when Paul awoke the next morning. He lay quiet a moment, trying to gather his wits. Suddenly he shot out of bed.

Today was Pony Penning Day! He dressed quickly and thudded barefoot down to the kitchen where Grandma stood over the stove, frying ham and making coffee for him as if he were man-grown! After a hurried breakfast, he ran out the door. He mounted Watch Eyes, a dependable pony that Grandpa had never been able to sell because of his white eyes. Locking his bare feet around the pony's sides, he jogged out of the yard.

Maureen came running to see him off.

"Whatever happens," Paul called back over his shoulder, "you be at Old Dominion Point at ten on a fresh pony."

"I'll be there, Paul!"

"And you, Paul!" yelled Grandpa. "Obey yer leader. No matter what!"

Day was breaking. A light golden mist came up out of the sea. It touched the prim white houses and the white picket fences with an unearthly light. Paul loped along slowly to save his mount's strength. All along the road, men were turning out of their gates.

"Where do you reckon you'll do most good, Bub?" taunted a lean sapling of a man. He guffawed loudly, then winked at the rest of the group.

Paul's hand tightened on the reins. "Reckon I'll do most good where the leader tells me to go," he said, blushing.

The day promised to be sultry. The marsh grass that usually billowed and waved stood motionless. The water of Assateague Channel glared like brass.

Now the cavalcade was thundering over a small bridge that linked Chincoteague Island to little Piney Island. At the far end of the bridge a scow with a rail fence around it stood at anchor.

In spite of light talk, the faces of the men were drawn tight with excitement as they led their mounts onto the scow. The horses felt the excitement, too. Their nostrils quivered, and their ears swiveled this way and that, listening to the throb of the motor. Now the scow began to nose its way across the narrow channel. Paul watched the White Hills of Assateague loom near. He watched the old lighthouse grow sharp and sharper against the sky. In a few minutes the ride was over. The gangway was being lowered. The horses were clattering down, each man taking his own.

All eyes were on Wyle Maddox, the leader.

"Split in three bunches," Wyle clipped out the directions loud and sharp. "North, south, and east. Me and Kim and the Beebe boy will head east, Wimbrow and Quillen goes north, and Harvey and Rodgers south. We'll all meet at Tom's Point."

Paul touched his bare heels into Watch Eyes' side. *They were off!* The boy's eyes were fastened on Wyle Maddox. He and Kim Horsepepper were following their leader like the wake of a ship.

As they rode on, Paul could feel the soft sand give way to hard meadowland, then to pine-laden trails. There were no paths to follow, only openings to skin through—openings that led to water holes or to grazing grounds. The three horses thrashed through underbrush, jumped fallen trees, waded brackish pools and narrow, winding streams.

Suddenly Paul saw Wyle Maddox' horse rear into the air. He heard him neigh loudly as a band of wild ponies

darted into an open grazing stretch some twenty yards ahead, then vanished among the black tree trunks.

The woods came alive with thundering hoofs and frantic horse calls. Through bush and brier and bog and hard marshland the wild ponies flew. Behind them galloped the three riders, whooping at the top of their lungs. For whole seconds at a time the wild band would be swallowed up by the forest gloom. Then it would reappear far ahead—nothing but a flash of flying tails and manes.

Suddenly Wyle Maddox was waving Paul to ride close. "A straggler!" he shouted, pointing off to the left. "He went that-a-way! Git him!" And with a burst of speed Wyle Maddox and Kim Horsepepper were after the band.

Paul was alone. His face reddened with anger. They wanted to be rid of him. That's what they wanted. Sent after a straggler! He was not interested in rounding up a straggler that couldn't even keep up with the herd! He wanted the Phantom. Then Grandpa's words flashed across his mind, "You, Paul, obey yer leader. No matter what!"

He wheeled his pony and headed blindly in the direction Wyle had indicated. He rode deeper into the pine thicket, trying to avoid snapping twigs, yet watching ahead for the slightest motion of leaf or bush. He'd show the men, if it took him all day! His thin shirt clung to him damply and his body was wet with sweat. A cobweb veiled itself across his face. With one hand he tried to wipe it off, but suddenly he was almost unseated. Watch Eyes was dancing on his hind legs, his nose high in the air. Paul stared into the sun-dappled forest until his eyes burned in his head. At last, far away and deep in the shadow of the pines, he saw a blur of motion. With the distance that lay between them, it might have been anything. A deer. Or even a squirrel. Whatever it was, he was after it!

Watch Eyes plunged on. There was a kind of glory in pursuit that made Paul and the horse one. They were trailing nothing but swaying bushes. They were giving chase to a mirage. Always it moved on and on, showing itself only in quivering leaves or moving shadows.

What was that? In the clump of myrtle bushes just ahead? Paul reined in. He could scarcely breathe for the wild beating of his heart. There it was again! A silver flash. It looked like mist with the sun on it. And just beyond the mist, he caught sight of a long tail of copper and silver.

He gazed awestruck. "It could be the Phantom's tail," he breathed. "It is! It is! It is! And the silver flash—it's not mist at all, but a brand-new colt!"

The blood pounded in his ears. No wonder the Phantom was a straggler! No wonder she let herself be caught. "She's got a baby colt!" he murmured.

He glanced about him helplessly. If he could only think! How could he drive the Phantom and her colt to Tom's Point?

Warily he approached the myrtle thicket. Just then the colt let out a high, frightened whinny. In that little second Paul knew that he wanted more than anything in the world to keep the mother and the colt together. Shivers of joy raced up and down his spine. His breath came faster. He made a firm resolution. "I'll buy you both!" he promised.

But how far had he come? Was it ten miles to Tom's Point or two? Would it be best to drive them down the beach? Or through the woods? As if in answer a loud bugle rang through the woods. It was the Pied Piper, the pinto stallion in command of the herd. And unmistakably his voice came from the direction of Tom's Point.

The Phantom pricked her ears. She wheeled around and almost collided with Watch Eyes in her haste to find the band. She wanted the Pied Piper for protection. Behind her trotted the foal, all shining and clean with its newness.

Paul laughed weakly. *He* was not driving the Phantom after all! She and her colt were leading him. They were leading him to Tom's Point!

Tom's Point was a protected piece of land where the marsh was hard and the grass especially sweet. About seventy wild ponies, exhausted by their morning's run, stood browsing quietly, as if they were in a corral. Only occasionally they looked up at their captors. The good meadow and their own weariness kept them peaceful prisoners.

At a watchful distance the roundup men rested their mounts and relaxed. It was like the lull in the midst of a storm. All was quiet on the surface. Yet there was an undercurrent of tension. You could tell it in the narrowed eyes of the men, their subdued voices and their too

174

easy laughter.

Suddenly the laughter stilled. Mouths gaped in disbelief. Eyes rounded. For a few seconds no one spoke at all. Then a shout that was half wonder and half admiration went up from the men. Paul Beebe was·bringing in *the Phantom and a colt!*

The roundup men were swarming around Paul, buzzing with questions. "Beats all!" he heard someone say. "For two years we been trying to round up the Phantom and along comes a spindling youngster to show us up."

" 'Twas the colt that hindered her."

" 'Course it was."   .

"It's the newest colt in the bunch; may not stand the swim."

"If we lose only one colt, it'll still be a good day's work."

The men accepted Paul as one of them now—a real roundup man. They were clapping him on the shoulder and trying to get him to talk. "Ain't they a shaggy-lookin' bunch?" Kim Horsepepper asked.

"Except for Misty," Paul said, pointing toward the Phantom's colt. "Her coat is silky." The mere thought of touching it sent shivers through him. "Misty," he thought to himself wonderingly. "Why, I've named her!"

He looked out across the water. Two lines of boats were forming a pony-way across the channel. He saw the cluster of people and the mounts waiting on the shores of Chincoteague and he knew that somewhere among them was Maureen. It was like a relay race. Soon she would carry on.

"Could I swim my mount across the

175

channel alongside the Phantom?" Paul asked Wyle Maddox anxiously.

Wyle shook his head. "Watch Eyes is all tuckered out," he said. "Besides, there's a kind of tradition in the way things is handled on Pony Penning Day. There's mounted men for the roundup and there's boatmen to herd 'em across the channel."

"Tide's out!" he called in clipped tones. "Current is slack. Time for the ponies to be swimmed across. Let's go!"

Suddenly the beach was wild with commotion. From three sides the roundup men came rushing at the ponies, their hoarse cries whipping the animals into action. They plunged into the water, the stallions leading, the mares following, neighing encouragement to their colts.

"They're off!" shouted Wyle Maddox, and everyone felt the relief and triumph in his words.

On the shores of Chincoteague the people pressed forward, their faces strained to stiffness, as they watched Assateague Beach.

"Here they come!" The cry broke out from every throat.

Maureen, wedged in between Grandpa Beebe on one side and a volunteer fireman on the other, stood on her mount's back. Her arms paddled the air as if she were swimming and struggling with the wild ponies.

Suddenly a fisherman, looking through binoculars, began shouting in a hoarse voice, "A new-borned colt is afeared to swim. Wait! A wild pony is breaking out from the mob! Swimming around the mob! Escaping!"

An awed murmur stirred the crowds. Maureen dug her toes in her mount's back. She strained her eyes to see the fugitive, but all she could make out was a milling mass of dark blobs on the water.

The fisherman leaned far out over the water. "It's the Phantom!" he screamed.

The people took up the cry, echoing it over and over. "It's the Phantom! She's escaped again!"

Maureen felt tears on her cheek, and impatiently brushed them away.

The fisherman was waving for quiet. "It's the *Phantom's* colt that won't swim!" he called out in a voice so hoarse it cracked. "The Phantom got separated from a bran'-fire new colt. She's gone back to get it!"

The people whooped and hollered at the news. "The Phantom's got a colt," they sang. "The Phantom's got a colt!"

Again the fisherman was waving for silence.

"She's reached her colt!" he crowed. "But the roundup men are closing in on her! They're making her shove the colt in the water. Look! She's makin' it swim!"

Grandpa Beebe cupped his hands around his mouth. "Can the little feller make it?" he boomed.

The crowd stilled, waiting for the hoarse voice. For long seconds no answer came. The fisherman remained as fixed as the piling he stood on. Wave after wave of fear swept over Maureen. She felt as if she were drowning. And just when she could stand the silence no longer, the fisherman began reporting in short, nervous sentences.

"They're half-ways across. Jumpin' Jupiter! The colt! It's bein' sucked down in a whirlpool. I can't see it now. My soul and body! A boy's jumped off the scow. He's swimming out to help the colt."

The onlookers did not need the fisherman with the binoculars any more. They could see for themselves. A boy swimming against the current. A boy holding a colt's head above the swirling water.

Maureen gulped great lungfuls of air. "It's Paul!" she screamed. "It's Paul!"

On all sides the shouts went up. "Why, it's Paul!"

Grandpa leaped up on his mount's back as nimbly as a boy. He stood with his arms upraised, his fists clenched.

"God help ye, Paul!" his words carried out over the water. "Yer almost home!"

Grandpa's voice was as strong as a tow rope. Paul was swimming steadily toward it, holding the small silver face of the colt above the water. He was almost there. He *was* there!

Maureen slid down from her mount, clutching a handful of mane. "You made it, Paul! You made it!" she cried.

The air was wild with whinnies and snorts as the ponies touched the hard sand, then scrambled up the shore, their wet bodies gleaming in the sun. Paul half-carried the little colt up the steep bank; then suddenly it found its own legs. Shouts between triumph and relief escaped every throat as the little filly tottered up the bank.

For a brief second Paul's and Maureen's eyes met above the crowds. It was as if they and the mare and her foal were the only creatures on the island. They were unaware of the great jostling and fighting as the stallions sorted out their own mares and colts. They were unaware of everything but a sharp ecstasy. Soon the Phantom and her colt would belong to them. Never to be sold.

Dodging horses and people, Grandpa Beebe made his way over to Paul.

"Paul, boy," he said, his voice unsteady, "I swimmed the hull way with you. Yer the most wonderful and the craziest young'un in the world. Now git home right smart quick," he added, trying to sound very stern. "Yer about done up, and Grandma's expectin' ye. Maureen and I'll see to it that the Phantom and her colt reach the pony pens."

Time for Laughter

Stories from The Peterkin Papers

By Lucretia P. Hale

THE LADY WHO PUT SALT IN HER COFFEE

THIS was Mrs. Peterkin. It was a mistake. She had poured out a delicious cup of coffee, and, just as she was helping herself to cream, she found she had put in salt instead of sugar! It tasted bad. What should she do? Of course she couldn't drink the coffee; so she called in the family, for she was sitting at a late breakfast all alone. The family came in; they all tasted, and looked, and wondered what should be done, and all sat down to think.

At last Agamemnon, who had been to college, said, "Why don't we go over and ask the advice of the chemist?" (For the chemist lived over the way, and was a very wise man.)

Mrs. Peterkin said, "Yes," and Mr. Peterkin said, "Very well," and all the children said they would go too. So the little boys put on their india-rubber boots, and over they went.

Now the chemist was just trying to find out something which should turn everything it touched into gold; and he had a large glass bottle into which he put all kinds of gold and silver, and many other valuable things, and melted them all up over the fire, till he had almost found what he wanted. He could turn things into almost gold. But just now he had used up all the gold that he had round the house, and gold was high. He had used up his wife's gold thimble and his great-grandfather's gold-bowed spectacles; and he had melted up the gold head of his great-great-grandfather's cane; and, just as the Peterkin family came in, he was down on his knees before his wife, asking her to let him have her wedding-ring to melt up with all the rest, because this time he knew he should succeed, and should be able to turn everything into gold; and then she could have a new wedding-ring of diamonds, all set in emeralds and rubies and topazes, and all the furniture could be turned into the finest of gold.

Now his wife was just consenting when the Peterkin family burst in. You can imagine how mad the chemist was! He came near throwing his crucible—that was the name of his melting-pot—at their heads. But he didn't. He listened as calmly as he could to the story of how Mrs. Peterkin had put salt in her coffee.

At first he said he couldn't do anything about it; but when Agamemnon said they would pay in gold if he would only go, he packed up his bottles in a leather case, and went back with them all.

First he looked at the coffee, and then stirred it. Then he put in a little chlorate of potassium, and the family tried it all round; but it tasted no better. Then he stirred in a little bichlorate of magnesia.

But Mrs. Peterkin didn't like that. Then he added some tartaric acid and some hypersulphate of lime. But no; it was no better. "I have it!" exclaimed the chemist, —"a little ammonia is just the thing!" No, it wasn't the thing at all.

Then he tried, each in turn, some oxalic, cyanic, acetic, phosphoric, chloric, hyperchloric, sulphuric, boracic, silicic, nitric, formic, nitrous nitric, and carbonic acids. Mrs. Peterkin tasted each and said the flavor was pleasant, but not precisely that of coffee. So then he tried a little calcium, aluminum, barium, and strontium, a little clear bitumen, and a half of a third of a sixteenth of a grain of arsenic. This gave rather a pretty color; but still Mrs. Peterkin ungratefully said

it tasted of anything but coffee. The chemist was not discouraged. He put in a little belladonna and atropine, some granulated hydrogen, some potash, and a very little antimony, finishing off with a little pure carbon. But still Mrs. Peterkin was not satisfied.

The chemist said that all he had done ought to have taken out the salt. The theory remained the same, although the experiment had failed. Perhaps a little starch would have some effect. If not, that was all the time he could give. He should like to be paid, and go. They were all much obliged to him, and willing to give him $1.37½ in gold. Gold was now $2.69¾, so Mr. Peterkin found in the newspaper. This gave Agamemnon a

181

pretty little sum. He sat himself down to do it. But there was the coffee! All sat and thought awhile, till Elizabeth Eliza said, "Why don't we go to the herb-woman?" Elizabeth Eliza was the only daughter. She was named after her two aunts—Elizabeth, from the sister of her father; Eliza, from her mother's sister. Now, the herb-woman was an old woman who came round to sell herbs, and knew a great deal. They all shouted with joy at the idea of asking her, and Solomon John and the younger children agreed to go and find her too. The herb-woman lived down at the very end of the street; so the boys put on their india-rubber boots again, and they set off. It was a long walk through the village, but they came at last to the herb-woman's house, at the foot of a high hill. They went through her little garden. Here she had marigolds and hollyhocks, and old maids and tall sunflowers, and all kinds of sweet-smelling herbs, so that the air was full of tansy-tea and elder-blow. Over the porch grew a hop-vine, and a brandy-cherry tree shaded the door, and a luxuriant cranberry-vine flung its delicious fruit across the window. They went into a small parlor, which smelt very spicy. All around hung little bags full of catnip, and peppermint, and all kinds of herbs; and dried stalks hung from the ceiling; and on the shelves were jars of rhubarb, senna, manna, and the like.

But there was no little old woman. She had gone up into the woods to get some more wild herbs, so they all thought they would follow her—Elizabeth Eliza, Solo-mon John, and the little boys. They had to climb up over high rocks, and in among huckleberry-bushes and blackberry vines. But the little boys had their india-rubber boots. At last they discovered the little old woman. They knew her by her hat. It was steeple-crowned without any vane. They saw her digging with her trowel round a sassafras bush. They told her their story—how their mother had put salt in her coffee, and how the chemist had made it worse instead of better, and how their mother couldn't drink it, and wouldn't she come and see what she could do? And she said she would, and took up her little old apron, with pockets all round, all filled with everlasting and pennyroyal, and went back to her house.

There she stopped, and stuffed her huge pockets with some of all the kinds of herbs. She took some tansy and pep-permint, and caraway-seed and dill, spear-mint and cloves, pennyroyal and sweet marjoram, basil and rosemary, wild thyme and some of the other time—such as you have in clocks—sappermint and opper-mint, catnip, valerian, and hop; indeed, there isn't a kind of herb you can think of that the little old woman didn't have done up in her little paper bags, that had all been dried in her little Dutch-oven. She packed these all up, and then went back with the children, taking her stick.

Meanwhile Mrs. Peterkin was getting quite impatient for her coffee.

As soon as the little old woman came she had it set over the fire, and began to stir in the different herbs. First she put in a little hop for the bitter. Mrs. Peterkin said it tasted like hop-tea, and not at all like coffee. Then she tried a little flagroot and snakeroot, then some spruce gum, and some caraway and some dill, some rue and rosemary, some sweet marjoram and sour, some oppermint and sappermint, a little spearmint and peppermint, some wild thyme, and some of the other tame time, some tansy and basil, and catnip and valerian, and sassafras, ginger, and penny-royal. The children tasted after each mixture, but made up dreadful faces. Mrs. Peterkin tasted, and did the same. The more the old woman stirred, and the more she put in, the worse it all seemed to taste.

So the old woman shook her head, and muttered a few words, and said she must go. She believed the coffee was bewitched. She bundled up her packets of herbs, and took her trowel, and her basket, and her stick, and went back to her root of sassafras, that she had left half in the air and half out. And all she would take for pay was five cents in currency.

Then the family were in despair, and all sat and thought a great while. It was growing late in the day, and Mrs. Peterkin hadn't had her cup of coffee. At last Elizabeth Eliza said, "They say that the lady from Philadelphia, who is staying in town, is very wise. Suppose I go and ask her what is best to be done." To this they all agreed, and off Elizabeth Eliza went.

She told the lady from Philadelphia the whole story—how her mother had put salt in the coffee; how the chemist had been called in; how he tried everything but could make it no better; and how they went for the little old herb-woman, and how she had tried in vain, for her mother couldn't drink the coffee. The lady from Philadelphia listened very attentively, and then said, "Why doesn't your mother make a fresh cup of coffee?" Elizabeth Eliza started with surprise. Solomon John shouted with joy; so did Agamemnon, who had just finished his sum; so did the little boys, who had followed on. "Why didn't we think of that?" said Elizabeth Eliza; and they all went back to their mother, and she had her cup of coffee.

Elizabeth Eliza Peterkin had a present of a piano, and she was to take lessons from the postmaster's daughter.

They decided to have the piano set across the window in the parlor, and the moving men brought it in, and left.

After they had gone the family all came in to look at the piano; but they found the men had placed it with its back turned towards the middle of the room, standing close against the window.

How could Elizabeth Eliza open it?

How could she reach the keys to play upon it?

Solomon John proposed that they should open the window. Agamemnon could do that with his long arms. Then Elizabeth Eliza could go around to the porch and open the piano from there. Then she could have her music-stool on the porch and play on the piano through the window from the outside.

So they tried this; and they all thought it was a very pretty sight to see Elizabeth Eliza playing on the piano while she sat

on the porch with the honeysuckle vines behind her.

It was very pleasant, too, moonlight evenings. Mr. Peterkin liked to take a nap on his sofa in the room; but the rest of the family liked to sit on the porch. So did Elizabeth Eliza; only she had to have her back to the moon.

All this did very well through the summer; but, when the fall came, Mr. Peterkin thought the air was too cold from the open window, and the family did not want to sit out on the porch.

Elizabeth Eliza practiced in the mornings with her coat on; but she had to give up her music in the evenings, the family shivered so.

One day, when she was talking with the lady from Philadelphia, she spoke of this trouble.

The lady from Philadelphia looked surprised, and then said, "But why don't you turn the piano round?"

One of the little boys pertly said, "It is a square piano."

But Elizabeth Eliza went home at once, and, with the help of Agamemnon and Solomon John, turned the piano around.

"Why did we not think of that before?" said Mrs. Peterkin. "What shall we *ever* do when the lady from Philadelphia goes home again?"

THE PETERKINS' TREE

EARLY in the autumn the Peterkins began to prepare for their Christmas-tree. Everything was done in great secrecy as it was to be a surprise to the neighbors as well as to the rest of the family. Mr. Peterkin had been up to Mr. Bromwick's wood-lot, and, with his consent, selected the tree. Agamemnon went to look at it occasionally after dark, and Solomon John made frequent visits to it mornings, just after sunrise.

Mr. Peterkin drove Elizabeth Eliza and her mother that way, and pointed furtively to it with his whip. But none of them ever spoke of it aloud to each other. It was suspected that the little boys had been to see it Wednesday and Saturday afternoons. But they came home with their pockets full of chestnuts and said nothing about it.

At last Mr. Peterkin had it cut down and brought secretly into the Larkins' barn. A week or two before Christmas a measurement was made of it with Elizabeth Eliza's tape-measure. To Mr. Peterkin's great dismay it was too high to stand in the back parlor. This was brought out at a secret council of Mr. and Mrs. Peterkin, Elizabeth Eliza, and Agamemnon.

Agamemnon suggested that it might be set up slanting; but Mrs. Peterkin was sure that would make her dizzy, and the candles would drip.

But a brilliant idea came to Mr. Peterkin. He proposed that the ceiling of the parlor should be raised to make room for the top of the tree.

Elizabeth Eliza thought the space would need to be quite large. It must not be like a small box, or you could not see the tree.

"Yes," said Mr. Peterkin, "I should have the ceiling lifted all across the room; the effect would be finer."

Elizabeth Eliza objected to having the whole ceiling raised, because her room was over the back parlor and she would have no floor while the alteration was going on and that would be very awkward. Besides, her room was not very high now, and, if the floor were raised, perhaps she could not walk in it upright.

Mr. Peterkin explained that he didn't propose altering the whole ceiling, just to lift up a ridge across the room at the back where the tree was to stand. This would make a hump, to be sure, in Elizabeth Eliza's room; but it would go across the whole room.

Elizabeth Eliza said she would not mind that. It would be like the thing that comes up on the deck of a ship that you sit against, only here you would not have the sea-sickness. She thought she should like it, for a rarity. She might use it for a divan.

Mrs. Peterkin thought it would come in the worn place of the carpet, and might be a convenience in making the carpet over.

Agamemnon was afraid there would be trouble in keeping the matter secret, for it would be a long piece of work for a carpenter; but Mr. Peterkin proposed having the carpenter for a day or two, for a number of jobs.

One of them was to make all the chairs in the house of the same height, for Mrs. Peterkin had nearly broken her spine by sitting down in a chair that she had supposed was her own rocking-chair, and it had proved to be two inches lower. The little boys were now large enough to sit in any chair; so a medium was fixed upon to satisfy all the family, and all the chairs were made the same height.

On consulting the carpenter, however, he insisted that the tree could be cut off at the lower end to suit the height of the parlor, and objected to so great a change as altering the ceiling. But Mr. Peterkin had set his mind on the improvement, and Elizabeth Eliza had cut her carpet to prepare for it.

So the folding-doors into the back parlor were closed and for nearly two weeks before Christmas there was great litter of fallen plastering and laths and chips and shavings; and Elizabeth Eliza's carpet was taken up, and the furniture had to be changed, and one night she had to sleep at the Bromwicks', for there was a long dangerous hole in the floor.

All this delighted the little boys. They could not understand what was going on. Perhaps they suspected a Christmas-tree, but they did not know why a Christmas-tree should have so many chips, and they were still more astonished at the hump that appeared in Elizabeth Eliza's room. It must be a Christmas present, they decided.

Some aunts and uncles arrived a day or two before Christmas, with some small cousins. These cousins occupied the attention of the little boys, and there was a great deal of whispering and mystery behind doors and under the stairs.

Solomon John was privately busy making candles for the tree. He had been collecting bayberries, as he understood they made very nice candles, and then it would not be necessary to buy any.

The elders of the family never all went into the back parlor together, and they all tried not to see what was going on. Mrs. Peterkin would go in with Solomon John, or Mr. Peterkin with Elizabeth Eliza, or Elizabeth Eliza and Agamemnon and Solomon John. The little boys and the small cousins were never allowed even to look inside the room.

Elizabeth Eliza meanwhile went into town a number of times. She wanted to consult Amanda as to how much ice-cream they should need, and whether they could make it at home with their own cream and ice. Then, too, she was pretty busy in her own room where the furniture had to be changed and the carpet altered. The "hump" was higher than she expected. There was danger of bumping her own head whenever she crossed it. She had to nail some padding on the ceiling for fear of accidents.

The afternoon before Christmas, Elizabeth Eliza, Solomon John, and their father collected in the back parlor for a council. The carpenters had done their work and the tree stood at its full height at the back of the room, the top stretch-ing up into the space arranged for it. All the chips and shavings were cleared away, and the tree stood on a neat box. But what were they to put on the tree?

Solomon John had brought in his supply of candles; but they proved to be very "stringy" and there were very few of them. How many bayberries it took to make a few candles! The little boys had helped him, and he had gathered a whole bushel of bayberries. He had put them in water, and skimmed off the wax, according to the directions; but there was so little wax!

Solomon John had given the little boys some of the bits sawed off from the legs of the chairs. He had suggested that they cover them with gilt paper, to answer for gilt apples.

These apples, a little blunt at the end, and the candles, were all they had for the tree! After all her trips into town Elizabeth Eliza had forgotten to bring anything for it!

"It is odd I should have forgotten, that day I went in on purpose to get the things," mused Elizabeth Eliza. "But I went from shop to shop and didn't know exactly what to get. I saw a great many gilt things for Christmas-trees; but I knew the little boys were making the gilt apples. There were plenty of candles in the shops too, but I knew Solomon John was making the candles."

Mr. Peterkin thought it was quite natural. Solomon John wondered if it were too late for them to go into town now. But Elizabeth Eliza could not go in the next morning, for there was to be a grand

Christmas dinner, and Mr. Peterkin could not be spared, and Solomon John was sure he and Agamemnon would not know what to buy. Besides, they would want to try the candles tonight.

Mr. Peterkin asked if the presents everybody had been preparing would not answer. But Elizabeth Eliza knew they would be too heavy. A gloom came over the room. There was only a flickering gleam from one of Solomon John's candles that he had lighted by way of trial.

Solomon John again proposed going into town. He lighted a match to examine the newspaper about the trains. There were plenty of trains coming out at that hour, but none going in.

Agamemnon was summoned. Mrs. Peterkin was entertaining the uncles and aunts in the front parlor. Agamemnon wished there was time to study up something about electric lights. Solomon John's candle sputtered and went out.

At this moment there was a loud knocking at the front door. The little boys and the small cousins and the uncles and aunts and Mrs. Peterkin all hurried to see what was the matter. The uncles and aunts thought somebody's house must be on fire. They opened the door, and there was a man, white with flakes, for it was beginning to snow, and he was pulling in a large box.

Mrs. Peterkin supposed it contained some of Elizabeth Eliza's purchases, so she ordered it to be pushed into the back

parlor and hastily called back her guests and the little boys into the other room. The little boys and the small cousins were sure they had seen Santa Claus himself.

The box was addressed to Elizabeth Eliza Peterkin. It was from the lady from Philadelphia! She had gathered a hint from Elizabeth Eliza's letters that there was to be a Christmas-tree, and had filled this box with decorations.

There was every kind of gilt hanging-thing, from gilt pea-pods to butterflies on springs. There were shining flags and lanterns and birdcages and nests with birds sitting on them, baskets of fruit, gilt apples and bunches of grapes, and, at the very bottom, a large box of candles and a box of Philadelphia bonbons!

Elizabeth Eliza and Solomon John could scarcely keep from screaming with joy. The little boys and the small cousins knocked on the folding-doors to ask what was the matter.

Hastily Mr. Peterkin and the rest took out the things, hung them on the tree, and put on the candles. When all was done, it looked so well that Mr. Peterkin exclaimed, "Let's light the candles now, and invite all the neighbors in and have the tree tonight on Christmas Eve!"

And so it was that the Peterkins had their Christmas-tree the day before, and were free on Christmas night to go and visit their neighbors.

THE PETERKINS TRY TO BECOME WISE

THE PETERKINS were sitting around the breakfast table and wondering what they should do because the lady from Philadelphia had gone away. "If," said Mrs. Peterkin, "we could only be more wise as a family!"

How could they manage it? Agamemnon had been to college, and the children all went to school; but still as a family they were not wise.

"It comes from books," said one of them. "People who have a great many books are very wise."

Then they counted up that there were very few books in the house; a few school-books and Mrs. Peterkin's cookbook were all.

"That's the thing!" said Agamemnon. "We want a library."

"We want a library!" said Solomon John. And all of them exclaimed, "We want a library!"

"Let us think how we shall get one," said Mrs. Peterkin. "I have observed that other people think a great deal of thinking."

So they all sat and thought a great while.

Then said Agamemnon, "I will make a library. There are some boards in the

189

wood-shed, and I have a hammer and some nails, and perhaps we can borrow some hinges, and there we have our library!"

They were all very much pleased at the idea.

"That's the bookcase part," said Elizabeth Eliza. "But where are the books?"

So they sat and thought a little while; then Solomon John exclaimed, "I will make a book!"

They all looked at him in wonder.

"Yes," said Solomon John. "Books will make us wise; but first I must make a book."

So they went into the parlor, and sat down to make a book. But there was no ink. What should he do for ink? Elizabeth Eliza said she had heard that nutgalls and vinegar made very good ink. So they decided to make some. The little boys said they could find nutgalls up in the woods. So they all agreed to set out and pick some. Mrs. Peterkin put on her cape and bonnet, and the little boys got into their rubber boots, and off they went.

The nutgalls were hard to find. There was almost everything else in the woods—chestnuts and walnuts, and small hazelnuts, and a great many squirrels; and they had to walk a great way before they found any nutgalls. At last they came home with a large basket and two nutgalls in it.

Then came the question of the vinegar. Mrs. Peterkin had used her very last on some beets they had the day before.

"Suppose we go and ask the minister's wife," said Elizabeth Eliza.

So they all went to the minister's wife. She said if they wanted some good vinegar they had better set a barrel of cider down in the cellar, and in a year or two it would make very nice vinegar. But they said they wanted it that very afternoon. When the minister's wife heard this she said she should be very glad to let them have some vinegar, and gave them a cupful to carry home. So they stirred in the nutgalls, and by the time evening came they had very good ink.

Then Solomon John wanted a pen. Agamemnon had a steel one, but Solomon John said, "Poets always used quills."

Elizabeth Eliza suggested that they should go out to the poultry-yard and get a quill. But it was already dark. They had, however, two lanterns, and the little boys borrowed the neighbors'. They set out in procession for the poultry-yard. When they got there the fowls were all at roost, so they could look at them quietly. But there were no geese! There were Shanghais, and Cochin-Chinas, and Guinea hens, and Barbary hens, and speckled hens, and Poland roosters, and bantams, and ducks, and turkeys, but not one goose!

"No geese but ourselves," said Mrs. Peterkin, wittily, as they returned to the house.

The sight of this procession roused up the village. "A torchlight procession!" cried all the boys of the town; and they gathered round the house, shouting for the flag; and Mr. Peterkin had to invite them in and give them cider and gingerbread before he could explain to them

that it was only his family visiting his hens.

After the crowd had dispersed, Solomon John sat down to think of his writing again. Agamemnon agreed to go over to the bookstore to get a quill. They all went over with him. The bookseller was just shutting up his shop. However, he agreed to go in and get a quill, which he did, and they hurried home.

So Solomon John sat down again, but there was no paper. And now the bookstore was shut up. Mr. Peterkin suggested that the mail was about in, and perhaps he should have a letter, and then they could use the envelope to write on. So they all went to the post-office, and the little boys had their rubber boots on, and they all shouted when they found Mr. Peterkin had a letter. The postmaster inquired what they were shouting about; and when they told him he said he would give Solomon John a whole sheet of paper for his book. And they all went back rejoicing.

So Solomon John sat down, and the family all sat round the table looking at him. He had his pen, his ink, and his paper. He dipped his pen into the ink and held it over the paper, and thought a minute, and then said, "But I haven't got anything to say."

The Baker's Daughter

By Margery Williams Bianco

O BUT the Baker's Daughter is beautiful!

The Baker's Daughter has yellow hair, and every night it is curled with rags, and every morning it stands out in a frizzy fluff round her head. The Baker's Daughter has blue dresses and pink dresses and spotted dresses, with flounces and flounces on them; she has beads around her neck and jingly bracelets and a ring with a real stone. All the girls in class sigh with envy of the Baker's Daughter.

But the Baker's Daughter is proud. She points her chin and she turns up her nose, and she is very, very superior. You never see her in the Baker's shop. She strolls up and down the sidewalk, sucking her beads.

You all know the Baker's shop, two steps down. It is warm in there, and busy. It smells of hot bread, and every few minutes the Baker, a hot untidy little man in shirt sleeves, comes up from the basement carrying a big tray of crullers, or shiny rolls, or twisted currant buns. The Baker works hard all day and he never has time to do more than just poke his nose outside the doorway, every hour or so, for a sniff of cool air. It is hard to believe that anything so beautiful as the Baker's Daughter could ever come out of the Baker's shop!

There was only one thing in the Baker's shop that at all came up in magnificence to the Baker's Daughter herself, and that was the big round cake that sat in the place of honor, right in the middle of the Baker's window. It was a chocolate cake, with all sorts of twirls and twiddles of lovely icing on it, and the word B I R T H D A Y written in pink sugar letters. For some reason or other the Baker would never sell that cake. Perhaps he was afraid he would never be able to make another one quite so beautiful. He would sell you any other cake from his window but that one, and even if you went there very early of a Friday morning, which is cruller day, when there are no cakes at all, and asked him for a nice party cake, he would say:

"I can let you have one by three o'clock!"

And if you then asked: "But how about the cake in the window?" he would reply:

"That's not for sale. You can have one by three o'clock!"

For though you should offer him dollars and dollars, he would never sell that cake!

I seldom dare to speak to the Baker's Daughter. I am much too humble. But still she has friends. Never little boys; these she points her chin at, from across the street. But there are little girls with whom she is on friendly terms for as much as a week at a time. Naturally they are very proud. If you can't be a princess or a movie star perhaps the next best thing is to be seen walking up to the drug store soda fountain with the Baker's Daughter, and sitting there beside her on a tall stool eating pineapple sundae.

Now there was one little girl with whom the Baker's Daughter condescended at one time to be friends. Perhaps her name had something to do with it. She was called Carmelita Miggs, and Carmelita is a very romantic and superior name. She had black hair and a pair of bronze slippers, and she was the only little girl ever seen to stroll publicly with the Baker's Daughter, arm in arm. What they talked about no one knew. But Carmelita sometimes wore the Baker's Daughter's beads, and the Baker's Daughter would wear Carmelita's beads, and altogether they were very, very special friends while it lasted.

And it lasted until Carmelita had a birthday party.

The Baker's Daughter of course was invited, and several other of Carmelita's school friends. It was to be a real party, at four in the afternoon, with ice cream. And the Baker's Daughter said, very grandly, that she would bring a cake.

"I will bake you a nice one," said her father, "with orange icing on it. Now let me see . . . how many of you will there be?"

But that wasn't at all what the Baker's Daughter wanted. Anyone at all could bring a cake with orange icing. "I will choose my own cake!" thought the Baker's Daughter.

But all she said was: "That will be very nice!"

And in the afternoon, while her father was down in the bake-shop kitchen putting the last twiddle on the orange cake (for he wanted to make it something very special), and while her mother was taking forty winks in the back parlor, and the bakery cat was sound asleep, with her four paws curled under her, behind the counter, the Baker's Daughter crept into the shop on tiptoe, in all her finery, and stole—yes, *stole*—that big magnificent cake from the very middle of the shop window!

You see, she had had her eye on it, all along!

She lifted it up—and a nice, light cake it seemed—wooden platter and all, and she covered it over with sheets of waxy paper and carried it round to Carmelita's house.

O but she looked proud, walking down the street with that big cake in her arms! Everyone turned to look at her.

"What a lovely cake!" cried all the little boys and girls when she arrived at Carmelita's house.

And the wrappings were taken off, very carefully, and it was set right in the middle of the table, with candles all around it.

"*What* a nice light cake!" said Carmelita's mother.

"All good cakes are light!" said the Baker's Daughter.

"It was very, very kind of your father

to make such a splendid cake," said Carmelita's mother.

"I chose it myself!" said the Baker's Daughter, tossing her head.

They talked a little, very politely, and Carmelita Miggs showed all her birthday presents. And at last came the moment for the ice cream to be handed round on little glass plates.

"And now," said Carmelita's mother, "we'll all have some of that delicious cake!"

Carmelita had to cut it, because it was her birthday. She stood there feeling very shy, for there was a great silence all round; everyone's eyes were fixed on the cake, and all one could hear was Tommy Bates busily sucking his ice-cream spoon, so as to get through first.

Only the Baker's Daughter sat there proudly, with her skirts spread out, looking indifferent, as though cakes like this were quite an everyday affair with her! Carmelita took the knife and stuck it into the very middle of the pink icing, and pushed. You could have heard a pin drop.

But the knife didn't go in. Carmelita turned very red, and took a long breath and tried again.

Still the knife wouldn't go in.

"You must try harder, dear," said Carmelita's mother, smiling pleasantly. "I expect the top icing is a little bit stiff! Do you want me to help you?"

Now Carmelita knew that she had been pushing just as hard as she could. It came upon her, all at once, that there must be something very very queer about that cake! But she took another long breath, again, and this time her mother put *her* hand on the knife, too.

You could have heard *two* pins drop!

And then, suddenly, there was a funny "plop," and the knife went in. And as it went in the cake slipped and turned a sort of somersault, and there it was, upside down, sticking on the tip of the knife that Carmelita's mother was still holding, and everyone looking most surprised. And that wasn't the worst of it!

It was all hollow inside!

In fact, it was just a big pasteboard shell covered over with icing, and *that* was why the Baker would never sell it to anyone!

Can you imagine how the party felt? How the little boys and girls whispered and giggled, how Carmelita wept, and the Baker's Daughter grew redder and redder, and snifflier and snifflier, and how Carmelita's mother tried to smooth everything over and pretend that it was really all very funny, and quite the nicest thing that could happen at any birthday party? And how, at the very last minute, while the ice cream was all melting away, they had to send out and buy a real cake, *somewhere else!*

But Carmelita Miggs didn't think it was a joke. She never, never forgave the Baker's Daughter for spoiling her party. For quite a long time she wouldn't speak to her at all. As for the other boys and girls, whenever they met Carmelita or the Baker's Daughter they would say:

"Now we'll all have some cake!"

You would think, after this, that the

Baker's Daughter would have changed her ways. But not a bit of it! I saw her, only the other day, strolling up and down the sidewalk and sucking her beads just as proud as ever.

As I went past her I whispered very softly: "Now we'll all have some cake!"

And do you know what the Baker's Daughter did? I hate to tell you.

She stuck—out—her—her—tongue!

There, in the middle of the Baker's window, is another cake. This time it has green icing and pink roses, and two little sugar doves on top. It is even grander than the old one, and will probably last twice as long.

Unless, of course, someone else should have a birthday party!

Mr. A and Mr. P

By Margery Williams Bianco

OF ALL the storekeepers in town there are none so merry as Mr. A and Mr. P.

They have quite the grandest store on the street. Outside it is painted a bright cheerful red, and inside it is full of all the things that a grocery store should have—soap and crackers and sardines and tubs of butter and red shiny apples, besides shelves of anything you could possibly think of, all put up in cans.

Mr. A is tall and thin, and Mr. P is short and stout. Mr. A has red hair, and Mr. P has very little hair at all. Mr. A can reach all the things off the top shelves, and Mr. P can get all the things off the bottom shelves. If there is anything on the very top shelf of all, and they have to get the long poker and poke it down, then Mr. A pokes and Mr. P catches, because Mr. P's lap is the widest.

In fact they do everything together. Mr. A takes the money and Mr. P rings the bell. Mr. A counts the groceries, and Mr. P writes them down. Mr. A makes the jokes, and Mr. P laughs at them.

And of an evening, when the store is closed and work is over, then Mr. A plays the flute and Mr. P plays the accordion.

You would think that when two people get along together so well, they would never have a quarrel in the world. But once upon a time they did, and this is how it happened.

For a long time they had been wondering what to do to make their life even merrier than it was. They had tried playing baseball with the soup cans, and football with the watermelons, and building all sorts of castles out of ketchup bottles and breakfast foods, just to see them come tumbling down again. But after a while they got tired of all this, and there just didn't seem anything new to play at.

Then Mr. A had a grand idea. He thought he would change the prices of everything in the store, over-night, just to see how surprised the customers would look when they came around next morning. He didn't want Mr. P to know about it, so that it might be a nice surprise for him, too. For Mr. A was always trying to think of something that would please Mr. P.

But Mr. P, too, was always trying to think of something that would please and surprise Mr. A. And unfortunately he happened to think of exactly the same thing, and he thought of it at almost exactly the same moment as Mr. A.

So each of them, very secretly, set about writing a whole set of new tickets, and each of them, also very secretly, went about sticking the new tickets just where

GRACE PAULL

they thought it would be most fun.

Mr. A would turn his head suddenly and want to know what Mr. P was giggling about, and Mr. P would stop writing his secret tickets long enough to ask *why* Mr. A was chuckling so, and they would both go off into peals of laughter and then look very solemn and begin working away again faster than ever.

Finally they locked up their store and went home for the night.

The first customer to come next morning was a housewife, and she wanted three cakes of soap for a quarter.

"Twelve cents a-piece!" said Mr. A, for he had changed the tickets from the breakfast cereal.

"But they're always three for a quarter," said the housewife.

"Not now, not now!" said Mr. A. "Maybe you're thinking of soup. Soup's three for a quarter. To-day," he added, and then began to giggle. He couldn't help it.

"Why, no it isn't!" cried Mr. P, beginning to giggle too. "It's two for nineteen. Look at that!"

And he winked at Mr. A, but for some reason Mr. A didn't seem to think it was funny at all.

"I tell you it's three for a quarter!" he said indignantly. "The whole week, too!"

"Two for nineteen, two for nineteen!" chanted Mr. P, in an irritating sort of way, and he went about the store humming "Two for nineteen, two for nineteen!"

"Just like a hen that's laid an egg!" thought Mr. A, beginning to get very annoyed, as people do when their jokes don't turn out to be funny after all.

The next customer wanted sugar and potatoes.

"Six for fifteen!" shouted Mr. P loudly.

"Two for forty-nine!" yelled Mr. A, banging his fist on the counter.

The customers began to get worried. They didn't know what to make of it at all. And the more Mr. A chuckled, the madder Mr. P got, and every time Mr. P giggled, Mr. A was cross enough to bite his head off.

In the afternoon it was worse. No one knew what anything cost at all. Half the customers were buying all sorts of things they didn't need just because they were cheap, and the other half were shouting that they wanted their money back. As fast as Mr. A stuck a ticket on one shelf Mr. P tore it down and put a different one in its place. They kept rushing round and round the store, doing nothing but change the tickets, and the last straw was when Mr. A marked a whole crate of watermelons four for fifteen cents, and all the boys from the neighborhood came pouring into the store so fast one couldn't even count them. And above all the turmoil, and the customers snatching this thing and that—for by this time they were so confused that they started waiting on one another—you might hear Mr. A's high squeaky voice shouting "Six for nineteen! Six for nineteen, I tell you!" and Mr. P's deep bass rumbling "Three for a quarter! Three for a quarter!"

It was like a nightmare!

When six o'clock came round Mr. A and Mr. P were both exhausted. Mr. A just threw his apron over his head and started rushing off down the street on his long thin legs, looking neither to right nor left, while Mr. P shooed the last customer out of the store and then sank right down on the onion crate and burst out sobbing.

He sobbed for quite a long time. When he had finished he felt a little bit better. So he mopped his eyes and blew his nose, and then he jumped up off the onion crate and rushed out of the store, not even banging the door behind him, and pattered off along the sidewalk as fast as he could go.

It was the very first time in all their lives that Mr. A and Mr. P had not walked home together. For years they had hung their two little aprons up side by side at exactly six o'clock, and at exactly two minutes past six they had taken their two hats and locked the store and strolled home side by side.

But this time Mr. A hadn't even gone home at all. He was far too upset. He went striding along through the town very fast, not caring at all which way he went, till he came to the place where the sidewalk ended and the country began, and there Mr. P finally saw him, still striding along with his nose in the air and his apron flapping in the breeze.

Now Mr. A was walking much faster than Mr. P, and so Mr. P had to make his stout little legs work very hard indeed to catch up with him, but catch up he did. And as soon as Mr. A heard that little patter-patter coming along behind him he slowed down a bit, and pretended to be looking at the landscape. So side by side, but neither looking at the other, they went along the road and across a field, until they came to a big log that was lying under a hickory tree, and there they both sat down side by side—plump!

Mr. A was still very cross, and Mr. P was still very hot and out of breath, so for a long while neither of them spoke. Then Mr. A looked round at Mr. P and gave a

big sniff. And Mr. P looked at Mr. A, and he gave a sniff, too. And then they both began to wriggle their toes on the ground.

Presently Mr. P said:

"I shouldn't think you need be so mean, just because I did something to please you!"

And Mr. A said:

"Well, you didn't have to be so cross, just because I wanted to give you a s-surprise!"

"I only did it to make you laugh!" said Mr. P.

"I thought you'd be very pleased and m-merry!" said Mr. A.

Then Mr. A pulled a packet of lemon drops out of his apron pocket.

"Have one," he said to Mr. P.

Mr. P took it and sucked it, and then he pulled a little packet out of *his* apron pocket, and he said to Mr. A:

"Don't you want some chewing gum?"

Half an hour later, just as the sun was setting, anyone looking out of the front window might have seen two little figures, one very tall and thin and the other very short and stout, trudging arm in arm along the sidewalk.

They were Mr. A and Mr. P, going back to their grocery store.

And from what I can hear, they have never quarreled since.

GRACE PAULL

The Doughnuts

Written and Illustrated by Robert McCloskey

ONE Friday night in November Homer overheard his mother talking on the telephone to Aunt Agnes over in Centerburg. "I'll stop by with the car in about half an hour and we can go to the meeting together," she said, because tonight was the night the Ladies' Club was meeting to discuss plans for a box social and to knit and sew for the Red Cross.

"I think I'll come along and keep Uncle Ulysses company while you and Aunt Agnes are at the meeting," said Homer.

So after Homer had combed his hair and his mother had looked to see if she had her knitting instructions and the right size needles, they started for town.

Homer's Uncle Ulysses and Aunt Agnes have a very up and coming lunch room over in Centerburg, just across from the court house on the town square. Uncle Ulysses is a man with advanced ideas and a weakness for labor saving devices. He equipped the lunch room with automatic toasters, automatic coffee maker, automatic dish washer, and an automatic doughnut maker. All just the latest thing in labor saving devices. Aunt Agnes would throw up her hands and sigh every time Uncle Ulysses bought a new labor saving device. Sometimes she became unkindly disposed toward him for days and days. She was of the opinion that Uncle Ulysses just frittered away his spare time over at the barber shop with the sheriff and the boys, so, what was the good of a labor saving device that gave you more time to fritter?

When Homer and his mother got to Centerburg they stopped at the lunch room, and after Aunt Agnes had come out and said, "My, how that boy does grow!" which was what she always said, she went off with Homer's mother in the car. Homer went into the lunch room and said, "Howdy, Uncle Ulysses!"

"Oh, hello, Homer. You're just in time," said Uncle Ulysses. "I've been going over this automatic doughnut ma-

201

chine, oiling the machinery and cleaning the works . . . wonderful things, these labor saving devices."

"Yep," agreed Homer, and he picked up a cloth and started polishing the metal trimmings while Uncle Ulysses tinkered with the inside workings.

"Opfwo-oof!!" sighed Uncle Ulysses and, "Look here, Homer, you've got a mechanical mind. See if you can find where these two pieces fit in. I'm going across to the barber shop for a spell, 'cause there's somethin' I've got to talk to the sheriff about. There won't be much business here until the double feature is over and I'll be back before then."

Then as Uncle Ulysses went out the door he said, "Uh, Homer, after you get the pieces in place, would you mind mixing up a batch of doughnut batter and put it in the machine? You could turn the switch and make a few doughnuts to have on hand for the crowd after the movie . . . if you don't mind."

"O. K." said Homer, "I'll take care of everything."

A few minutes later a customer came in and said, "Good evening, Bud."

Homer looked up from putting the last piece in the doughnut machine and said, "Good evening, Sir, what can I do for you?"

"Well, young feller, I'd like a cup o' coffee and some doughnuts," said the man.

"I'm sorry, Mister, but we won't have any doughnuts for about half an hour, until I can mix some dough and start this machine. I could give you some very fine sugar rolls instead."

"Well, Bud, I'm in no real hurry so I'll just have a cup o' coffee and wait around a bit for the doughnuts. Fresh doughnuts are always worth waiting for is what I always say."

"O. K.," said Homer, and he drew a cup of coffee from Uncle Ulysses' super automatic coffee maker.

"Nice place you've got here," said the customer.

"Oh, yes," replied Homer, "this is a very up and coming lunch room with all the latest improvements."

"Yes," said the stranger, "must be a good business. I'm in business too. A traveling man in outdoor advertising. I'm a sandwich man, Mr. Gabby's my name."

"My name is Homer. I'm glad to meet you, Mr. Gabby. It must be a fine profession, traveling and advertising sandwiches."

"Oh no," said Mr. Gabby, "I don't advertise sandwiches, I just wear any kind of an ad, one sign on front and one sign on behind, this way . . . Like a sandwich. Ya know what I mean?"

"Oh, I see. That must be fun, and you travel too?" asked Homer as he got out the flour and the baking powder.

"Yeah, I ride the rods between jobs, on freight trains, ya know what I mean?"

"Yes, but isn't that dangerous?"

"Of course there's a certain amount a risk, but you take any method a travel these days, it's all dangerous. Ya know what I mean? Now take airplanes . . ."

Just then a large shiny black car stopped in front of the lunch room and a chauffeur helped a lady out of the rear door.

They both came inside and the lady smiled at Homer and said, "We've stopped for a light snack. Some dough-nuts and coffee would be marvelous."

Then Homer said, "I'm sorry, Ma'm, but the doughnuts won't be ready until I make this batter and start Uncle Ulysses' doughnut machine."

"Well now aren't *you* a clever young man to know how to make *doughnuts!*"

"Well," blushed Homer, "I've really never done it before but I've got a receipt to follow."

"Now, young man, you simply must allow me to help. You know, I haven't made doughnuts for years, but I know the best receipt for doughnuts. It's marvelous, and we really must use it."

"But, Ma'm . . ." said Homer.

"Now just *wait* till you taste these doughnuts," said the lady. "Do you have an apron?" she asked, as she took off her fur coat and her rings and her jewelry and rolled up her sleeves. "Charles," she said to the chauffeur, "hand me that baking powder, that's right, and, young man, we'll need some nutmeg."

So Homer and the chauffeur stood by and handed things and cracked the eggs while the lady mixed and stirred. Mr. Gabby sat on his stool, sipped his coffee, and looked on with great interest.

"There!" said the lady when all of the ingredients were mixed. "Just *wait* till you taste these doughnuts!"

"It looks like an awful lot of batter," said Homer as he stood on a chair and poured it into the doughnut machine with the help of the chauffeur. "It's about *ten*

times as much as Uncle Ulysses ever makes."

"But wait till you taste them!" said the lady with an eager look and a smile.

Homer got down from the chair and pushed a button on the machine marked, "*Start.*" Rings of batter started dropping into the hot fat. After a ring of batter was cooked on one side an automatic gadget turned it over and the other side would cook. Then another automatic gadget gave the doughnut a little push and it rolled neatly down a chute, ready to eat.

"That's a simply *fascinating* machine," said the lady as she waited for the first doughnut to roll out.

"Here, young man, *you* must have the first one. Now isn't that just *too* deli-cious!? Isn't it simply marvelous?"

"Yes, Ma'm, it's very good," replied Homer as the lady handed doughnuts to Charles and to Mr. Gabby and asked if they didn't think they were simply divine doughnuts.

"It's an old family receipt!" said the lady with pride.

Homer poured some coffee for the lady and her chauffeur and for Mr. Gabby, and a glass of milk for himself. Then they all sat down at the lunch counter to enjoy another few doughnuts apiece.

"I'm so glad you enjoy my dough-nuts," said the lady. "But now, Charles, we really must be going. If you will just take this apron, Homer, and put two dozen doughnuts in a bag to take along, we'll be on our way. And, Charles, don't forget to pay the young man." She rolled down her sleeves and put on her jewelry, then Charles managed to get her into her big fur coat.

"Good night, young man, I haven't had so much fun in years. I *really* haven't!" said the lady, as she went out the door and into the big shiny car.

"Those are sure good doughnuts," said Mr. Gabby as the car moved off.

"You bet!" said Homer. Then he and Mr. Gabby stood and watched the automatic machine make doughnuts.

After a few dozen more doughnuts had rolled down the little chute, Homer said, "I guess that's about enough doughnuts to sell to the after theater customers. I'd better turn the machine off for a while."

Homer pushed the button marked *Stop* and there was a little click, but nothing happened. The rings of batter kept right on dropping into the hot fat, and an automatic gadget kept right on turning them over, and another automatic gadget kept right on giving them a little push and the doughnuts kept right on rolling down the chute, all ready to eat.

"That's funny," said Homer, "I'm sure that's the right button!" He pushed it again but the automatic doughnut maker kept right on making doughnuts.

"Well, I guess I must have put one of those pieces in backwards," said Homer.

"Then it might stop if you pushed the button marked *Start*, said Mr. Gabby.

Homer did, and the doughnuts still kept rolling down the little chute, just as regular as a clock can tick.

"I guess we could sell a few more doughnuts," said Homer, "but I'd better telephone Uncle Ulysses over at the bar-ber shop." Homer gave the number and while he waited for someone to answer he counted thirty-seven doughnuts roll down the little chute.

Finally someone answered "Hello! This is the sarber· bhop, I mean the barber shop."

"Oh, hello, sheriff. This is Homer. Could I speak to Uncle Ulysses?"

"Well, he's playing pinochle right now," said the sheriff. "Anythin' I can tell 'im?"

"Yes," said Homer. "I pushed the button marked *Stop* on the doughnut machine but the rings of batter keep right on dropping into the hot fat, and an automatic gadget keeps right on turning them over, and another automatic gadget keeps giving them a little push, and the doughnuts keep right on rolling down the little chute! It won't stop!"

"O. K. Wold the hire, I mean, hold the wire and I'll tell 'im." Then Homer looked over his shoulder and counted another twenty-one doughnuts roll down the little chute, all ready to eat. Then the sheriff said, "He'll be right over. . . . Just gotta finish this hand."

"That's good," said Homer. "G'by."

The window was full of doughnuts by now so Homer and Mr. Gabby had to hustle around and start stacking them on plates and trays and lining them up on the counter.

"Sure are a lot of doughnuts!" said Homer.

"You bet!" said Mr. Gabby. "I lost count at twelve hundred and two and that was quite a while back."

People had begun to gather outside the lunch room window, and someone was saying, "There are almost as many doughnuts as there are people in Centerburg, and I wonder how in tarnation Ulysses thinks he can sell all of 'em!"

Every once in a while somebody would come inside and buy some, but while somebody bought two to eat and a dozen to take home, the machine made three dozen more.

By the time Uncle Ulysses and the sheriff arrived and pushed through the crowd, the lunch room was a calamity of doughnuts! Doughnuts in the window, doughnuts piled high on the shelves, doughnuts stacked on plates, doughnuts lined up twelve deep all along the counter, and doughnuts still rolling down the little chute, just as regular as a clock can tick.

"Hello, sheriff, hello, Uncle Ulysses, we're having a little trouble here," said Homer.

"Well, I'll be dunked!!" said Uncle Ulysses.

"Dernd ef you won't be when Aggy

206

gits home," said the sheriff.

"Mighty fine doughnuts though. What'll you do with 'em all, Ulysses?"

Uncle Ulysses groaned and said, "What will Aggy say? We'll never sell 'em all."

Then Mr. Gabby, who hadn't said anything for a long time, stopped piling doughnuts and said, "What you need is an advertising man. Ya know what I mean? You got the doughnuts, ya gotta create a market . . . Understand? . . . It's balancing the demand with the supply . . . That sort of thing."

"Yep!" said Homer. "Mr. Gabby's right. We have to enlarge our market. He's an advertising sandwich man, so if we hire him, he can walk up and down in front of the theater and get customers."

"You're hired, Mr. Gabby!" said Uncle Ulysses.

Then everybody pitched in to paint the signs and to get Mr. Gabby sandwiched between. They painted "SALE ON DOUGHNUTS" in big letters on the window too.

Meanwhile the rings of batter kept

207

right on dropping into the hot fat, and an automatic gadget kept right on turning them over, and another automatic gadget kept right on giving them a little push, and the doughnuts kept right on rolling down the little chute, just as regular as a clock can tick.

"I certainly hope this advertising works," said Uncle Ulysses, wagging his head. "Aggy'll throw a fit if it don't."

The sheriff went outside to keep order, because there was quite a crowd by now —all looking at the doughnuts and guessing how many thousand there were, and watching new ones roll down the little chute, just as regular as a clock can tick. Homer and Uncle Ulysses kept stacking doughnuts. Once in a while somebody bought a few, but not very often.

Then Mr. Gabby came back and said, "Say, you know there's not much use o' me advertisin' at the theater. The show's all over, and besides almost everybody in town is out front watching that machine make doughnuts!"

"Zeus!" said Uncle Ulysses. "We must get rid of these doughnuts before Aggy gets here!"

"Looks like you will have ta hire a truck to waul 'em ahay, I mean haul 'em away!!" said the sheriff who had just come in. Just then there was a noise and a shoving out front and the lady from the shiny black car and her chauffeur came pushing through the crowd and into the lunch room.

"Oh gracious!" she gasped, ignoring the doughnuts, "I've lost my diamond bracelet, and I know I left it here on the counter," she said, pointing to a place where the doughnuts were piled in stacks of two dozen.

"Yes, Ma'm, I guess you forgot it when you helped make the batter," said Homer.

Then they moved all the doughnuts around and looked for the diamond bracelet, but they couldn't find it anywhere. Meanwhile the doughnuts kept rolling down the little chute, just as regular as a clock can tick.

After they had looked all around the sheriff cast a suspicious eye on Mr. Gabby, but Homer said, "He's all right, sheriff, he didn't take it. He's a friend of mine."

Then the lady said, "I'll offer a reward of one hundred dollars for that bracelet! It *must* be found! . . . it *really* must!"

"Now don't you worry, lady," said the sheriff. "I'll get your bracelet back!"

"Zeus! This is terrible!" said Uncle Ulysses. "First all of these doughnuts and then on top of all that, a lost diamond bracelet . . ."

Mr. Gabby tried to comfort him, and he said, "There's always a bright side. That machine'll probably run outta batter in an hour or two."

If Mr. Gabby hadn't been quick on his feet Uncle Ulysses would have knocked him down, sure as fate.

Then while the lady wrung her hands and said, "We must find it, we *must!*" and Uncle Ulysses was moaning about what Aunt Agnes would say, and the sheriff was eyeing Mr. Gabby, Homer sat down and thought hard.

Before twenty more doughnuts could roll down the little chute he shouted,

"SAY! I know where the bracelet is! It was lying here on the counter and got mixed up in the batter by mistake! The bracelet is cooked inside one of these doughnuts!"

"Why . . . I really believe you're right," said the lady through her tears. "Isn't that *amazing?* Simply *amazing!*"

"I'll be durn'd!" said the sheriff.

"Oh-h-h!" moaned Uncle Ulysses. "Now we have to break up all of these doughnuts to find it. Think of the pieces! Think of the *crumbs!* Think of what *Aggy* will say!"

"Nope," said Homer. "We won't have to break them up. I've got a plan."

So Homer and the advertising man took some cardboard and some paint and printed another sign. They put this sign

FRESH DOUGHNUTS
2 for 5¢
While They Last
$100.00 PRIZE
A BRACELET
INSIDE A DOUGHNUT
P.S. YOU HAVE TO GIVE THE
BRACELET BACK

in the window, and the sandwich man wore two more signs that said the same thing and walked in the crowd out front.

THEN . . . The doughnuts began to sell! *Everybody* wanted to buy doughnuts, *dozens* of doughnuts!

And that's not all. Everybody bought coffee to dunk the doughnuts in too. Those that didn't buy coffee bought milk or soda. It kept Homer and the lady and the chauffeur and Uncle Ulysses and the sheriff busy waiting on the people who wanted to buy doughnuts.

When all but the last couple of hundred doughnuts had been sold, Rupert Black shouted, "I GAWT IT!!" and sure enough . . . there was the diamond bracelet inside of his doughnut!

Then Rupert went home with a hundred dollars, the citizens of Centerburg went home full of doughnuts, the lady and her chauffeur drove off with the diamond bracelet, and Homer went home with his mother when she stopped by with Aunt Aggy.

As Homer went out of the door he heard Mr. Gabby say, "Neatest trick of merchandising I ever seen," and Aunt Aggy was looking sceptical while Uncle Ulysses was saying, "The rings of batter kept right on dropping into the hot fat, and the automatic gadget kept right on turning them over, and the other automatic gadget kept right on giving them a little push, and the doughnuts kept right on rolling down the little chute just as regular as a clock can tick—they just kept right on a comin', an' a comin', an' a comin,' an' a comin'."

—From *Homer Price*

The 500 Hats of Bartholomew Cubbins

Written and Illustrated by Dr. Seuss

IN THE beginning, Bartholomew Cubbins didn't have five hundred hats. He had only one hat. It was an old one that had belonged to his father and his father's father before him. It was probably the oldest and the plainest hat in the whole Kingdom of Didd, where Bartholomew Cubbins lived. But Bartholomew liked it —especially because of the feather that always pointed straight up in the air.

The Kingdom of Didd was ruled by King Derwin. His palace stood high on the top of the mountain. From his balcony he looked down over the houses of all his subjects—first over the spires of the noblemen's castles, across the broad roofs of the rich men's mansions, then over the little houses of the townsfolk, to the huts of the farmers far off in the fields.

It was a mighty view and it made King Derwin feel mighty important.

Far off in the fields, on the edge of a cranberry bog, stood the hut of the Cubbins family. From the small door Bartholomew looked across the huts of the farmers to the houses of the townsfolk, then to the rich men's mansions and the noblemen's castles, up to the great towering palace of the King. It was exactly the same view that King Derwin saw from his balcony, but Bartholomew saw it backward.

It was a mighty view, but it made Bartholomew Cubbins feel mighty small.

Just after sunrise one Saturday morning Bartholomew started for town. He felt very happy. A pleasant breeze whistled through the feather in his hat. In his right hand he carried a basket of cranberries to sell at the market. He was anxious to sell them quickly and bring the money back home to his parents.

He walked faster and faster till he got to the gates of the town.

The sound of silver trumpets rang through the air. Hoof beats clattered on the cobbled streets.

"Clear the way! Clear the way! Make way for the King!"

All the people rushed for the sidewalks. They drove their carts right up over the curbstones. Bartholomew clutched his basket tighter.

Around the corner dashed fifty trumpeters on yellow-robed horses. Behind them on crimson-robed horses came the King's Own Guards.

"Hats off to the King!" shouted the Captain of the King's Own Guards.

On came the King's carriage—white and gold and purple. It rumbled like thunder through the narrow street.

It swept past Bartholomew. Then suddenly its mighty brakes shrieked. It lurched—and then it stopped. The whole procession stood still.

Bartholomew could hardly believe what he saw. Through the side window of the carriage, the King himself was staring back—straight back at him! Bartholomew began to tremble.

"Back up!" the King commanded the Royal Coachman.

The Royal Coachman shouted to the royal horses. The King's Own Guards shouted to their crimson-robed horses.

The trumpeters shouted to their yellow-robed horses. Very slowly the whole procession backed down the street, until the King's carriage stopped right in front of Bartholomew.

The King leaned from his carriage window and fixed his eyes directly on Bartholomew Cubbins. "Well . . . ? Well . . . ?" he demanded.

Bartholomew shook with fright. "I ought to say something," he thought to himself. But he could think of nothing to say.

"Well?" demanded the King again. "Do you or do you *not* take off your hat before your King?"

"Yes, indeed, Sire," answered Bartholomew, feeling greatly relieved. "I *do* take off my hat before my King."

"Then take it off this very instant," commanded the King more loudly than before.

"But, Sire, my hat *is* off," answered Bartholomew.

"Such impudence!" shouted the King, shaking an angry finger. "How dare you stand there and tell me your hat is off!"

"I don't like to say you are wrong, Sire," said Bartholomew very politely, "but you see my hat *is* off." And he showed the King the hat in his hand.

"If that's your hat in your hand," demanded the King, "what's that on your head?"

"On my head?" gasped Bartholomew. There *did* seem to be something on his head. He reached up his hand and touched a hat!

The face of Bartholomew Cubbins turned very red. "It's a hat, Sire," he stammered, "but it *can't* be mine. Someone behind me must have put it on my head."

"I don't care *how* it got there," said the King. "You take it off." And the King sat back in his carriage.

Bartholomew quickly snatched off the hat. He stared at it in astonishment. It was exactly the same as his own hat—the same size, the same color. And it had exactly the same feather.

"By the Crown of my Fathers!" roared the King, again leaning out of the carriage window. "Did I or did I *not* command you to take off your hat?"

"You did, Sire . . . I took it off . . . I took it off twice."

"Nonsense! There is still a hat upon your head."

"Another hat?" Again Bartholomew reached up his hand and touched a hat.

"Come, come, what is the meaning of all this?" demanded the King, his face purple with rage.

"I don't know, Sire," answered Bartholomew. "It never happened to me before."

The King was now shaking with such fury that the carriage rocked on its wheels and the Royal Coachman could hardly sit in his seat. "Arrest this impudent trickster," shouted the King to the Captain of the King's Own Guards. "We'll teach him to take off his hat."

The Royal Coachman cracked his long whip. The King's carriage swung forward up the street toward the palace.

But the Captain of the King's Own Guards leaned down from his big brass saddle and grabbed Bartholomew Cubbins by his shirt. Away flew Bartholomew's basket! The cranberries bounced over the cobblestones and rolled down into the gutter.

With a jangling of spurs and a clatter of horseshoes, the Captain and Bartholomew sped up the winding street toward the palace. Out of the narrow streets, on up the hill! Bartholomew clung to the Captain's broad back. On and on they galloped, past the bright gardens of the wealthy merchants. Higher and higher up the mountain, on past the walls of the noblemen's castles. . . .

Flupp! . . . the sharp wind whisked off Bartholomew's hat. *Flupp Flupp* . . . two more flew off. *Flupp Flupp Flupp* flew another . . . and another. ". . . 4 . . . 5 . . . 6 . . . 7 . . ." Bartholomew kept counting as the hats came faster and faster. Lords and ladies stared from the windows of their turrets, wondering what the strange stream of hats could mean.

Over the palace drawbridge they sped —through the great gates, and into the courtyard. The Captain pulled in his reins.

"His Majesty waits in the Throne Room," said a guard, saluting the Captain.

"The Throne Room!" The Captain dropped Bartholomew to the ground. "I'd certainly hate to be in your shoes," he said, shaking his head sadly.

For a moment Bartholomew was terribly frightened. "Still," he thought to himself, "the King can do nothing dreadful to punish me, because I really haven't done anything wrong. It would be cowardly to feel afraid."

213

Bartholomew threw back his shoulders and marched straight ahead into the palace. "Follow the black carpet," said the guard at the door. All through the long hallway Bartholomew could hear the muttering of voices behind heavy doors. "He won't take off his hat?" "No, he won't take off his hat."

Bartholomew walked on till he stood in the very middle of the Throne Room. The King, in a long scarlet robe, was sitting on his throne. Beside him stood Sir Alaric, Keeper of the King's Records. He wore in his belt, instead of a sword, a long silver ruler. Lords and noblemen of the court stood solemn and silent.

The King looked down at Bartholomew severely. "Young man, I'll give you one more chance. Will you take off your hat for your King?"

"Your Majesty," said Bartholomew as politely as he possibly could, "I will—but I'm afraid it won't do any good." And he took off his hat—and it didn't do any good. Another hat sat on Bartholomew's head. He took off hat after hat after hat

after hat until he was standing in the middle of a great pile of hats.

The lords and noblemen were so astonished they couldn't even speak. Such a thing had never happened in the Throne Room before.

"Heavens!" said Sir Alaric, Keeper of the Records, blinking behind his triangular spectacles. "He's taken off 45!"

"And there were 3 more down in the town," said the King.

"And you must add on 87 more that blew off my head as we galloped up the hill," said Bartholomew, trying to be helpful.

"One hundred and thirty-five hats! Most unusual," said Sir Alaric, writing it down on a long scroll.

"Come, come," said the King impatiently. "Sir Alaric, what do you make of all this nonsense?"

"Very *serious* nonsense, Your Majesty," answered Sir Alaric. "I advise you to call in an expert on hats."

"Excellent," agreed the King. "Ho, Guard! Fetch in Sir Snipps, maker of hats for all the fine lords."

Into the Throne Room marched the smallest man, wearing the tallest hat that Bartholomew had ever seen. It was Sir Snipps. Instead of a sword, he wore at his side a large pair of scissors.

"Take a look at this boy's hat," commanded the King. Sir Snipps looked at Bartholomew Cubbins' hat and sniffed in disgust. Then he turned to the King and bowed stiffly. "Your Majesty, I, Sir Snipps, am the maker of hats for all the fine lords. I make hats of cloth of gold, fine silks and gems and ostrich plumes. You ask *me* what I think of *this* hat? Pooh! It is the most ordinary hat I ever set eyes on."

"In that case," said the King, "it should be very simple for you to take it off."

"Simple, indeed," mumbled Sir Snipps haughtily, and, standing on his tiptoes, he pushed his pudgy thumb at Bartholomew's hat and knocked it to the floor. Immediately another appeared on Bartholomew's head.

"Screebees!" screamed Sir Snipps, leaping in the air higher than he was tall. Then he turned and ran shrieking out of the Throne Room.

"Dear me!" said the King, looking very puzzled. "If Snipps can't do it, this *must* be more than an ordinary hat."

"One hundred and thirty-six," wrote Sir Alaric, wrinkling his brow. "Your Majesty, I advise that you call in your Wise Men."

"A fine idea!" said the King. "Ho, Guard! bring me Nadd. Nadd knows about everything in all my kingdom."

In came an old, old man. He looked at the hat on Bartholomew's head, and he looked at the pile of hats on the floor.

"Nadd, my Wise Man, can you take off his hat?" asked the King. Nadd shook his head solemnly—solemnly no.

"Then fetch me the Father of Nadd," commanded the King. "He knows about everything in all my kingdom and in all the world beyond."

In came an even older man. But when he looked at Bartholomew's hats, the Father of Nadd merely locked his fingers across his beard and said nothing.

"Then bring me the Father of the Father of Nadd!" ordered the King. "He knows about everything in all my kingdom, in all the world beyond, and in all other worlds that may happen to be."

Then came the oldest man of them all. But he just looked at Bartholomew and nibbled nervously at the end of his beard.

"Does this mean there is *no one* in my whole kingdom who can take off this boy's hat?" bellowed the King in a terrifying voice.

A small voice came up through the balcony window. "What's the matter, Uncle Derwin?" To Bartholomew, it sounded like the voice of a boy.

The King stepped out on the balcony and leaned over the marble railing. "There's a boy in here . . . just about your age," the King said. "He won't take off his hat."

Bartholomew tiptoed up behind the King and looked down. There stood a boy with a big lace collar—a very proud little boy with his nose in the air. It was the Grand Duke Wilfred, nephew of the King.

"You send him down here," said the Grand Duke Wilfred. "*I'll* fix him."

The King thought for a minute. He pushed back his crown and scratched his head. "Well . . . maybe you can. There's no harm trying."

"Take him to the Grand Duke Wilfred!" commanded the King. And two of the King's Own Guards led Bartholomew out of the Throne Room.

"Pooh!" said the Grand Duke Wilfred,

looking at Bartholomew's hat and laughing meanly. "*That* hat won't come off? You stand over there." He pointed to a corner where the wall curved out. "I need a little target practice with my bow and arrow."

When Bartholomew saw that the Grand Duke Wilfred had only a child's bow he didn't feel frightened. He spoke up proudly, "I can shoot with my father's big bow."

"My bow's plenty big enough for shooting hats—especially hats like yours," answered Wilfred. And he let fly an arrow. ZZZ! . . . it grazed Bartholomew's forehead and nipped off his hat. Away it blew, and over the parapet. But another hat appeared on his head. ZZZ! . . . ZZZ! . . . . ZZZ! . . . the arrows flew . . . till the Grand Duke's whole bagful of arrows was gone. And still a hat sat upon Bartholomew's head.

"It's not fair," cried the Grand Duke. "It's not fair!" He threw down his bow and stamped upon it.

"One hundred and fifty-four hats!" gulped Sir Alaric.

"These hats are driving me mad!" The King's voice rang out through all the palace. "Why waste time with a *child's* bow and arrow. Fetch me the mightiest bow and arrow in all my realm—fetch the Yeoman of the Bowmen!"

"Yeoman of the Bowmen," echoed all the lords and noblemen of the court.

A gigantic man strode out across the terrace. His bow was as big as the branch of a tree. The arrow was twice as long as Bartholomew, and thicker than his wrist.

"Yeoman of the Bowmen," said the King, "shoot off this boy's hat . . . and make it *stay* off!"

Bartholomew was trembling so hard that he could scarcely stand straight. The Yeoman bent back his mighty bow.

G—r—r—zibb! . . . Like a mad giant hornet the arrow tore through the air toward Bartholomew Cubbins.

G—r—r—zapp! . . . The sharp arrowhead bit through his hat and carried it off—on and on for a full half mile.

G—r—r—zopp! . . . It plunked to a stop in the heart of an oak tree. Yet there on Bartholomew's head sat another hat.

The face of the Yeoman of the Bowmen went white as the palace walls. "It's black magic!" he shrieked.

"Black magic, that's *just* what it is," sighed the King with relief. "I should have thought of that before. That makes things simple. Back to the Throne Room! Call my magicians!"

In the whole Throne Room there wasn't a sound as loud as a breath. But from the spiral stairs that led down from the southwest tower came the shuffling of slow, padded feet. The magicians were coming! Low and slow, they were chanting words that were strange. . . .

"Dig a hole five furlongs deep,
Down to where the night snakes creep;
Mix and mold the mystic mud,
Malber, Balber, Tidder, Tudd."

In came seven black-gowned magicians, and beside each one stalked a lean black cat. They circled around Bartholomew Cubbins muttering deep and mysterious sounds.

"Stop this useless muttering," ordered the King. "I want a chant that will charm away this boy's hat."

The magicians huddled over Bartholomew and chanted:

"Winkibus
Tinkibus
Fotichee
Klay,
Hat on the demon's head,
Fly far away!
Howl, men, howl away,
Howl away, howl away,
Yowl, cats, yowl away,
Yowl away, yowl away!
Hat on this demon's head,
Seep away, creep away, leap away,
*   gleap away,*
*   Never come back!"*

"A mighty good chant," said the King, looking very pleased. "Are you sure it will work?"

All the magicians nodded together.

"But," said the King, looking puzzled, "there still *seems* to be a hat upon his head. How long will it take for the charm to work?"

"Be calm, oh, Sire, and have no fears," chanted the magicians.
"Our charm will work in ten short years."

"*Ten years!*" gasped the King. "Away, fools!" he shouted. "Out of my sight! I can't wait *ten years* to get rid of his hat. Oh, dear, what *can* I do . . . what CAN I do?"

"If I were King," whispered the Grand Duke Wilfred, "I'd chop off his head."

"A dreadful thought," said the King, biting his lip. "But I'm afraid I'll have to."

"Young man," he said to Bartholomew Cubbins, and he pointed to a small door at the end of the room, "march down those steps to the dungeon and tell the executioner to chop off your head."

Bartholomew's heart sank into his boots, but he did as the King commanded. "I *must* take off my hat," he said to himself as he started down the long black stairway. "This is my last chance." One hat after another he tore from his head ". . . 156 . . . 157 . . . 158 . . ." It grew colder and damper. ". . . 217 . . . 218 . . . 219 . . ." Down . . . down . . . down. ". . . 231 . . . 232 . . . 233 . . ." It seemed to Bartholomew he must be in the very heart of the mountain.

"Who's there?" said a voice from the blackness.

Bartholomew turned a corner and stepped into the dungeon.

The executioner was whistling and swinging his axe idly because at the moment he had nothing to do. In spite of his business, he really seemed to be a very pleasant man.

"The King says you must chop off my head," said Bartholomew.

"Oh, I'd hate to," said the executioner, looking at him with a friendly smile. "You seem like such a nice boy."

"Well . . . the King says you have to," said Bartholomew, "so please get it over with."

"All right," sighed the executioner, "but first you've got to take off your hat."

"Why?" asked Bartholomew.

"I don't know," said the executioner, "but it's one of the rules. I can't execute anyone with his hat on."

"All right," said Bartholomew, "you take it off for me."

The executioner leaned across the chopping block and flipped off Bartholomew's hat.

"What's this?" he gasped, blinking through the holes in his mask, as another hat sat on Bartholomew's head. He flipped this one off . . . then another and another.

"Fiddlesticks!" grunted the executioner, throwing his axe on the floor. "I can't execute you at all." And he shook hands with Bartholomew and sent him back upstairs to the King.

The King had been taking a nap on the throne. "What are you doing back here?" he said to Bartholomew, angry at being awakened.

"I'm sorry, Your Majesty," explained Bartholomew. "My head can't come off with my hat on. . . . It's against the rules."

"So it can't," said the King, leaning back wearily. "Now how many hats does that make altogether?"

"The executioner knocked off 13 . . . and I left 178 more on the dungeon steps," answered Bartholomew.

"Three hundred and forty-six ·hats," mumbled Sir Alaric from behind his scroll.

"Uncle Derwin," yawned the Grand Duke Wilfred, "I suppose I'll have to do away with him. Send him up to the highest turret and I, in person, will push him off."

"Wilfred! I'm surprised at you," said the King. "But I guess it's a good idea."

So the King and the Grand Duke led Bartholomew Cubbins toward the highest turret.

Up and up the turret stairs he climbed behind them.

"This is my *last—my very last* chance," thought Bartholomew. He snatched off his hat. "Three hundred and forty-

219

seven!" He snatched off another. He pulled and he tore and he flung them behind him. ". . . 398 . . . 399 . . ." His arms ached from pulling off hats. But still the hats came. Bartholomew climbed on.

". . . 448 . . . 449 . . . 450 . . ." counted Sir Alaric, puffing up the stairs behind him.

Suddenly Sir Alaric stopped. He looked. He took off his triangular spectacles and wiped them on his sleeve. And then he looked again. *The hats began to change!* Hat 451 had not one but *two* feathers! Hat 452 had three . . . and 453 also had three *and a little red jewel!* Each new hat was fancier than the hat just before.

"Your Majesty! Your Majesty!" cried out Sir Alaric.

But the King and the Grand Duke were 'way up where they couldn't hear. They had already reached the top of the highest turret. Bartholomew was following just behind.

"Step right out here and get out on that wall," snapped the Grand Duke Wilfred. "I can't wait to push you off."

But when Bartholomew stepped up on the wall they gasped in amazement. He was wearing the most beautiful hat that had ever been seen in the Kingdom of Didd. It had a ruby larger than any the King himself had ever owned. It had ostrich plumes, and cockatoo plumes, and mockingbird plumes, and paradise plumes. Beside *such* a hat even the King's Crown seemed like nothing.

The Grand Duke Wilfred took a quick step forward. Bartholomew thought his end had come at last.

"Wait!" shouted the King. He could not take his eyes off the magnificent hat.

"I *won't* wait," the Grand Duke talked back to the King. "I'm going to push him off now! That new big hat makes me madder than ever." And he flung out his arms to push Bartholomew off.

But the King was quicker than Wilfred. He grabbed him by the back of his fine lace collar. "This is to teach you," His Majesty said sternly, "that Grand Dukes *never* talk back to their King." And he turned the Grand Duke Wilfred over his knee and spanked him soundly, right on the seat of his royal silk pants.

"And now," smiled the King, lifting Bartholomew down from the wall, "it would be nice if you'd sell me that wonderful hat!"

". . . 498 . . . 499 . . ." broke in the tired voice of Sir Alaric, who had just arrived at the top of the steps, "and *that* . . ." he pointed to the hat on Bartholomew's head, "makes exactly 500!"

"*Five hundred!*" exclaimed the King. "Will you sell it for 500 pieces of gold?"

221

"Anything you say, Sire," answered Bartholomew. "You see . . . I've never sold one before."

The King's hands trembled with joy as he reached for the hat.

Slowly, slowly, Bartholomew felt the weight of the great hat lifting from his head. He held his breath. . . . Then suddenly he felt the cool evening breezes blow through his hair. His face broke into a happy smile. The head of Bartholomew Cubbins was bare!

"Look, Your Majesty! *Look!*" he shouted to the King.

"No! *You* look at *me*," answered the King. And he put the great hat on right over his crown.

Arm in arm, the King and Bartholomew went down to the counting room to count out the gold. Then the King sent Bartholomew home to his parents . . . no basket on his arm, no hat on his head, but with five hundred pieces of gold in a bag.

And the King commanded that the hat he had bought, and all the other hats, too, be kept forever in a great crystal case by the side of his throne.

But neither Bartholomew Cubbins, nor King Derwin himself, nor anyone else in the Kingdom of Didd could ever explain how the strange thing had happened. They only could say it just "happened to happen" and was not very likely to happen again.

The Middle Bear

By Eleanor Estes

WHEN a play was given at the town hall, Sylvie was usually the only one of the four Moffats who was in it. However, once in a while the others were in a play. For instance, Rufus had been the smallest of the seven dwarfs. And once Janey had been a butterfly. She had not been an altogether successful butterfly, though, for she had tripped on the sole of her stocking, turning a somersault all across the stage. And whereas Joey was rarely in a play, he was often in charge of switching the lights on and off.

Jane liked the plays at the Town Hall. In fact she liked them better than the moving pictures. In the moving pictures Jane always found it difficult to tell the good man from the bad man. Especially if they both wore black mustaches. Of course the pianist usually played ominous music just before the bad man came on the scene, and that helped. Even so, Jane preferred the plays at the Town Hall. There she had no trouble at all telling the good from the bad.

Now there was to be a play at the Town Hall, "The Three Bears," and all four of the Moffats were going to be in it. Miss Chichester, the dancing school teacher, was putting it on. But the money for the tickets was not going into her pocket or into the Moffats' pocket, even though they were all in the play. The

money was to help pay for the new parish house. The old one had burned down last May and now a new one was being built. "The Three Bears" was to help raise the money to finish it. A benefit performance, it was called.

In this benefit performance, Sylvie was to play the part of Goldilocks. Joey was to be the big bear, Rufus the little bear, and Janey the middle bear. Jane had not asked to be the middle bear. It just naturally came out that way. The middle Moffat was going to be the middle bear.

As a rule Joey did not enjoy the idea of acting in a play any more than he liked going to dancing school. However, he felt this play would be different. He felt it would be like having a disguise on, to be inside of a bear costume. And Jane felt the same way. She thought the people in the audience would not recognize her as the butterfly who turned a somersault across the stage, because she would be comfortably hidden inside her brown bear costume. As for Rufus, he hoped that Sylvie, the Goldilocks of this game, would not sit down too hard on that nice little chair of his and really break it to bits. It was such a good chair, and he wished he had it at home.

Mama was making all the costumes, even the bear heads. A big one for Joey, a little one for Rufus, and a middle-sized

one for Jane. Of course she wasn't making them out of bear fur; she was using brown outing flannel.

Now Jane was trying on her middle bear costume. She stepped into the body of the costume and then Mama put the head on her.

"Make the holes for the eyes big enough," Jane begged. "So I'll see where I'm going and won't turn somersaults."

"Well," said Mama, "if I cut the eyes any larger you will look like a deep sea diver instead of a bear."

"Oh, well . . ." said Jane hastily. "A bear's got to look like a bear. Never mind making them any bigger, then."

Besides being in the play, each of the Moffats also had ten tickets to sell. And since Rufus really was too little to go from house to house and street to street selling tickets, the other three Moffats had even more to dispose of. Forty tickets!

At first Jane wondered if a girl should sell tickets to a play she was going to be in. Was that being conceited? Well, since the money was for the new parish house and not for the Moffats, she finally decided it was all right to sell the tickets. Besides, she thought, who would recognize her as the girl who sold tickets once she was inside her bear costume?

Sylvie sold most of her tickets like lightning to the ladies in the choir. But Joey's and Janey's tickets became grimier and grimier, they had such trouble disposing of them. Nancy Stokes said she would help even though she went to a different parish house. She and Joey and Jane went quietly and politely up on people's verandas and rang the bell.

"Buy a ticket for the benefit of the new parish house?" was all they meant to say. But very often no one at all answered the bell.

"They can't all be away," said Nancy. "Do you think they hide behind the curtains when they see us coming?"

"Oh, no," said Jane. "You see it'd be different if the money was for us. But it isn't. It's a benefit. Why should they hide?"

One lady said she was very sorry but she was making mincemeat. "See?" she said, holding up her hands. They were all covered with mincemeat. So she could not buy a ticket. Not possibly, and she closed the door in their faces.

"She could wash her hands," said Nancy angrily. The children called this lady "mincemeat," ever after. Of course she never knew it.

Yes, the tickets were very hard to sell. But little by little the pile did dwindle. If only everybody were like Mrs. Stokes, they would go very fast. She bought four tickets! Jane was embarrassed.

"Tell your mother she doesn't have to buy all those tickets just 'cause all of us are in the play," she instructed Nancy.

But all the Stokes insisted they really wanted to go. And even if none of the Moffats were in it, they would still want to go, for the play would help to build a new parish house. What nice people! thought Jane. Here they were, a family who went to the white church, buying tickets to help build a parish house for Janey's church. She hoped she would be a good middle bear, so they would be proud they knew her.

At last it was the night of the play. The four Moffats knew their lines perfectly. This was not surprising, considering they all lived in the same house and could practice their lines any time they wanted to. And, besides this, they had had two rehearsals, one in regular clothes and one in their bear costumes.

When Jane reached the Town Hall, she was surprised to find there were many features on the program besides "The Three Bears." The Gillespie twins were going to give a piano duet. "By the Brook," it was called. A boy was going to play the violin. Someone else was going to toe dance. And Miss Beale was going to sing a song. A big program. And the Moffats, all of them except Mama, were going to watch this whole performance from behind the scenes. They could not sit in the audience with the regular people with their bear costumes on, for that would give the whole show away.

Jane fastened her eye to a hole in the curtain. Mama had not yet come. Of course Mama would have to sit out front there with the regular people, even though she had made the costumes. The only people who had arrived so far were Clara Pringle and Brud. They were sitting in the front row and Jane wondered how they had gotten in because the front door that all the regular people were supposed to use wasn't even open yet.

When Jane wasn't peering through a hole in the curtain, Joey or Rufus was. Each one hoped he would be the first to

see Mama when she came in. Or now and then they tried to squeeze through the opening at the side of the asbestos curtain. But the gnarled little janitor shook his head at them. So they stayed inside.

Sylvie was busy putting make-up on herself and on the dancers' faces. Jane watched them enviously. The only trouble with wearing a bear costume, she thought, was that she couldn't have her face painted. Well, she quickly consoled herself, she certainly would not have stage fright inside her bear head. Whereas she might if there were just paint on her face. "Somebody has been sitting in my chair," she rehearsed her lines. She stepped into her bear costume. But before putting on her head, she helped Rufus into his bear uniform. He didn't call it a costume. A uniform. A bear uniform. Jane set his head on his shoulders, found his two eyes for him so he could see out, and the little bear was ready.

Joey had no difficulty stepping into his costume and even in finding his own two eyes. Now the big bear and the little bear were ready. Jane looked around for her head, to put it on. Where was it?

"Where's my head?" she asked. "My bear head."

Nobody paid any attention to her. Miss Chichester was running back and forth

226

and all around, giving an order here and an order there. Once as she rushed by, causing a great breeze, Jane yelled to make herself heard, "How can we act 'The Three Bears' unless I find my middle bear head?"

"Not just now. I'm too busy," was all Miss Chichester said.

Everybody was too busy to help Jane find her head. Sylvie was helping the toe dancer dress. Joey was busy running around doing this and doing that for Miss Chichester. And the little old janitor was busy tightening ropes and making sure the lights were working. Rufus could not be torn from a hole in the curtain. He was looking for Mama.

Jane sighed. Everybody's busy, she thought. She rummaged around in a big box of costumes. Maybe her bear head had been stuck in it. She found a dragon head and tried it on. How would that be? She looked in the mirror. The effect was interesting. But, no, she could not wear this, for a bear cannot be a dragon.

Goodness, thought Jane. The curtain will go up, and the middle bear won't be a whole bear. This was worse than tripping over her stocking the time she was a butterfly. Maybe Joey and Rufus somehow or another had two heads on. They didn't, though, just their own. Phew, it was warm inside these bear costumes. Jane stood beside Rufus and looked through another small hole in the curtain. Oh! The big door was open! People were beginning to arrive. And what kind of a bear would she be without a head? Maybe she wouldn't be allowed to be a bear at

all. But there certainly could not be three bears without a middle one.

"Don't worry," said Rufus, not moving an inch from his spot. "Lend you mine for half the play . . ."

"Thanks," said Jane. "But we all have to have our heads on all through the whole thing."

The Stokes were coming in! Jane felt worried. The only person who might be able to fix a new bear head for her in a hurry was Mama. Oh, if she had only made a couple of spare heads. But Mama wasn't coming yet. Jane resolved to go and meet her. She put on her tam and her chinchilla coat over her bear costume. Then she ran down the three narrow steps into the Hall. She crouched low in her coat in order not to give away the fact that she was clad in a bear costume. Nobody on this side of the curtain was supposed to know what people on her side of the curtain had on until the curtain rolled up. Surprise. That's what was important in a play.

Mr. Buckle was coming in now, walking towards the front row. Jane stooped low, with her knees bent beneath her. In front her coat nearly reached the ground. From the way she looked from the front, few would guess that she was the middle bear. Of course her feet showed. They were encased in the brown costume. But she might be a brownie or a squirrel.

"Hello, Mr. Buckle," said Jane. "I'm in a hurry . . ."

"Where are you going, middle Moffat?" he asked. "Aren't you the prima donna?"

"No. Just the middle bear."

"Well, that's fine. The middle Moffat is the middle bear."

"Yes. Or I was until I lost my head."

"Oh, my," said Mr. Buckle. "This then is not your head?" he asked, pointing to her tam.

"Yes, but not my bear head. I don t mean bare head. Bear head! B-e-a-r. That kind of head."

"Mystifying. Very mystifying," said Mr. Buckle, settling himself slowly in a seat in the front row.

"You'll see later," said Jane, running down the aisle.

She ran all the way home. But the house was dark. Mama had already left. And she must have gone around the other way or Jane would have passed her. Jane raced back to the Town Hall. There! Now! The lights were dim. The entertainment had begun. Jane tried to open the side door. Chief Mulligan was guarding this entrance. He did not want to let her in at first. He thought she was just a person. But when she showed him her costume, he opened the door just wide enough for her. The bear costume was as good as a password.

The toe dancer was doing the split. Jane tiptoed up the three steps and went backstage, wondering what would happen now. The show always goes on. There was some comfort in that thought. Somehow, someone would fix her head. Or possibly while she was gone her middle bear head had been found. She hoped she would not have to act with her head bare.

Miss Chichester snatched her.

"Oh, there you are, Jane! Hop into your costume, dear."

"I'm in it," said Jane. "But I can't find my middle bear head."

"Heavens!" said Miss Chichester, grasping her own head. "What else will go wrong?"

Jane looked at her in surprise. What else *had* gone wrong? Had others lost worse than their heads?

"Where's the janitor?" Miss Chichester asked. "Maybe he let his grandchildren borrow it."

Jane knew he hadn't, but she couldn't tell Miss Chichester for she had already flown off. And then Janey had an idea.

"I know what," she said to Joey. "Pin me together." And she pulled the neck part of her costume up over her head. Joey pinned it with two safety pins, and he cut two holes for her eyes. This costume was not comfortable now. Pulling it up and pinning it this way lifted Jane's arms so she had trouble making them hang down the way she thought a bear's should. However, at any rate, she now had a bear head of sorts.

"Do I look like a bear?" she asked Rufus.

"You look like a brown ghost," Rufus replied.

"Don't you worry," said Sylvie, coming up. "You look like a very nice little animal."

"But I'm supposed to be a bear, not a nice little animal," said Jane.

"Well," said Sylvie, "people will know you are supposed to be a bear because

Rufus and Joey both have their bear heads on."

So Jane resigned herself to not being a perfect bear. She tried to comfort herself with the thought that she would still be in disguise. She hoped her acting would be so good it would counterbalance her bad head. "Somebody has been eating my porridge," she practiced.

Miss Chichester appeared. "The janitor said 'No,'" she said. She thoughtfully surveyed Jane a moment. "Hm-m-m, a make-shift," she observed. "Well, it's better than nothing," she agreed with Jane. But she decided to switch the order of the program around in order to give everybody one last chance to find the middle bear's real head. She sent Miss Beale out onto the stage. Everybody hoped that while Miss Beale was singing "In an Old-fashioned Garden," the head would appear. But it didn't.

"Keep a little in the background," said Miss Chichester to Jane. "Perhaps people will not notice."

"If I can only see where the background is," thought Jane. For she found it even harder to keep her eyes close to the holes cut in her costume than it had been to the real ones in her regular bear head.

Now the heavy curtain rolled up. It didn't stick halfway up as it sometimes did, and Sylvie, Goldilocks, in a blue pinafore and socks, ran out onto the stage midst loud applause. The play had begun! Sylvie had a great deal of acting to do all by herself before the three bears came home. But she wasn't scared. She was used to being on the stage alone.

Jane's heart pounded as she and Joey and Rufus waited for their cue to come home. If only she didn't trip and turn a somersault, for she really could not see very well. Somehow she managed to see out of only one eye at a time. These eye holes must have been cut crooked. One hole kept getting hooked on her nose.

"Now!" Miss Chichester whispered. "Cue! Out with you three bears."

Joe, Jane, and Rufus, the three bears, lumbered out onto the stage. They were never supposed to just walk, always lumber and lope.

The applause was tremendous. It startled the three bears. The Town Hall was packed. Somebody must have sold a lot of tickets.

"There's Mama," said Rufus. He said it out loud.

He wasn't supposed to say anything out loud except about his porridge, his chair, and his bed. But anyway he said, "There's Mama." Jane could not see Mama. Lumbering out onto the stage had dislocated her costume so that now she could not see at all. Fortunately the footlights shone through the brown flannel of her costume so she could keep away from the edge of the stage and not fall off.

The Moffats all knew their lines so well they did not forget them once. The only trouble was they did not have much chance to say them because the applause was so great every time they opened their mouths. At last, however, they reached the act about the three beds. An extra platform had been set up on the

229

stage to look like the upstairs of the three bears' house. The three bears lumbered slowly up the steps.

Suddenly shouts arose all over the Hall:

"Her head! Her head! The middle bear's head!"

"Sh-sh-sh," said others. "See what's going to happen."

As Jane could not see very well she had no idea what these shouts referred to. She had the same head on now that she had had on all during this play so far. Why then all these shouts? Or had she really stayed in the background the way Miss Chichester had asked her to, and the audience had only just discovered about the make-shift?

"Oh," whispered Joey to Jane. "I see it. It's your real bear head and it's on the top of my bed post."

"O-o-o-h!" said Jane. "Get it down."

"How can I?" said Joe. "With all these people watching me?"

"Try and get it when you punch your bed," urged Jane.

Joey was examining his big bear's bed now. "Hm-m-m," he said fiercely. "Somebody has been lying on my bed. . . ." But he couldn't reach the middle bear's head. He did try. But he couldn't quite reach it, and there was more laughter from the audience.

Jane pulled her costume about until she could see through the eyehole. Ah, there was her head! On the post of the

230

big bear's bed. No wonder people were laughing. What a place for the middle bear's head. Here she was, without it. And there it was, without her. Jane resolved to get it. Somehow or other she would rescue her head before this play was completely over. Now was her chance. It was her turn to talk about her bed. Instead, Jane said:

"Somebody has been trying on my head, and there it is!"

Jane hopped up on Joey's bed. She grabbed her middle bear head.

"Yes," she repeated. "Somebody has been trying on my head," but as she added, "and here it is!" the safety pins that held her make-shift head together popped open. The audience burst into roars of laughter as Janey's own real head emerged. Only for a second though. For she clapped her middle bear head right on as fast as she could, and hopped off the bed. Goodness, she thought, I showed my real face and I didn't have any paint on it.

Unfortunately Jane still could not see, for she had stuck her bear head on backwards. But the audience loved it. They clapped and they stamped. "Bravo! Bravo! Bravo, middle bear!" Big boys at the back of the hall put their fingers in their mouths and whistled. And it was a long, long time before Jane could say:

"Somebody has been sleeping in my bed," and the play could go on. At last Rufus discovered Goldilocks in his little bed, and she leaped out of the window.

That was the end of the play, and the curtain rolled down.

When the bowing began, Miss Chichester tried to send Jane in backwards, thinking the back of her was the front of her. Fortunately, Rufus held Jane by one paw, and Joey held the other. So she didn't get lost. And the three bears lumbered dizzily on and off many times, sometimes with Sylvie, and sometimes alone. And somebody yelled for "the mysterious middle bear!" It must have been the oldest inhabitant.

Miss Chichester turned Jane's head around for this bow and at last Jane really did look like a perfect middle bear. Furthermore, she could see out. There was Mama, laughing so hard the tears were rolling down her cheeks. And there was Nancy Stokes with all the Stokes, and Olga was there. And there was Mr. Buckle beaming up at the stage. Jane bowed and lumbered off the stage. She felt good now. Acting was fun, she thought, especially if you could be disguised in a bear uniform. And this time she had not turned a somersault across the stage as she had the time she was a butterfly. True, she had lost her head. But she had found it. And the show had gone on, the way people always say shows do.

Moreover, the Moffats had nice warm bear pajamas to sleep in for the rest of the winter. Of course they didn't go to bed with the bear heads on. But the rest of the costumes were nice and warm.

—From *The Middle Moffat*

The Teacup Whale

By Lydia Gibson

ONE day early in spring David was going along the road, splish, splash, squish, squash. In spring when the snow has melted, the road is very muddy. David came to a big puddle in the middle of the road. He had to walk around it because it was too big to jump over. Walking around took longer than jumping, so David got interested in the puddle on the way around, and he stopped to look in. He saw pebbles and he saw bubbles and he saw mud. He saw some sticks floating and he saw an early angleworm coming out for a springtime walk around the edge of the puddle. He saw a tiny river running in one end of the puddle and another tiny river running out the other end, made of wheel-tracks in the muddy road.

Then all of a sudden he saw a little black SOMETHING in the middle of the puddle. It wiggled. It blew a little tiny fountain. Then it went down out of sight under the muddy water. David crouched down to see better and leaned over so far he almost fell in. For a minute all he could see in the puddle was himself, as if he were looking into a mirror, and the white clouds overhead in the blue sky. Then the little tiny black thing came up to the top of the water and flopped its little tiny black tail—kersplash!

"Why, my goodness gracious me!" said David with his eyes bulging out. "It's a WHALE!"

He had a map of Nantucket on the wall beside his bed at home, with a picture of a whale on it. He knew exactly what a whale was like, from the spout that came out of his blowhole to the flukes of his spreading tail fully an inch away.

David luckily had his little tin bucket

232

with him. He hardly ever went out without his little red tin bucket, it was so very useful for carrying all sorts of things home. This time he worked hard and splashed and puffed and caught the whale in his hands and put it in the bucket with

make sense, but then very few things did. She went on: "It means very big indeed. Bigger than a horse. Bigger than a car. Bigger than an elephant. Whales are enormous. But what a VERY funny polliwog this is!"

enough water to swim in, and he carried it home.

The bucket was quite deep and dark for such a tiny whale, and you couldn't see him very well, so David went and climbed on a chair, and reached on the shelf, and got a white teacup and filled it with water before he put in the whale. The whale showed up very black and shiny and handsome in the nice white teacup. Then he carried it to his mother.

"Whatever have you got there?" asked David's mother. "Another polliwog?"

"No," said David, "that is a whale."

"Nonsense," said his mother. "Whales are enormous."

"What is a nor-mouse?" asked David.

"Whales are," said his mother; it didn't

Every day the whale grew. David fed him bits of chopped meat and he got bigger and bigger and he got stronger and stronger. One morning when David came down to breakfast the teacup was smashed into bits and the whale lay flopping in the saucer in a few drops of water. He had grown too big and too strong for the little white teacup. So David went to the kitchen and got a strong yellow bowl, the kind they mix ginger cookies in. The whale swam in that and it fitted him nicely. He went round and round and round to the left side and admired the scenery, and then he turned and went round and round and round to the right side and admired the scenery. He never seemed to get tired of doing it. For a good many days the whale swam in the yellow mixing bowl. But he was growing all the time. He ate boiled rice—at first ten grains a day and then more and more. He got bigger and bigger and he got stronger and stronger. One day he gave a JUMP, and landed on the floor. He was too big for the yellow bowl.

David sat down and put his elbows on his knees and put his chin in his hands. That was to make thinking easier. Then he thought what to do. The watering can was too small. The soup kettle was too small. The brass fruit bowl was too small. The wash basin was too small, and, besides, they couldn't wash their hands if there was a whale in it. So he asked his mother if he could borrow the wash boiler. She said yes, if he would be careful of it. So the whale lived in the wash boiler. All the time he was getting bigger and bigger and stronger and stronger, and the little fountains he blew through the blowhole in the top of his head were getting bigger too, and he couldn't turn around.

"I do declare," said David's mother, "I never in all my born days saw a polliwog blow fountains through the top of his head! What a VERY funny polliwog!"

The whale lived in the wash boiler about a week. He knocked over the wash boiler one day and made a big puddle on the floor. So David had to move him again. He thought and thought. There wasn't any place in the house now big enough for the whale to turn around in but the bathtub. So David moved the whale into the bathtub. By this time he was about as big as a big cat or a smallish dog, and a very pretty shiny black like patent leather shoes. He was getting so tame that he used to come swimming up to the top of the water and blow a fountain whenever David whistled for him.

But you can see that it wasn't very convenient to keep the whale in the bathtub, because whenever anybody wanted to take a bath, they had to bring the dishpan up from the kitchen to put the whale into, and it was hard to keep him from jumping out of the dishpan. He was so impatient to get back into the big tub where he could swim around in comfort, he simply wouldn't lie still long enough for anyone to take a bath. And every day the whale grew. By this time he was eating leftover tea biscuits, toast and vegetables. He got bigger and bigger and stronger and stronger. At last one day David's mother said, "I simply cannot and will not be bothered lifting out this great big clumsy heavy polliwog every time anyone in this house takes a bath!"

So David and his father got into the car and they drove down the hill to the Village. They went past the Grocery Store and the Butcher Store and the Drugstore and the Post Office and the Railroad Station till they came to Mister Barlow's Hardware Store.

"Good morning, Mister Barlow," said David.

."Good morning, David, fine weather we're having and what can I do for you this fine morning?" said Mister Barlow.

"I have a whale which is growing very fast," said David, "and I must have a tank to keep him in. Perhaps you keep tanks in your store?"

"Yes, indeed," said Mister Barlow proudly, and showed him several tanks. But they were goldfish tanks.

"Oh, dear no," said David, "these aren't NEARLY big enough! Show me some bigger tanks, please."

But Mister Barlow didn't have any bigger tanks. David had to order one made four times as big as the bathtub and twice as deep and all lined with tin to make it water-tight.

In two or three days the tank was finished and Mister Barlow brought it up to David's house. They put it in the garden right beside the porch so they could watch the whale easily, and they filled it with water. It was summertime now, so the whale enjoyed living in the garden. He grew very fast from being out in the sun. He got bigger and bigger and stronger and stronger. Pretty soon he got as big as a pony.

All the children in the neighborhood

LYDIA GIBSON

used to come to visit David's whale. They got sardines at the Grocery Store and threw them to the whale one at a time for a treat. They brought the whale ice cream cones, because whales come from polar regions and they thought he must miss the icebergs. But the whale didn't like ice cream which melted and made the water horrid and cloudy; so the children took turns changing the water in the tank, with the garden hose.

One day some visitors came a long way to see the whale. There was Mister Queebus and Missis Queebus and their little boy Alexander. They came in their car all the way from Woodstock, ninety miles away, and they were all dressed up in their Sunday-go-to-meeting clothes. They stood in a row on the porch and looked down on the whale in the tank, and admired him. The whale was so pleased with all this admiration that he blew an especially splendid fountain in honor of the Queebus family, when David whistled. It was his only way of thanking them. But now he was so big that his fountain was like the smoke that you see coming out of the smokestack of a locomotive, when you sit in the car at the railroad crossing gates and watch the express go roaring by. So the fountain blew all over the Queebus family and their best visiting clothes got soaking wet and it made them very cross. David's mother said, "REALLY we can't keep that ridiculous polliwog of David's any longer. It's MUCH too big. And I don't believe it will ever be a frog anyway!"

David was getting quite tired of chang-ing the water in the big tank with the garden hose every few days, and of running around the Village with his red bucket collecting bread and scraps from all the neighbors to feed the hungry whale, who ate a great deal. And the whale was growing all the time. Day by day he was getting bigger and he was getting stronger.

So David telephoned to Tony, the Express Man, to bring up his truck. And he telephoned to Nick, the Garage Man, to bring his wrecking car, and all together they hoisted the whale onto the truck by means of the derrick on the wrecking car. They pinned wet bath towels around his head to keep him from drying out on the ride.

David climbed up on the driver's seat beside Tony the Express Man and they went down the hill to the Village. They went past the Grocery Store and past the Butcher Store and past the Drugstore and past the Post Office and past the Railroad Station till they came to Mister Barlow's Hardware Store. There David bought a very long strong chain, and then they drove the whale down to the wharf that stuck out into the river. They hooked the whale to the wharf with the chain around his tail because he hadn't any neck, and David promised to come down every day to visit him.

Every day David's father drove him down to the wharf and David whistled to his whale. The whale came up close alongside the wharf and blew lovely fountains for David. He was a very happy and comfortable whale, swimming around the wharf and eating fresh fish right out of the river, and sleeping under the wharf at night like a dog in his kennel. He was a great pet with all the people in the Village. The Grocer brought his three little boys to see him, and the Butcher brought his little girl, and the Postman brought his twins, and the old Station Agent who sold railroad tickets for train rides brought his little golden-haired grandchild.

They all admired the whale and some of them brought him sardines out of a can. But catching fresh fish out of the river had spoiled the whale for sardines out of a can, and he would spit them out for the crabs and fish to eat.

People used to come out from the City on Sundays just to see David's whale. The man who owned the wharf was planning to charge ten cents admission from everyone, to pay him for his trouble. But David couldn't see what trouble the man had; David took care of the whale, David had tied him up, and David had collected food for him in his bucket all the while he was growing! But all the time the whale was getting stronger and stronger.

One morning David went down to the wharf to visit the whale as usual. He whistled and whistled for the whale. But the whale didn't come to blow him a fountain. Then David noticed that the wharf was all broken at the end; planks were ripped apart, and the big heavy piles were pulled sidewise.

The whale had broken the wharf in the night. He had broken loose and had swum majestically down the river to the sea, a mighty full-grown whale, towing a piece of chain behind him.

David went home and told his mother the whale had gone, and his mother said, "Well, David, it WAS a whale after all!"

Oscar, the Trained Seal

By Mabel E. Neikirk

OSCAR and Mr. Zabriski were on their way to a big fair in California. Oscar was a trained seal. He was going to do circus tricks at the fair, and Mr. Zabriski was going to take care of him.

"Now, how shall we go?" asked Mr. Zabriski when they planned the trip. "Shall we go by air, by water, or by land?"

"By air, by water, or by land," repeated Oscar. "What kind of traveling is that?"

"Why, you silly seal!" replied Mr. Zabriski. "By air means flying, of course. Would you like to go in an airplane? By water means on a boat, and land means on a train. I think perhaps the train would be best."

"None of them are any good," remarked the seal. "I couldn't take my bathtub on a plane. Now, could I?"

"No, I suppose not," his master replied. "It would be too heavy."

"And s'pose I got seasick on the boat, and I can't go on the train—"

"Well, why not?" he was asked.

"Just because, just because," said Oscar convincingly, "and *anyway*, I want to ride in a truck."

Mr. Zabriski was an agreeable man, and he always tried to please Oscar, so they started off across the country in a Ford truck, Mr. Zabriski sitting in front driving, and Oscar riding in back, taking baths all the way. When the truck went over a bumpy road, the water swished and splashed, and Oscar would roll about in his tub, diving and swimming and making seal noises. It was a great lark.

Oscar pretended that his tub was an ocean. But so many waves splashed out that the floor of the truck dripped like an ice wagon, and they had to stop at almost every gas station for water.

Mr. Zabriski would drive up to a station and say to the attendant, "Will you please put some water in my car?"

Then he and Oscar would chuckle because the man always went to the front

238

of the car and seemed surprised when he found the radiator full.

"You've plenty of water, sir," he usually said.

"I mean I need water for the tank in the back of my truck," Mr. Zabriski would explain.

Then the man would go around and almost fall over backward in his surprise, because Oscar always stuck out his head and shouted, "Boo!"

They had lots of fun for two days and, then, they had lots of trouble, because Oscar's bathtub sprung a leak. They filled it up and they filled it up, and the leak kept getting worse and worse.

Finally Mr. Zabriski stopped the truck and he and Oscar got out and sat down beside the road to think.

"Now we *are* in a jam," groaned Mr. Zabriski. "We simply must get to California. The people at the fair are looking for us even now."

"We can't go by plane. There's no airport here," grumbled Oscar.

"And we can't go by boat. There's no

water," Mr. Zabriski added. He put his head in his hands, and Oscar put *his* head in his flippers, and they began to think.

Then suddenly, a loud "Whoo-oo-oo!" screeched through the air, and looking up, they saw a column of black smoke shooting to the sky, and they heard the roar and puff-puff of a big steam engine rushing nearer every minute. The seal jumped up.

"We've got to go by train," he shouted. "And here it comes. Grab your baggage and make it snappy!"

They made a dash for it. There wasn't even time to buy tickets. They called to the station master to take care of their truck, and they climbed on board. Mr. Zabriski rode in the Pullman, but Oscar had to ride in the baggage car.

"You arrange for my bath," he whispered when they parted, and Mr. Zabriski said that he would see what he could do.

Now the train on which they were riding was a very fine one, streamlined, of course. There were observation and club cars in which you could read or watch the country flying by, and there was a dining-car. You could sit at a table and eat turkey dinners with cranberry sauce and ice cream while you looked out of the window. There were large dressing-rooms and even a bathroom with a big tub. A man called a porter made the passengers comfortable. He gave them pillows for their heads when they were tired, and footstools for their feet, and he put clean towels in the bathroom.

Mr. Zabriski called the porter. "My seal wants a bath."

"Can't be done! Can't be done!" said the porter crossly. "This isn't a circus train. This is first-class passenger train."

"You're right. This *is* a very fine train, and that's a very nice bathroom, and all the better, because my seal *must* have a bath. He's used to it," said Mr. Zabriski firmly. Then he put his hand into his pocket and gave the porter two shiny quarters.

"That's all right, Boss. That's all right. I'll fix it up. Thank you, sir," the porter answered at once, grinning when he saw the nice, new money. "*Sure*, your seal can have a bath. Now when we get to the next station, and everybody is looking out of the windows, then's your chance. For if anyone saw a seal going through the car, they'd have fits! Yes, sir!"

Mr. Zabriski agreed that was an excellent plan. The train began to slow up, so he hurried to tell Oscar. And when all the passengers were looking out at the people on the platform, Oscar slid quietly down the Pullman aisle to the bathroom and nobody saw him at all.

In a jiffy Mr. Zabriski had drawn a big tub full of cold water, and Oscar dived in.

"Are you all right?" Mr. Zabriski asked.

"Fine," replied the seal. "This is keen. You go and have a smoke."

So everything was fixed up. Mr. Zabriski was enjoying a cigar in the club car and Oscar was enjoying his bath. Mr. Zabriski thought that the porter was watching the bathroom and the porter thought that Mr. Zabriski was watching, but no one was there except Oscar, splashing about in the tub.

By and by, a young lady passenger said to her friend, "It's awfully hot, isn't it? I think I'll take a bath and see if I can get cooled off." She gathered up her toilet articles and went down the aisle. Opening the bathroom door, she started in, but hastily backed out with a terrible shriek.

"Oh-o-o-o!" she screamed. "Help! Help! Save me! Save me!"

All the people jumped from their seats and came crowding around her. "Save you from what?" asked a man anxiously.

"There's a bear in the bathroom," the frightened girl cried. "I saw his trunk— oh-o-o-o! Oh-o-o!"

"Stop it!" said the man sharply. "Bears don't have trunks. *I'll* look."

He opened the door cautiously and stuck in his head, and just then Oscar rolled over with a tremendous splash, throwing water in every direction; and the man shut the door with a *bang!*

"It's a w-w-w-whale!" he sputtered, mopping water out of his eyes and nose and hair and off his new necktie. "I saw his long neck."

"I knew it was a ferocious animal," cried the young lady. "I knew it! Just listen to him barking!"

"Fiddlesticks!" an old lady spoke up. "Are you both crazy? There aren't any whales or bears in that bathroom. I'll bet it's a cat. You're both so scared you don't know what you are saying. Who ever heard of bears with elephants' trunks on their noses, or of whales with their heads on top of giraffes' necks? Ridiculous! And as for barking, it might very well be a dog. I'll call it."

She began: "Here, kitty, kitty, kitty. Nice doggy. Come, Fido. Come here, sir!" She turned the knob ever so carefully, and peeked through the crack.

"Mercy me!" she exclaimed. "It's a whole Noah's Ark and a flood, too." And she slammed the door shut just as fast as she could while rivers of water came running along the floor and out into the corridor.

By this time everybody was greatly excited. A crowd had gathered around the bathroom door, and some of the people were trying to peek through the keyhole.

"Oh-o-o-o!" the young lady kept on screaming.

"Ring for the porter!" someone yelled.

"Yes, the porter! The porter! Call him," several people cried all at once. The men rumpled their hair in their excitement, the women twisted their handkerchiefs into thin rings. And they all rang their bells for the porter.

He came running, and Mr. Zabriski came, too.

"I'll lose my job," muttered the porter.

"They'll put us off the train," Mr. Zabriski worried out loud, "and then how'll we get to California?" But suddenly an idea flashed into Mr. Zabriski's head. As he reached the end of the car near the bathroom, he jumped up on a seat and raised his hand for silence.

"La-dies and gen-tle-men," he shouted. "Quiet. Please! I have a surprise for you. We have with us today, Oscar! Oscar, the *famous* trained seal! And what is he going to do, my friends? He is going to perform his circus tricks for your entertainment."

"Hurrah! Hurrah! Yip-ee!" cried the passengers.

"He has been limbering up in his bath," called Mr. Zabriski, "and now, if you will all be kind enough to take your places in the club car, the show will be ready to begin in a few minutes."

"Three cheers for the seal," the passengers shouted, and they all rushed for the club car, each trying to be there first in order to get a seat in the front row.

Then Mr. Zabriski opened his suitcase, and hurriedly put on his pink velvet suit, and his shiny black silk hat, and he and Oscar entered the club car. Mr. Zabriski cracked a whip while Oscar did all sorts of marvelous tricks. He balanced colored balls on his nose, he wheeled a baby buggy, he danced, and he even sang, "Yankee Doodle."

The people clapped their hands and cried for more, and more, and more, and they slapped each other on the back. And the conductors of the train were so pleased because everyone was having such a good time that they decided to have a party. They sent the porter to the dining-car for refreshments, and everybody had cinnamon toast, and chocolate cookies and tea. Mr. Zabriski had some, too.

And Oscar, what did *he* have? Why, a nice big fish.

Children in America
Then and Now

Waukewa's Eagle

By James Buckham

ONE day, when the Indian boy Waukewa was hunting along the moun-
tainside, he found a young eagle with a
broken wing, lying at the base of a cliff.
The bird had fallen from a ledge, and being too young to fly, had fluttered down
the cliff and hurt itself so severely that it
was likely to die. When Waukewa saw it
he was about to drive one of his sharp
arrows through its body, for the passion
of the hunter was strong in him, and the
eagle plunders many a fine fish from the
Indian's drying frame. But a gentler impulse came to him as he saw the young
bird quivering with pain and fright at his
feet, and he slowly stooped over the panting eaglet. For fully a minute the wild
eyes of the wounded bird and the eyes of
the Indian boy, growing gentler and
softer as he gazed, looked into one another. Then the struggling and panting of
the young eagle ceased; the wild fright-

ened look passed out of its eyes, and it suffered Waukewa to pass his hand gently over its ruffled and draggled feathers. The fierce instinct to fight, to defend its threatened life, yielded to the charm of the tenderness and pity expressed in the boy's eyes; and from that moment Waukewa and the eagle were friends.

Waukewa went slowly home to his father's lodge, bearing the wounded eaglet in his arms. He carried it so gently that the broken wing gave no twinge of pain, and the bird lay perfectly still, never offering to strike with its sharp beak the hands of the boy.

Warming some water over the fire at the lodge, Waukewa bathed the broken wing of the eagle, and bound it up with soft strips of skin. Then he made a nest of ferns and grass inside the lodge, and laid the bird in it. The boy's mother looked on with shining eyes. Her heart was very tender. From girlhood she had loved all the creatures of the woods, and it pleased her to see some of her own gentle spirit waking in the boy.

When Waukewa's father returned from hunting, he would have caught up the young eagle and wrung its neck. But the boy pleaded with him so eagerly, stooping over the captive and defending it with his small hands, that the stern warrior laughed and called him his "little squawheart." "Keep it, then," he said, "and nurse it until it is well. But then you must let it go, for we will not raise up a thief in the lodges." So Waukewa promised that when the eagle's wing was healed and grown so that it could fly, he would

carry it forth and give it its freedom.

It was a month—or, as the Indians say, a moon—before the young eagle's wing had fully mended and the bird was old enough and strong enough to fly. And in the meantime Waukewa cared for it and fed it daily, and the friendship between the boy and the bird grew very strong.

But at last the time came when the willing captive must be freed. So Waukewa carried it far away from the Indian lodges, where none of the young braves might see it hovering over and be tempted to shoot their arrows at it, and there he let it go. The young eagle rose toward the sky in great circles, rejoicing in its freedom and its strange new power of flight. But when Waukewa began to move away from the spot, it came swooping down again; and all day long it followed him through the woods as he hunted. At dusk, when Waukewa shaped his course for the Indian lodges, the eagle would have accompanied him. But the boy suddenly slipped into a hollow tree and hid, and after a long time the eagle stopped sweeping about in search of him and flew slowly and sadly away.

Summer passed, and then winter; and spring came again, with its flowers and birds and swarming fish in the lakes and streams. Then it was that all the Indians, old and young, braves and squaws, pushed their light canoes out from shore and with spear and hook waged pleasant war against the salmon and the red spotted trout. After winter's long imprisonment, it was such joy to toss in the sunshine and the warm wind and catch savory fish to take the place of dried meats and corn!

Above the great falls the salmon sported in the cool, swinging current, darting under the lee of the rocks and leaping full length in the clear spring air. Nowhere else were such salmon to be speared as those which lay at the head of the rapids. But only the most daring braves ventured to seek them there, for the current was strong, and should a light canoe once pass the danger point and get caught in the rush of the rapids, nothing could save it from going over the roaring falls.

Very early in the morning of a clear April day, just as the sun was rising splendidly over the mountains, Waukewa launched his canoe a half mile above the rapids and floated downward, spear in hand, among the salmon. He was the only one of the Indian lads who dared to fish above the falls. But he had been there often, and never yet had his watchful eye and his strong paddle suffered the current to carry his canoe beyond the danger point. This morning he was alone on the river, having risen long before daylight to be first at the sport.

The riffles were full of salmon, big, lusty fellows, who glided about the canoe on every side in an endless silver stream. Waukewa plunged his spear right and left, and tossed one glittering victim after another into the bark canoe. So absorbed in the sport was he that for once he did not notice when the canoe began to glide more swiftly among the rocks. But suddenly he looked up, caught his paddle, and dipped it wildly in the swirling water. The canoe swung sidewise, shivered, held

its own against the torrent, and then slowly inch by inch began to creep upstream toward the shore. But suddenly there was a loud, cruel snap, and the paddle parted in the boy's hands, broken just above the blade! Waukewa gave a cry of despairing agony. Then he bent to the gunwale of his canoe and with shattered blade fought desperately against the current. But it was useless. The racing torrent swept him downward; the hungry falls roared tauntingly in his ears.

Then the Indian boy knelt calmly upright in the canoe, facing the mist of the falls, and folded his arms. His young face was stern and lofty. He had lived like a brave—now he would die like one.

Faster and faster sped the doomed canoe toward the great cataract. The black rocks glided away on either side like phantoms. The roar of the terrible waters became like thunder in the boy's ears. But still he gazed calmly and sternly ahead, facing his fate as a brave Indian should. At last he began to chant the death-song, which he had learned from the older braves. In a few minutes all would be over. But he would come before the Great Spirit with a fearless hymn upon his lips.

Suddenly a shadow fell across the canoe. Waukewa lifted his eyes and saw a great eagle hovering over, with dangling legs, and a spread of wings that blotted out the sun. Once more the eyes of the Indian boy and his old friend the eagle met; but now the eagle was master!

With a glad cry the Indian boy stood up in his canoe, and the eagle hovered

247

lower. Now the canoe tossed up on that great swelling wave that climbs to the cataract's edge, and the boy lifted his hands and caught the legs of the eagle. The next moment he looked down into the awful gulf of waters. The canoe was snatched from beneath him and plunged down the black wall of the cataract; but he and the struggling eagle were floating outward and downwards through the cloud of mist. The cataract roared terribly, like a wild beast robbed of its prey. The spray beat and blinded, the air rushed upward as they fell. But the eagle struggled on with his burden. He fought his way out of the mist and the flying spray. His great wings threshed the air with a whistling sound. Down, down, they sank, the boy and the eagle, but ever farther from the precipice of water and the boiling whirlpool below.

At length, with a fluttering plunge, the eagle dropped on a sand bar below the whirlpool, and he and the Indian boy lay there a minute, breathless and exhausted. Then the eagle slowly lifted himself, took the air under his free wings, and soared away, while the Indian boy knelt on the sand, and watched with shining eyes the great bird until he faded into the cliffs.

The Big Green Umbrella

By Elizabeth Coatsworth

Mr. THOMAS THOMAS had an umbrella. It was a very fine umbrella, made of dark green silk, with an ivory tip and a round ivory handle.

Mr. Thomas's umbrella was a very large umbrella. It was really like a small silk roof. It would keep Mr. Thomas and Mrs. Thomas and young Tom and little Amanda all dry on a rainy day. At least if the rain came down straight, they would be dry.

On rainy days the whole family walked together, under Mr. Thomas's big green umbrella. The umbrella would keep them dry, going to church, or going down the street in the little town of Newcastle, Delaware, under the rows of elm trees, past the little red brick houses with their small-paned windows.

People looking out from upstairs windows would say, "There goes Mr. Thomas's big green umbrella!"

Everyone knew it. There were many big umbrellas in Newcastle, but Mr. Thomas's was the biggest, the greenest, and the silkiest.

He was very proud of it, and so were Mrs. Thomas and Tom and Amanda.

But one day the umbrella seemed to grow tired of its life in Newcastle. It grew tired of keeping the rain off the Thomases on rainy days and on sunny days standing in the dark corner behind the door. It had heard the talk of the winds from far away. It had listened to the whispering of raindrops which had seen all the world at one time or another. Goodness knows what thoughts the umbrella had been thinking during all the long hours behind the door! But when the moment came, the umbrella acted.

It was a Saturday morning in April. The wind blew fresh, the clouds raced overhead, the sun shone brightly when it shone at all. The birds sat among the budding trees and sang for joy, though sometimes they had to stop their singing when a sudden flurry of wind almost blew their tails inside out. It was a wild day, but a lovely day. The dogs barked, the little boys flew their plunging kites, the horses clattering over the cobbled streets threw up their heads at the blowing bits of paper, and the Thomas family went for a walk. Mr. Thomas took the umbrella along, because in April a shower may come up at any minute.

When people in Newcastle went for a walk, they always went to the river, the Delaware River whose wide waters ran along the back of the gardens of the red brick houses on the strand. There were always things to be seen on the river, a flock of wild ducks bobbing about, or fishermen in their small boats. Or it might be a big clipper ship with its white sails

249

spread, sailing down the river for South America, or the ports of Russia, or far-away China.

On this April morning, such a ship was standing off the shore, its sails taut.

"She's from Philadelphia," Mr. Thomas remarked, "probably bound for the Pagoda Anchorage."

"I wish I were on her," said Tom.

"So do I," said little Amanda.

"Pooh, you'd be sick!" cried Tom.

"No more than you!" cried Amanda.

"Hush, children," said gentle Mrs. Thomas, "see, it's beginning to rain."

Yes, the clouds had suddenly gathered. A minute ago the sun was shining, and now the rain was falling!

Mr. Thomas put up the big green silk umbrella, and all the Thomases gathered under it like chickens under a bush when the rain begins. Had the umbrella heard what the children said? Who will ever know?

Suddenly an unexpected gust of wind arose, stronger than any of the others. It pushed its way under the green umbrella. Umbrella and wind together struggled to pull the ivory handle out of Mr. Thomas's grasp. They tugged, they jerked, they plunged.

Mrs. Thomas smothered a scream, the children knocked against Mr. Thomas's elbows, the umbrella like a thing gone mad whacked against Mr. Thomas's fine beaver hat and sent it spinning. As Mr. Thomas reached one hand out to catch his hat, the umbrella gave a wicked twist—and it was free with its friend the wind.

Above the meadow the umbrella went, now near the ground, now high in the air, like a big green flower, like a tumbling toadstool. Now it floated like a jellyfish, now it soared upward like a kite, now it turned head-over-heels like a boy at play.

It was over the river now, frightening a flock of ducks which flew up quacking and spattering water.

The rain had stopped already. The sun was out again. In a row the Thomases stood and watched the great green umbrella, which had been their pride, dancing and bowing and pirouetting above the river. Sometimes they couldn't see it and then they would catch a glimpse of it again, dark against the white sails of the clipper ship which it seemed to be approaching. Then they saw it no more.

"If only my hat hadn't blown off!" sighed Mr. Thomas. "I might have held it."

"No one could have held that big umbrella in such a wind," soothed Mrs. Thomas.

"We'll never have another umbrella like that," whimpered Amanda.

"There's not another umbrella like it in the world," said young Tom solemnly.

"The wind's gone down," said Mr. Thomas. "I suppose our umbrella's in the Delaware by now."

"It will float for a while," murmured Mrs. Thomas, "and then it will sink."

"And scare the fishes," Tom suggested.

"Perhaps it will keep the sunshine off the fishes as it used to keep the rain off us," said Amanda.

"Anyhow it's at the bottom of the Delaware by now," said Mr. Thomas. "I'm

sorry, for it was a fine umbrella. We'll never see it again."

Mr. Thomas was an upright man, a deacon in the church, a kind husband, and an indulgent father. He set the children a splendid example by never making a remark unless he was sure that he was right.

But on this fine blowy April Saturday morning Mr. Thomas was wrong as wrong could be. The umbrella was *not* at the bottom of the Delaware, nor even at the top of it among the waves. And he was mistaken in other ways besides.

Captain John De Witt of the clipper ship *Commerce* was walking the deck on this fine April morning thinking what a fine ship his was, and what a good crew he had signed on, and how well the first mate was handling the business of sailing the vessel down the river.

Off for China! That was an exciting thought at the beginning of each voyage. To sail halfway round the world and trade with the Chinese, to fill the hold with sweet-smelling tea and buy fine porcelain and embroidered shawls for his wife, surely that was a fine kind of voyage to make.

Suddenly, something caught his eye; it bobbed and winked at the captain.

"That's a funny bird," he thought. But his sharp sailor's eyes told him immediately that it was no bird.

"A kite?" But it hadn't a kite's shape. Dancing, leaping, tumbling, the thing approached nearer.

"An umbrella!" exclaimed the captain and laughed. The umbrella seemed to be on a frolic, so full of high spirits that it couldn't behave the same way for two seconds on end. Now it appeared about to leap into the river, now it changed its course, to skim over the masts. At the last moment it did neither, but with a final tumble landed in the rigging and stuck.

Now a sailor was scrambling up to where the umbrella rested. The thing heaved and moved. It seemed asking the wind not to press it against the ropes but to let it go again to play about in the air. But the wind was a joker, too, turning the umbrella around just as the sailor's brown hand reached for it. Now he had the handle. Now he was working his fingers up to the catch. Now the umbrella had suddenly ceased to be a great green toadstool; it was furled and helpless, only a stick in petticoats.

The sailor brought the closed umbrella to the captain, who examined it.

"A very fine umbrella and not a bit the worse for its cruise," he said. "I'll put it in my cabin and show the Chinese what a good umbrella looks like."

Although the umbrella stood for long weeks behind the cabin door, it was not like standing in the hallway of a house. The air smelled of salt and tarry ropes. The umbrella heard the creaking of cordage and the whistle of wind. It moved up and down, up and down with the motion of the vessel. Although nothing could be seen from the corner of the cabin behind the door, a great deal could be heard and imagined.

Land air has a different smell; first come the sea-birds on the borders of the ocean, and then one hears the land birds singing

and twittering. The *Commerce* moved smoothly now on a quiet river. There were cries of men, unlike the sounds of American voices, and smells of gardens and incense and dead fish.

When the *Commerce* came to anchor there were temple bells, too, in the distance, and Chinese voices conferring with Captain De Witt in the cabin. But still nothing to be seen.

Then one day it rained, slats of rain falling on the cabin roof like a bamboo curtain falling with a sharp sound, and that day the great green umbrella with

the ivory handle came out of its hiding and saw China.

If I should tell you all that the umbrella saw, I should have to tell you all about China, for it saw everything. It saw the blue-clothed crowds, with pigtails hanging down their backs, the women with bound feet in little embroidered slippers, the children in bright clothes. It saw the river boats with big eyes painted on each side of the prows, the dark temples opening on streets so narrow that the umbrella touched walls on each side.

Indeed the streets were so very narrow

and the green umbrella was so very large that hundreds of Chinese had to pass under it as it moved along, and they all gave it a glance of interest and admiration.

The merchant who was in charge of loading the *Commerce* looked at the umbrella with interest and admiration too.

"A fine umbrella," he said in Chinese.

"A very fine umbrella," the interpreter repeated in English.

"It is yours," declared Captain De Witt, for the captain and the merchants were always giving each other presents.

So that afternoon the umbrella started off with a slim yellow hand on its ivory handle, and a grave Chinese face like an old idol's in its green shade.

When the merchant reached his home, he went directly into the part of his house where the women of the family lived, to show them the new umbrella, for the women liked to see things which came from across the sea. They were used to smaller parasols made of glazed paper. They laughed and stared at the great big green umbrella as large as a little house.

Peach Blossom, the merchant's youngest daughter, was more interested than anyone else. "It is so curious," she exclaimed. "I have never seen such a thing."

The merchant smiled at her. "It is yours," he said, "but you must have one of the servants hold it for you when it rains. It is too large for your little hands."

So the umbrella became Peach Blossom's. It went out into the garden in the courtyard to keep her dry when it rained. A big peasant woman held it, while Peach Blossom tripped along on her tiny feet, with food for the goldfish in the rain-speckled pond under the moon-shaped bridge. More rarely it took her to a temple or to visit at some other house where her relatives lived. Then all the children crowded under the umbrella and laughed because they had seen nothing like it before.

A month went by and one afternoon the merchant noticed that Peach Blossom was looking more thoughtful than usual.

"What are you thinking about, Peach Blossom?" he asked.

"I had a dream last night, my father," Peach Blossom replied, bowing.

"Tell me," he said.

Again Peach Blossom bowed. "I dreamed," she went on, "I was walking out in the rain, holding the foreign umbrella in my hand. And I heard it sigh and I looked up. It seemed then that it was a huge bird which was struggling to get away. But I was not afraid.

"Why do you sigh?" I asked, and it replied, "I am weary for my own place and my own people."

"Then I looked again and it seemed to be only the foreign umbrella. But this morning when Green Bamboo held it over me during a shower, it tugged and struggled so that she could hardly hold it." The merchant nodded slowly. "It is homesick," he said. "Things can no doubt be homesick too. I will take it back to the Captain and explain. If it stayed here it would not be lucky. Fortunately the *Commerce* has not yet sailed."

So that was how it came about that the big green umbrella found itself once more

behind the door in the captain's cabin. Once more it smelled and heard and felt the life of a ship, leaving the port for the open sea. Once more it shared in the life of a long voyage, heard the talk and felt the rise and fall of the vessel beneath it. Once more it came through storms and calms to the quiet of a great river, but this time the odors that blew from the land and the far-off sounds of the shores were as familiar as sun and rain to the umbrella.

Then once more the ship came up into the wind and the anchor chains rattled and the captain's gig was lowered and the captain and the umbrella were rowed ashore across the ripples of the river.

At the little Newcastle customs house the officer bowed politely to Captain De Witt. "I trust that you had a good voyage to China, sir. Are you putting goods ashore at Newcastle this trip?"

Captain De Witt laughed. "Only this stowaway which signed on from here without papers," and he held out the big green umbrella.

"By thunder, sir, that's Mr. Thomas's umbrella which blew away over a year ago. It was the biggest umbrella in town. He never expected to lay eyes on that again, I do assure you."

So the captain explained how the umbrella had chosen to come aboard and the customs officer laughed and nodded, and called a boy.

"Here, Jim, take this to Mr. Thomas's house with my compliments, and tell him

255

that it went on a voyage to China along with Captain De Witt on the *Commerce*. In China, it was given to a little Chinese girl who had a dream and sent it back because she thought the umbrella was homesick. Amanda will like to hear that."

"Tell Amanda that the little girl's name was Peach Blossom and that she was eight years old," Captain De Witt joined in.

"That's about Amanda's age," said the customs officer, "or thereabouts. Children keep changing their ages so fast, I can't keep track of them."

The boy, Jim, started up the street under the elms, whistling and swinging the big green umbrella by the ivory handle. It was so tall he had to keep his hand above his shoulder so the ivory tip wouldn't hit the paving stones.

"What have you got there, Jim?" one of his friends asked him. "Look out or it will run away with you."

"That's Mr. Thomas's green umbrella and it's been on a cruise to China," Jim explained.

"Whew!" said the boy falling in beside Jim, "what do you know about that?"

Just then a lady who was passing stopped, looking sharply at the umbrella. "Isn't that Mr. Thomas's big green umbrella?" she demanded. "What are you doing with it, boy?"

When she heard the story, she nodded her head a couple of times.

"I'll go along to see that you don't break it," she declared. "I do want to see Mrs. Thomas's face when she comes to the door. I've seen that umbrella too many times to be mistaken about it."

So the umbrella went on its triumphant way, and more and more people joined the procession. There were children and dogs of course, and grown-up people too, just to see what the Thomases would say when they saw their big green umbrella returned from faraway China.

Jim knocked on the big shiny knocker on the white door, and the maid came, and was soon followed by Mr. and Mrs. Thomas and young Tom and little Amanda, pouring out onto the steps to see the big green umbrella. Mr. Thomas opened it, and there it was, as big and sheltering as ever and not a tear or wear in all its dark green surface.

Mrs. Thomas kept repeating, "Well, I never in all my born days!"

Young Tom grinned and went out into the street to see the *Commerce* standing offshore, sails set for Philadelphia.

But Amanda went over when no one was looking and kissed the handle of the runaway umbrella to welcome it home.

It was she who found fastened below the ivory handle a colored cord from which hung an embroidered peach with a tassel at its end, filled with sandalwood, as a remembrance.

But Peach Blossom must have been right: the umbrella apparently wanted to be home where it belonged. For never again did it attempt to leave Newcastle, where it lived in great splendor as the umbrella which had been to China; yes, and had come back again.

Caleb's Luck

By Laura Benét

URSULA KOERING

"COULD I sit here a spell, ma'am?"
Miss Cranston looked up from her desk and saw a drooping small figure in one of the seats. So noiselessly had the boy entered that she had not even heard him come. After school that day, she had settled down in the empty schoolroom to plan examination questions. The first of June spelled closing time for the High Ridge Community School in the North Carolina mountains.

"Who is it?" she asked quickly. The tired voice replied in deep satisfaction: "This is the finest sittin' I ever sat."

"Did you want to see me?" asked the teacher, kindly.

"I reckon so," was the placid response. Still the boy made no motion to get up.

Pushing aside papers, Miss Cranston walked down the aisle. A glance had already told her that this twelve-year-old mountaineer was completely exhausted.

"What's your name?" she said.

"Caleb Waters."

257

"Have you come far?"

"Nigh onto fifteen miles. It's a long way to Turkey Creek Bottom."

"Have you had anything to eat?"

"Piece o' corn pone, ma'am."

She brought him the remains of her lunch and his eyes brightened. "It's a purty place here. I'm comin' for schoolin' next year."

"That's good news," said Miss Cranston encouragingly. "We think it's a nice place, but it's too far for you to walk. Is some neighbor going to carry you in to school each day?"

His face fell. "No; ain't nobody to fetch me. Say, ma'am, can I stop here by the week?"

"Yes, if you pay for your board, Caleb. The people who could board you are poor, too, you know. Could you pay a little?"

"No," he answered, decidedly. "I can't pay anything."

The teacher reflected: "Could you take a job this summer—or"—a bright idea occurred to her, "do you know the rock near High Ridge called Garnet Rock? Summer visitors are interested in the garnets."

"I've heard talk about it."

"While you're here, Caleb, go to see Ed Jones who runs the hotel. He'll have someone going out there, I'm sure. Pick up a big sackful of the best stones and you can sell them." And she added: "I'll have my landlady fix you up at our house tonight." She gave him directions as to how to find the place. "Can you read and write and do easy sums?"

"No'm. That's why I want to go to school."

Miss Cranston sighed. They shook hands and Caleb limped wearily off to the Jones House, the country hotel on High Ridge's one long street. Ed Jones, the proprietor as well as postmaster, eyed him curiously. Yes, he said, a farmer was riding out Garnet Rock way and maybe he could get a lift behind him on his horse.

Caleb got the lift and when he arrived at the Rock he used his time well. He had quick eyes and nimble fingers and spent the afternoon diligently mining garnets, getting together a packet of really good ones.

The farmer returned for him, good-naturedly. "Right smart lot o' stones ye have thar," he remarked.

Caleb gave him one of the largest in return for the ride.

"It's a purty place here," he said, repeating his stock phrase amiably.

"Well, son, you take them garnets to Ed Jones. He'll advertise 'em for ye 'mong the summer folks."

Caleb hurried off to see Ed Jones, a close bargainer, who appraised the garnets slyly. "Not worth a sick chicken's crop," he said, "but rub 'em up and I'll trade 'em for ye at a few cents apiece. Come by in a week."

Caleb ached with disappointment. He had pictured himself making several dollars from his finds. It would take quite a few of those scarce dollars to get him through the winter. Ma wanted that he should have learnin'. Well, he'd go back to that teacher lady.

At her boarding house he had supper, a good night's sleep, and breakfast. Then the fifteen miles home seemed less difficult. And Miss Cranston told him that ten dollars in his pocket would cover the whole winter's schooling.

"I'll try to help you," said Miss Cranston, "when I get back from vacation. The schoolbooks will be free. You must have one whole suit and a pair of shoes and some board money. I'll help you all I can." She waved a friendly good-by.

Caleb tugged at his bleached hair badly in need of cutting. Then he set off for his far hills without a backward look. On the outskirts of High Ridge, the county seat and highest point in these mountains, he paused for the view before descending into the bottom land. Leaning against a stalwart rock, he looked his fill. Fragments of the rock had broken off and a large white piece of quartz lay at his feet. His eyes rested on it eagerly. Ma had asked him to fetch a stone for propping the cabin's door, for there were few good-sized rocks to be had on their own acre of muddy ground. This shining stone was mighty pretty and not too large to carry. He picked it up and went on his way.

It was dark night when he reached the hillock where the home cabin adjoined those dense woods where his father ran a still.

"Caleb!" his mother's voice said. "So it's you, boy? I was studyin' the ridge since sundown. Thought you was fixin' to come back last night. You ain't forgot th' rock?"

"No. But Ma, I can't make th' winter schoolin'." And Caleb's eyes flashed in despair.

"Sit a spell, Caleb. Tell me about it. I got some black-eyed peas for you."

They talked in whispers. The moon rose over the cabin which, with its spring and a rickety shed for the cow and chickens, stood alone in a clearing. The cabin was lonely, but the pungent pines and balsams, the sound of Turkey Creek, and Ma's burned-out patch of flowers spelled home as much as did Ma herself.

"You got to git schoolin', Caleb. Your skull-piece is better'n your Pa's and ye're twelve and can't read nor write. No sense in knockin' round these hills makin' stills and shootin' up revenue men like your Pa has. Mebbe I kin slip ye some o' the egg money."

Caleb shyly laid his hand on hers.

Before they went to bed, Ma propped the cabin door open with the new stone. "Such a purty, shiny one," she said.

"I brung you a garnet too, Ma. I want you should wear it in a gold ring some day."

"Mercy, what could I do with a fancy piece like a gold ring, Caleb? Hush your talk. We're nothin' but rabbits. When the sheriff's gun goes bang, we run for cover."

A week passed. Caleb had to do the several chores that made up daily life. But one day when his father was at the still and his mother at a quilting bee down the creek, two miles away, he was left to tend his small sister. He sat at the cabin door, contemplating the piece of white quartz. It would set a little firmer if he tilted it over on the side—so. As Caleb did this, something caught his eye—a sharp glitter from the quartz. The bright speck was embedded too deep for him to pick it out.

Going to the shed, he fetched Pa's ax. Whack, whack! After half an hour of work, he detached the glittering bit that had winked at him. It was encrusted with other material but its color was a deep greenish blue. He hid it carefully away.

That evening Pa came home in a temper. "Someone is watchin' my still," he said. "I got to move it further off into the cave by the stream. We got to lay low. Caleb, don't ye let me hear ye say ye'r a-goin' to High Ridge! Sheriff's men might catch ye."

"But, Pa, my garnets—?"

"Just let me find ye gone and I'll"—he raised his hand threateningly.

Ma was silent. Often in the days that followed, her eyes met her son's, the same question in both. But when Pa had wild spells like this it was best to lie low.

The long hot summer days dragged on, each one bitterer than the last. But the sheriff never did find the still and after some weeks they could relax. When Caleb needed courage he looked at the blue stone—for he couldn't go after his garnet money. But now it seemed as if Pa was possessed to discover the piece of white quartz—it had been so handy for the door. But Caleb kept the pretty blue stone well hidden, for it was his one bit of hope. He put it in a hollow tree, then moved it from there on account of thieving squirrels who might mistake it for a nut.

Then one day a dreadful thing happened! The stone had finally been placed in an empty tobacco sack hanging from the peg where he kept his few clothes. His father, in a tantrum, found the tobacco pouch, shook it out and, since there was no tobacco in it, tossed it away.

Caleb heard the precious blue stone rattle on the floor boards of the cabin before it slipped through a crack. Then followed a frantic hunt. While Ma was at the spring, he spent an hour under the house, half-sobbing as he frantically clawed up dirt with his hands. A skunk and her family had found a home there. Just as Caleb finally spied the treasure beside one of the upright posts that supported the cabin, the mother skunk deluged him with her scent!

There was a reckoning. When Pa came home he cut a hickory switch from the grove, a stout new one that would hurt, and took his son out to the shed to be whipped "for turnin' thet skunk loose." Then Caleb, along with his scented shirt and trousers, was put to soak in a tub for dismal hours. But he'd put the stone safely in a new place.

When but two weeks remained before the High Ridge School was to re-open for the fall session, Pa announced that he was going away to do some "hoss swappin'" in Cutter County.

"Yer cousin at the Falls kin take you-all in for a night or so," he decreed. "I aim to be gone a short spell."

Ma's face was hard to read. When her husband had gone to get in the corn, she

 URSULA KOERING

said, "Caleb, boy, here's your chance. We'll go along to Cousin Cassie's. Ye make tracks tomorrow for High Ridge. Ye might get a lift."

Sure enough Caleb met a mountaineer who was taking his wife to the doctor at High Ridge. Never had the boy imagined that it would be so easy to ride in one of these Fords. The miles melted away. When they got to the county seat, he was promised a return trip at the end of the day. Caleb ran to the Jones House but found its owner was at the post office. He made tracks across the mountain village street. What if—what if—he should get two dollars for those garnets? Schooling seemed nearer and nearer. Life wouldn't be so lonely any more.

Ed Jones, postmaster, looked at the ragged mountain lad as though he had never seen him. "Well?"

"I aimed to get the—what the summer folk gave for my garnets I left with ye," gulped Caleb.

"Garnets! Left 'em months ago, ye young rascal! Never sent no word nor come after 'em. I sold some and threw the rest out. Give ye twenty-five cents for the lot." Grudgingly he pushed two dimes and a nickel over the sill.

"Ye mean—ye cast them away?" Caleb asked darkly. Caleb's spirits fell like the charred stick of a skyrocket. Out went a hard fist. In another instant Ed Jones' large nose would have been double its size. But the postmaster slammed down the window. "Git out o' here, varmint, or I'll have ye run out of town!" he shouted.

The mountain boy sat down on the

261

post office steps, heavily. He felt very sick at his stomach and dizzy too. It was the hot time of the day and few people passed in and out for letters. At last he heard a deep unfamiliar voice saying to him: "You're from these parts. Whereabouts is the Garnet Rock?"

He opened his eyes and saw a broad-shouldered, middle-aged man who looked very wise. In a dazed voice, Caleb answered: "I can't rightly remember."

"But I am interested in stones, you see." The man bent down towards him. "Have you mined garnets 'round here in your hills?"

"I ain't from here. I'm from Turkey Creek Bottom." Then Caleb fumbled in his shirt and brought out the blue stone: "Can ye tell me what it is?" he mumbled.

The man's eyes brightened: "Let me examine it," he said.

The boy clutched it distrustfully. "*He* cast away my garnets," he stammered, chest heaving. "Them garnets I was aimin' to get schoolin' with."

"This isn't a garnet." The man knelt down beside him on the steps. "This is something very different. Come over to my room."

They went to the hotel across the street and up to the man's room—a more comfortable-looking place than Caleb had ever seen. While his new friend, who was a geologist, occupied himself with a magnifying glass and tools, Caleb munched chocolate and crackers.

At last the examination was finished: "Looks very favorable," the man, whose name was Wilkinson, announced. "Caleb, you're a lucky boy. You've got a precious stone here—a rare, blue beryl as sure as I'm alive."

The owner of the stone looked up languidly: "A-burril? I ain't never heard o' *them*. Is it a kind o' garnet?"

"Better. What did that postmaster give you for your garnets, boy?"

"Twenty-five cents."

"I'll pay you ten dollars for this stone, just as it is."

Caleb stared at him. His face grew dark red. "Ten dollars? You're foolin', mister. Pa'd take it fer a hoss for sure."

"Tell me a little about yourself," he said and listened to Caleb's story of the summer.

"I'm staying here several weeks longer," he said. "I'll see that teacher and arrange about your winter term." And Caleb knew by his voice that he meant it. "Here's the ten dollars—but you'd better let me be your banker. Some day you'll show me where you found the stone?"

"Sure," said Caleb with satisfaction. "This here"—he fingered his change—"it'll buy my Ma a new calico dress length. And say, mister, we got to chip 'nuff off the ten dollars to buy her a ring. More garnets are easy to come by."

Henry Wilkinson looked hard at Caleb and smiled. "Easier than some other things," he said. "A lot easier than courage and patience and really working for an education."

Katie Meets Buffalo Bill

By Katharine Koch

KATIE was turning round and round the smooth iron crossbar of the hitching post, her black braids swinging wildly in time with her revolutions.

"Katie! Oh, Katie-e-e! Here comes the iceman!" screamed Francie.

At her sister's shriek Katie brought herself gradually to a stop, slid down the sidebar, and stood clutching it until the earth stopped moving in waves up and down. She let go the post and sat down suddenly and hard. Giggling, she wiped her hot face with a grimy hand and looked up the street.

"The ice wagon and the horses are going round and round—and so's my stomach," she gasped.

Katie closed her eyes to shut out the whirling sight. Clearly through the sleepy quiet of the little town she heard the familiar sounds of creaking wheels and the heavy clop of horses' hoofs. She jumped to her feet and stood wavering unsteadily as the iceman pulled his two white horses

URSULA KOERING

263

to a stop. Water dripped from the sides of the rickety old wagon and made little plop-plopping sounds in the yellow dust. How nice it would be to stick bare toes under the cool dripping water! But Mom wouldn't let Katie go barefooted and said there were plenty of other ways she could get hurt without stepping on broken glass or running a splinter into her foot. Katie had to admit honestly that Mom was probably right, for all kinds of things did have a funny way of happening to her.

"Sakes alive, Katie! The way you were spinning around that post," said the iceman. "You'll break your neck some day, sure. Wasn't it just last week that you knocked out a tooth?"

Katie ran her tongue into the empty spot in her mouth. Yes, the tooth was still gone and the spot felt as big as a cave. She grinned at the iceman, showing a gaping hole. Katie liked the iceman. He was big and jolly, always making jokes with the boys who followed his wagon and letting them climb on the back step to pick up small pieces of ice that lay in the straw.

She watched as he climbed down from the driver's seat and looped the reins around the hitching post. Scrambling up beside him, she waited expectantly while he chipped off a piece of ice from a large block, ducking to escape the small pieces that flew in a shower from his ice pick. She scooped up a handful and dropped them into Francie's upstretched hands. Little Francie squealed when some of the cold slivers slid down her arm, and she squealed still more when Katie popped a

tiny piece down the back of her neck.

"Now, Katie, you oughtn't to tease your little sister like that," said the iceman as he deftly dropped a fairly large piece of ice down Katie's neck.

Since Katie was two years older than Francie, she could squeal considerably louder. She did now.

"S'pose you know Buffalo Bill's Wild West Show is coming to town?" said the iceman, raising his voice to be heard.

Katie stopped in the middle of an extra loud howl and stared, her eyes and mouth making three big O's.

"Buffalo Bill! The real Buffalo Bill? Is he coming here?"

"That's right. The signs are up on the billboard down by the livery stable. Here's a handbill that tells about it. I'm helping to pass out a few on my rounds today."

Two eager hands reached for the crumpled handbill that the iceman pulled from his pocket.

"Let go, Francie. I'm older—and you can't read, anyway."

"I can, too, read, and I'm almost as old as you are."

Katie's face flushed in quick temper. "Give it to me. You're too little," she shrilled, stamping her foot.

Francie relinquished her hold.

"You can have it," she said with dignity. "Mom says you'll be sorry some day when you lose your temper. She says it's your worst enemy—and you're an old meanie," she added in a burst of indignation. Turning, she ran after the iceman who had shouldered the block of ice and was dripping his way to the kitchen door.

Katie walked slowly toward the front porch. There was an uneasy sinking feeling in her stomach, and it wasn't the hitching post that caused it. She and Francie could have looked at the handbill together. It would have been fun to read it to Francie. And now her quick temper had spoiled things again.

Miserably she looked at the paper which had caused the trouble. In spite of her gloomy thoughts, her attention was attracted by a picture of some yelling Indians pursuing a stagecoach.

Presently Katie was so absorbed in the marvelous handbill that she didn't even hear the iceman as he called giddap to his horses and drove down the street. The poster read:

Coming!   Coming!   Coming!

Buffalo Bill's
Wild West Show

BUFFALO BILL

The Famous Indian Fighter

Annie Oakley—Little Sure Shot
The Original and Authentic
Deadwood Mail Coach
Hundreds of Painted Savages

A Year's Visit West in 3 Hours

AMUSEMENT — EDUCATION

Coming Aug. 26, 1906

Katie knew a great deal about Buffalo Bill. Last time they had gone to the farm to visit Grandma, she had found a pile of paper-bound books up in the attic. She had read all of *Jesse James and His Demon Horse; or, A True Pard to the Outlaw King*, and had almost finished *Buffalo Bill's Red Trail; or, The Road-Rider Renegade's Run Down*, when Mom had discovered her. In spite of her tearful protests, the fascinating story books had been whisked away.

"No wonder you were yelling in your sleep last night," Mom had said. "Dime novels weren't meant for children."

Katie wondered if Wild West Shows were meant for children. Thoughtfully she considered the most favorable way to convince Mom that no little girl should miss such an educational opportunity.

But it was Papa who brought up the subject that very evening. After supper he pulled two slips of yellow cardboard from his pocket and announced, "A man from the Buffalo Bill show was in the newspaper office this afternoon. He gave me two passes to the performance."

He looked at Katie and his face was serious as he went on slowly, "I'd like to take you, Katie, but I've been noticing lately how often you lose your temper. I saw you push Francie away from the swing yesterday, and this morning you were very ugly to Barbie."

Baby Barbie banged her spoon on the highchair and laughed when she heard her name, but Katie hung her head.

"I'll make a bargain with you, Katie. It may help you to remember to hold your hair-trigger temper. I'll take you with me to the Wild West Show if you can control your temper till the day of the show. Is it a bargain?"

"Yes, Papa, I'll try," promised Katie.

And Katie did try. When she felt the familiar upsurging of temper, she reminded herself, "Remember Buffalo Bill!" Francie helped, too. "Remember the show!" she warned when she saw a certain glint in Katie's eye. Even Baby Barbie caught the spirit of the thing and would bang her rag doll happily against the floor, chanting, "Show! Show!"

It wasn't easy. Time after time, quick harsh words were hastily swallowed. Then, the day before the show, in an argument over paper dolls, Katie forgot and stamped her foot. All day she struggled with her conscience. Should she tell Papa? She knew that Francie would keep her secret. But when she told him that evening, Papa smiled at the sober-faced little girl.

"Well, Katie," he said, "it seems to me that one little stamp in two weeks' time shouldn't count as a fit of temper. You've done well, Katie."

So next day a radiant-faced Katie in a new pink jumper dress set off with Papa for the old Fair Grounds where the show tent was staked.

"You can play with my paper dolls," she told Francie. She felt sorry for Francie who must stay home with Mom and Barbie, though Francie didn't seem to mind at all.

"Have a good time, Katie," called Mom. "But do be careful."

"Oh, nothing can happen to me at the show," called back Katie.

But Katie was wrong about that.

When they reached the Fair Grounds, Katie held tight to Papa's hand. Such crowds! Such hustle and bustle! Such color and excitement! And everywhere voices shouting:

"Right this way! Right this way! This way to the big tent."

"Buy a souvenir, Ladies and Gentlemen. Buy a souvenir."

"Read all about him, folks! The true story of Buffalo Bill. He traces his ancestry to Irish Kings!"

"Over here! Over here! Rosa Bonheur's famous picture of Buffalo Bill."

"Tickets! Get your tickets here!"

It seemed dark inside the tent after the bright sunshine outside, and Katie first blinked and then stared with curious eyes. Rows and rows of wooden planks ran around the tent and they seemed filled with thousand of faces. Papa found some places for them in the second row up near the entrance to the dressing rooms.

"We can see all the performers come in and go out of the main tent," he explained, "and you can sit here by the edge and hold on to this tent pole."

Suddenly there sounded the thunder of hoofs, the crack of rifles and blood-curdling yells. Katie jumped and reached for Papa's hand. The show had begun!

Whooping cowboys on bucking broncos galloped past Katie's seat beside the post and on into the big ring. Their lariats whizzed through the air as they roped and tied Texas steers. Gauchos from the plains

of Patagonia swung their heavy iron bolas. Bearded Cossacks, wearing knee-length coats belted at the waist, and armed with daggers and long Caucasian rifles, balanced themselves on their heads as they rode their ponies around the ring.

A covered wagon drove slowly through the dust. Hideous war-whoops rang out, and painted savages dashed after the wagon. The pioneers fought bravely but they were outnumbered. Just as all seemed lost, hundreds of American soldiers galloped to the rescue. Katie let out her breath in a long sigh of relief.

Then Katie stared in astonishment, for into the ring rode a woman dressed in fringed buckskin and carrying a rifle.

"Ladies and Gentlemen!" bellowed the announcer. "Presenting the famous Annie Oakley, Little Sure Shot!"

Annie Oakley laid her gun on the ground, threw glass balls into the air, snatched up the gun, and shot the balls before they reached the ground. Watching wide-eyed, Katie wondered if she could persuade Papa to get her a gun for Christmas.

Now there was a hush and Katie felt tingly all over. Something was going to happen. Katie stood up to see better, holding the tent pole.

A bugle blared and a spotlight shifted to the entrance. In its glare a white horse pranced and curvetted. A man, tall and straight and broad-shouldered, sat easily in the saddle. He was dressed in buckskin and wore leather gauntlets and long boots. His hair was white and flowed to his shoulders. He had a silky mustache and a

267

little goatee. Katie's heart throbbed and she swallowed hard. It was Buffalo Bill!

Slowly he rode around the ring, reining the high-stepping horse with one hand and flourishing his sombrero in greeting with the other. Instinctively Katie felt that this was a man who loved the spotlight and the applause, who took delight in swaggering before cheering crowds. "Just the way I feel when I get up in school to speak a piece," she thought sympathetically.

Buffalo Bill spurred his horse to a gallop and rode swiftly around the ring, jumping from his horse to the ground and back into the saddle many times. He picked up colored kerchiefs from the ground as the white horse galloped past them. He shot glass balls which an Indian threw into the air. Ping! Ping! Ping! sang the colored balls as each was shattered. Not one was missed. In all too short a time Buffalo Bill was leaving the ring. The white horse, daintily sidestepping, came nearer and nearer to the place' where Katie leaned farther and farther forward. And then—

Katie's foot slipped. Wildly she clutched for the tent pole but her fingers brushed past. Head over heels went Katie into the dust—right in front of the prancing white horse.

Buffalo Bill leaned far down, caught Katie's skirt and pulled her into the saddle. He hesitated a moment, then, holding Katie in his arm, he wheeled his horse and galloped completely around the ring and out of the tent. The horse came to a stop. But the riders sat still. It seemed very quiet in the field outside the performers' quarters.

"Well, Sis," said Buffalo Bill, "you're heavier than the handkerchiefs I pick off the ground."

Buffalo Bill looked at Katie and Katie looked at Buffalo Bill. Why, Buffalo Bill was an old man with a wrinkled face. Katie didn't know that Buffalo Bill was ill and tired and worried about debts, or that he needed money to keep his Wild West Show because many people were trying that new entertainment called "moving pictures." But Katie knew that his eyes were sad. Then Buffalo Bill smiled at her and Katie knew something else. She knew that Buffalo Bill was kind.

"Thank you," she said shyly. "I was afraid you'd be mad at me."

"Shucks, no!" said Buffalo Bill. "I learned long ago in my Indian fighting days that it doesn't pay to get mad too easily. You can't think with your head if you lose it! Now, when you fell in front of me, I figured I could use you in the act, so I galloped around the ring with you, and the people loved it!"

"Oh," breathed Katie. "I think you're wonderful. I read all about you in a dime novel."

"Gosh, the things they write," exclaimed Buffalo Bill. "You know, Sis, you mustn't believe everything you read in those books. I wrote some of those yarns myself and I had to stretch things considerably. Why, in one story, my hero killed more men in one war trail than I killed in all my life."

Katie's face clouded. "But you did

work for the Pony Express and fight Indians and kill buffaloes, didn't you?" she asked anxiously.

"Oh, yes, I did those things," the old scout reassured her. "They made up a song about me, and the cowboys used to sing it—still do, maybe."

The white horse tossed his head and Katie patted his smooth hair.

"He's beautiful," she said. "I 'spect he's proud to carry you."

Buffalo Bill looked pleased.

"Isham is one of the finest," he said, "and I've owned plenty. There was my first pony, Prince. Then in the army I had a horse called Buckskin Joe. When I went scouting for General Sheridan I rode a light-colored, fast-stepping pony named Powder Face. Yes, I've had some fine horses—but I think Isham will be my last."

Katie saw the sad look that came back to his eyes. Impulsively she threw her arms around his neck and planted a wet kiss on his leathery cheek. Then Papa was there and Katie was lifted down from Isham's back.

As in a dream Katie stumbled homeward by Papa's side. When they reached home Katie looked at the little gray house with dazed eyes. It seemed ages ago that she had left that familiar porch. But there was Mom holding Barbie, and there was Francie looking very sober.

"Oh, Katie," she cried. "I let Barbie hold your paper doll just a minute—the one with the red dress—and she tore off its head."

Katie came back to earth suddenly. "Francie! Not Rosemary Gwendolyn, my favorite doll! Oh, you—"

She stopped and swallowed hard.

"Never mind," she said. "Tomorrow we'll have a grand funeral—and you can help bury her."

Papa smiled, and Katie smiled back.

"You can't think with your head if you lose it," explained Katie.

The Family Who Had Never Had Roller Skates

Written and Illustrated by Hildegard Woodward

IT WAS springtime in the city. The hand organs were playing the Bella Bocca Polka and everyone was roller-skating. People whirled gaily along the sidewalks and through the park, in and out, in and out. Sometimes they fell on their elbows and often their feet flew up in the air.

This was quite long ago, that is, long before anyone knew about automobiles, for time was when the park was full of horses and carriages and some people scorched along on high-wheeled bicycles. But roller-skating was new and quite the thing. Yet, sad as it may seem, Emma, Alice and Louise Pettingill had never had roller skates.

"You would break your legs," said Pa-pa Pettingill.

"Dear me, yes," said Ma-ma Pettingill.

"Little ladies should not muss and tear their petticoats," said Cousin Margaret Pettingill.

So Emma, Alice, and Louise Pettingill just stood at the parlor window and gazed at the people skimming along through the park. They wished and wished their legs were not so brittle or their petticoats so stiff. They were quiet, good little girls who always did what they were told and never asked for anything they couldn't have. Dreams of roller skates rolled through their heads but they said nothing; they just sighed sadly and stood at the parlor window in their stiff petticoats, quietly humming the Bella Bocca Polka.

When Cousin Margaret Pettingill took them for their walk in the park she never seemed to notice that everyone was roller-skating; the boys and girls, the papas and mamas, the cousins and uncles, even the aunts, everyone was roller-skating, that is, everyone except Emma, Alice, and Louise Pettingill. When they went downtown shopping she didn't even seem to notice that the window of the Empire Emporium was just full of roller skates, beautiful, gleaming roller skates of all sizes. Emma, Alice, and Louise gazed longingly at them but it did no good. Cousin Margaret Pettingill walked right ahead, bent on buying yards of ribbon for more sashes and yards and yards of lace for petticoat frills.

"Why don't you roller-skate?" called Polly Polhemus as she whirled around them on one foot. "See what fun it is."

Emma, Alice, and Louise had nothing whatever to say. They just plodded along home in their button boots, looking very proper but feeling quite unhappy.

"What nice little ladylike girls we have," said Cousin Margaret Pettingill. "I am so glad they do not care to indulge in boisterous performances on roller skates."

"Yes, indeed," said Ma-ma Pettingill.

The three little girls grew sadder and quieter day by day. They didn't even care to eat. Their legs grew thinner and their cheeks grew paler, but the Pettingill petticoats were always clean and freshly starched and never torn.

Pa-pa Pettingill was far too busy at business to notice their plight. He dashed out of the house every morning after breakfast and when he slowly climbed the

brown front steps at night, he never even looked up from his evening paper.

One day, however, something happened. Pa-pa Pettingill forgot to get an evening paper. So when he came down the street to his house he did notice Emma, Alice, and Louise standing at the parlor window gazing out at the park. They looked so thin and sad that it quite wrung his heart. In fact he was so shocked that he suddenly darted for the front steps and ran right into a sailor who was swirling along the sidewalk on his roller skates. This did not particularly please Pa-Pa Pettingill and he flew up the brownstone steps in quite a state and started shouting in the front hall at Ma-ma Pettingill.

"What is the meaning of this! Our daughters look ill. We must get tonics and pills and medicines. They must be cured at once!"

"Yes, my dear," said Ma-ma Pettingill. "I'll send Peter for Doctor Martin tomorrow."

"Send for him immediately," roared Pa-pa Pettingill.

Emma, Alice, and Louise became frightened and paler than ever but still they didn't say anything at all. The whole family waited in the parlor while Peter Onderdouck, the coachman, hitched the horse and drove around to tell Doctor Martin, and Pa-pa Pettingill paced the parlor floor impatiently.

Finally after an hour or two Doctor Martin came, medicine bag in hand.

"Thank you for coming so promptly," said Ma-ma Pettingill. "We are very much worried about our little girls."

Emma, Alice, and Louise began to tremble with fear while Doctor Martin listened to their hearts and took their temperatures. He looked at their tongues and examined their throats. Then, humming the Bella Bocca Polka, he threw his things back in his bag.

"Pills! Tonics! Nonsense!" he cried.

"Perhaps they should be put to bed with flannel on their chests and keep out the air," said Cousin Margaret Pettingill.

"Yes," said Ma-ma Pettingill, "the spring air is so dangerous."

"Nonsense," roared Doctor Martin, "they must have fresh air and plenty of it. Flannel, indeed! Get out their roller skates and send them to the park."

"But we have no roller skates," murmured Emma, Alice, and Louise.

"What, no roller skates!" he shouted. "I am astounded!"

"Oh!" said Pa-pa Pettingill.

"Oh!" said Ma-ma Pettingill.

"So very unladylike," murmured Cousin Margaret Pettingill.

"Ridiculous!" said Doctor Martin, "everyone is roller-skating. Send out for some at once."

The next day Peter Onderdouck hitched up and drove Pa-pa Pettingill around to the Empire Emporium where he himself bought three pairs of the shiniest, most wonderful roller skates with wooden wheels that whirled like anything.

So Emma, Alice, and Louise began to roller-skate. They fell on their noses, their feet flew up in the air. Their petticoats grew mussed and torn but their cheeks grew rosy. Soon there were no finer roller skaters in the whole park than Emma, Alice, and Louise Pettingill.

Then Pa-pa and Ma-ma and Cousin Margaret Pettingill stood proudly watching from the parlor window.

"I have half a mind to try it one day myself," said Pa-pa Pettingill.

"Dear me," said Ma-ma Pettingill.

"Goodness gracious! What next!" exclaimed Cousin Margaret Pettingill, but, very softly, she began to hum the Bella Bocca Polka.

Indians in the House

By Laura Ingalls Wilder

Long ago, when wild Indians owned all the land that is now Oklahoma, a little girl named Laura lived in a little log house in that Indian country. In those days children called their fathers "Pa," and their mothers "Ma." Laura and her sister Mary and their baby sister Carrie had come with their Pa and Ma in a covered wagon, all the way from the Big Woods of Wisconsin. And Jack, the brindle bulldog, had walked all that long way under the wagon.

Pa had built the small log house on the wide and empty prairie. As far as the eye could see in all directions there was nothing but tall, wild grass rippling in the winds that always blew over the level land. There were no other houses, no fields or fences. There was not even a road.

No other white people lived in all that country. Indians lived there, but they were never seen. Perhaps they had gone away to hunt the buffaloes, or perhaps they were hidden in hollows somewhere on the enormous prairie. Laura had lived there a long time and she had never seen an Indian.

One morning Pa went hunting. Jack wanted to go, too. His eyes begged and his stumpy tail wagged pleadingly and whines quivered in his throat. But Pa chained him to the log barn.

"No, Jack," Pa said, "you stay here on guard." Then he said to Mary and Laura, "Don't let him loose, girls."

It was a disgrace to be chained, and poor Jack felt it deeply. He turned his head and would not watch Pa going away with his gun. Pa went farther and farther away until the prairie swallowed him and he was gone.

Laura tried to comfort Jack, but the more he thought about the chain, the worse he felt. So all that morning Laura and Mary stayed with him. They stroked his smooth brindled head and hugged his neck and told him how sorry they were, and they tried to cheer him up. But he was very sad.

Suddenly he stood up and growled fiercely. The hair on his neck bristled. All his savage teeth showed and his eyes glared red. Laura and Mary turned around quickly and they saw two naked wild men coming.

They were tall and thin and fierce-looking. They came walking one behind the other through the high wild grass and all their skin above the grass was bare. It was brownish red. Their heads seemed to go up to a peak, and the peak was a tuft of hair that stood straight up and ended in feathers. Their eyes were black and glittering and still, like snakes' eyes.

"Indians!" Mary whispered. Laura was

shivery; there was a queer feeling in her middle and her legs wobbled. Jack was growling ferociously. He had bounded clear off the ground, trying to get loose from the chain. Laura was glad that the chain kept him there with her.

"Jack won't let them hurt us," she whispered to Mary.

All this time the wild men were coming closer and closer. They came to the house and they went straight in through the open door.

"They are in the house," Mary whispered, "with Ma and Carrie." She clung tight to Laura and Laura clung to her and

URSULA KOERING

they shook all over. They did not know what those wild men were doing to Ma and to baby Carrie.

"Oh, what are they doing to Ma?" she whispered.

"Oh, I don't know!" Mary whispered. There was no sound at all from the house. Laura knew she must do something to save Ma and the baby. She couldn't think what to do. Then she thought of Jack. He had stopped growling; he was lunging at the chain, trying with all his might to break it so that he could get to those Indians. He hated Indians; if he could reach them he would kill them.

"I'm going to turn Jack loose," Laura said. She was too scared to speak out loud.

Mary whispered, "Pa said not to."

"He didn't know Indians would come," Laura answered.

"He said not to let Jack loose." Mary was almost crying.

Laura thought that surely, if Pa had known that Indians would come, he wouldn't have chained up Jack. If he knew, he would say she could turn Jack loose. She thought it would be right to disobey him, just this once. But she had never dared to disobey Pa. She thought of Ma and little baby Carrie, alone in the house with those terrible wild men; nobody was there to help them. They needed Jack. But she must always obey her father. And Pa had said not to let Jack loose.

"I'm going in there to help Ma!" she whispered. Then she clutched Jack and held on to him tightly. She didn't dare let him loose and she didn't dare leave him. She was safe with him; Jack wouldn't let anything hurt her.

But somehow she made her arms let go. She shut her eyes tight and ran toward the house as fast as she could go. Mary was close behind her. Laura fell down and her eyes popped open; she jumped up and kept on running. She came to the door and slipped into the house without making a sound.

The wild men were standing by the fireplace. Ma was bending over the fire, cooking something, and Carrie's head was hidden in Ma's skirts. Laura meant to run to Ma, but before she got so far she came to the bed and quick as a flash she hid behind the bedpost.

It was just wide enough to hide her eyes against, if she pressed her nose against it. She felt safer there because she couldn't see the Indians. But she couldn't help moving just enough to let one eye peep from behind the bedpost.

First, she saw the wild men's moccasins, then their sinewy, bare, red-brown legs, all the way up. Around their waists the wild men wore narrow leather thongs, and the furry skin of a small animal hung down in front. The fur was striped black and white and it made a horrid smell. It was a fresh skunk skin.

A knife like Pa's hunting knife and a sharp hatchet like Pa's hatchet were tied to each leather thong. Above them the Indians' ribs made little ridges up their bare sides. Their arms were folded on their breasts. At last Laura looked at their faces and she dodged behind the bedpost.

URSULA KOERING

Their faces were bold and strange. Their black eyes glittered. All around their heads where hair grows, these wild men had no hair. Only on top of their heads one tuft of hair stood straight up, and it was wound around with string, and feathers stuck upright in it.

When Laura peeked from the bedpost again, one of those Indians was looking straight at her. Her heart jumped into her throat and choked her. Two black eyes glittered into her eyes. The Indian didn't move, not a muscle of his face moved. Only his eyes twinkled at her. Laura didn't move, either. She didn't even breathe.

The Indian made two harsh sounds in his throat. The other Indian looked at Laura then, and he made one short sound, like "Ha!" Laura hid her eyes again.

After a long time she heard Ma take the cover off the iron bake-oven in the coals. She heard the Indians squat down on the hearth. She heard them eating.

Laura peeked and hid and peeked again while the wild men ate every morsel of the cornbread that Ma had baked. They even picked up the crumbs from the hearth. Ma stood watching them and stroking Carrie's head. Mary stood close behind Ma and held on to her sleeve. All the time Jack's chain was rattling; he was still trying to get loose.

When every crumb was eaten, the Indians stood up. The skunk smell was stronger when they moved. One of them

277

spoke to Ma. Ma looked at him with big
eyes; she did not know what those harsh
sounds meant. She did not say anything.
The Indians turned around and walked
out through the door. Their moccasins
did not make the least sound as they
went.

When they were surely gone, Ma
sighed a long, long sigh. She hugged
Laura tight in one arm and Mary tight
in the other, and through .the window
they watched those wild men going
away, one behind the other, through the
waving tall wild grasses.

"Are you scared, Ma?" Mary asked.

"Well," Ma said, "I'm thankful to
goodness they're gone."

Laura wrinkled her nose. "They smell
awful."

Then they told Ma how they had
come into the house to help her, and Ma
said, "That's my brave little girls."

"Now we must get dinner," she said.
"Pa will be here soon. Mary, bring some
wood. Laura, you may set the table."

The table was made of two slabs of
oak. One end of the slabs was stuck into
a crack between the logs of the wall, and
the other end was held up by pieces of
log. Laura spread a checked red-and-
white cloth on the table, and set on it the
tin plates and tin cups and the steel knives
and forks.

Ma stirred cornmeal and water together to make corn-cakes. She made two
thin cakes, each shaped in a half-circle.
She laid the cakes with their straight sides
together in the round bake-oven, and she
pressed her hand on top of each cake. Pa

URSULA KOERING

278

always said he didn't need any other sweetening, when Ma put the prints of her hands on the cornbread. Then the iron cover was put on the bake-oven and it sat in the hot coals, with more coals raked over the top.

The cornbread was baking and the table was set, when Pa came home. He had killed a big jack rabbit and two prairie hens. He dropped them by the door step, came in with his gun and said, "Whew! What a smell!"

Laura and Mary ran to him, both talking at once and holding to him while he put the gun on its pegs above the door.

"What's all this? What's all this?" he said, rumpling their hair. "So you've seen Indians at last, have you, Laura? I noticed they have a little camp in a valley west of here."

"They took all your tobacco, Charles," Ma said. "And they ate a lot of cornbread. They pointed to the cornmeal and made signs that they were hungry and I was afraid not to cook some."

"You did the right thing," Pa told her. "We don't want to make enemies of any Indians."

"They wore fresh skunk skins, and that was all they wore," said Ma. "We were short of cornmeal, too."

"Oh well. We can hold out awhile yet. And there's plenty of fresh meat running all over the country. Don't worry, Caroline," Pa said.

"But, Charles, they took all your tobacco."

"Never mind," said Pa.

But Laura could not forget the Indians. She said, "If I'd turned Jack loose, he'd 've eaten those smelly Indians right up!"

Pa stopped still. "Did you girls think of turning Jack loose?" he asked in a dreadful voice.

Laura murmured, "Yes, Pa."

"After I told you not to?" Pa said, in a more dreadful voice.

Laura's head hung down and she couldn't speak, but Mary choked, "Yes, Pa."

For a moment Pa was silent. Then he sighed a long sigh like Ma's sigh after the Indians went away.

"After this," he said in a terrible voice, "you girls remember you're to do as you're told. Don't you even think of disobeying me. Do you hear?"

"Yes, Pa," Laura and Mary whispered.

"Do you know what would have happened if you'd turned Jack loose?" Pa asked.

"No, Pa," they whispered.

"We'd be in trouble with the Indians. Bad trouble, do you understand?"

"Would they have killed Jack?" Laura quavered.

"Yes," said Pa. "And worse than that. But all you girls need to know is this: you do as you're told, no matter what happens."

"Yes, Pa," Laura said, and Mary said, "Yes, Pa." They were glad they had not turned Jack loose.

"Do as you're told," said Pa, "and no harm will come to you."

Blue Rocking Chair Tells A Story

By Carolyn Sherwin Bailey

THE blue rocking chair was the most alive piece of furniture that Ann had ever known. Rock, rock, it swayed back and forth. Rock, rock, it walked as it rocked over Great-granny Brown's smooth kitchen floor. The floor was painted gray and Great-granny Brown washed it with slippery soap suds. Across the slippery floor, as Ann sat and rocked, went the blue rocking chair from the window to the table, from the table toward the door, and then back again.

Creak, creak, said the blue rocking chair as Ann rocked her doll in it; creak, creak, as she rocked back and forth. It could talk as well as walk.

"What is the blue rocking chair saying?" Ann asked.

"It is trying to tell you a story, the story of its life," Great-granny Brown said.

"Oh, help it," Ann said.

"Once upon a time," Great-granny Brown began, "a pine tree grew on the side of our mountain. A settler cut down the pine tree. He chopped and sawed it. Then he chose the strongest, smoothest pieces of pine and took them into his log house, there on the side of our mountain, to dry. When winter came, when snow drifted over the windows, the man and his little boy sat in front of their fire with draw-knives and shaped the strong, smooth, dry pieces of pine.

"The boy carved four chair legs. His father carved a chair back and the little boy carved the rungs. Working together they carved a thick chair seat. The boy carved one chair arm and his father carved the other chair arm. Then came the hardest part of the work. On a broad pine board the father drew with a piece of charcoal two chair rockers, just alike, just as curving. Carefully he carved the chair rockers, just alike, just as curving. They put together the parts of the chair —legs, back, rungs, arms, and rockers— with wooden pegs that they had whittled. Last of all they painted the chair red. The little boy's mother sat in the rocking chair in front of the fire. There she knitted and told stories. Creak, creak. Rock, rock. The rocking chair talked and walked along the hearth."

"Then?" said Ann.

"Then," said Great-granny Brown, "the settler father and the mother and the little boy decided to move. They decided to move down our mountain to this valley where Hillsborough was beginning. Yes, our Hillsborough, with a sawmill to cut boards, a grist mill to grind grain, a church, a school, a store, and some frame houses with brick ends. So they loaded their beds and dishes, the table and chest, into their wagon. They hitched the oxen to draw the wagon and they tied the cow to the back. Then they put the red rocking chair in the wagon, and the little boy sat in it to keep it from falling out.

"The chair rocked as the wagon, drawn by the two oxen, bumped and jolted along. So they started down our mountain.

chair, alive and moving, talking to itself, they covered their heads. They ran back into the woods. The oxen pulled the family and their furniture, with the cow walking behind, down the side of our mountain to Hillsborough."

"Then?" asked Ann. Creak, creak, Ann rocked and rocked and the rocking chair went across the kitchen toward the door

"Deep dark woods were on both sides of the road. There were no houses or people. Suddenly a flash of bright feathers showed between the trees. Arrows whizzed about the wagon. Indians whooped as they ran out from the deep dark woods.

"The father drove the oxen faster. The cow trotted to keep up. The little boy rocked bravely—creak, creak—as the Indians made a circle around the wagon. But when the Indians saw the red rocking

to the garden.

"Then," went on Great-granny Brown, "the father and mother and the little boy lived in their own frame house with a brick end here in Hillsborough. They had a red barn, an apple orchard, a corn field, a vegetable garden and a flower garden. They had an iron stove with brass legs in the parlor. The red rocking chair lived in the parlor between the stove and the center table where the Bible and the family picture album lay.

It rocked and rocked, and held the boy until he grew older. Then he was a man and had his own little boy."

"Oh," said Ann.

"And then," went on Great-granny Brown, "the red paint wore off the rocking chair. Patches of wood showed through. The man who had cut down the pine tree and drawn the curving rockers on a pine board was now the grandfather. He liked to sit and rock on the back porch when the sun shone as it does today. He used to rock there in the sunshine, looking at the yellow roses and the golden corn, the gilt weathervane on the church steeple and the yellow leaves when the maple and beech trees turned.

"'We could paint the rocking chair yellow,' the grandfather said one day.

"So the new little boy and his father scraped the old red paint off the rocking chair. They rubbed the pine wood as smooth as glass with sandstone. They bought a pot of bright yellow paint at the store and the grandfather helped as they put three coats of paint on the rocking chair.

"The yellow rocking chair lived on the porch in the summer and in the kitchen in the winter because there were mahogany chairs with slippery hair-cloth seats in the parlor. But wherever it stood, it shone. As glowing as the sun or the gilt weathervane, as bright as an ear of yellow corn, as yellow as an autumn leaf! It rocked faster and moved farther. It creaked more loudly."

"Next?" Ann said.

"That new little boy in the brick-end house here in Hillsborough grew to be a man," said Great-granny Brown. "And he had his own little girl. That made the family happy, for there had not been a little girl in the house in all that time.

mary stevens

282

That new little girl loved the yellow rocking chair. She rocked and rocked in it. She rocked her dolls and her kittens. The little boy who had come in the first place down our mountain, the little boy who had frightened away the Indians as he rode in the rocking chair in the back of the wagon, was now the grandfather. And then the yellow paint wore off the rocking chair. Legs, back, seat, arms, and rockers needed new paint.

"They all knew what color the little girl liked. Blue cornflowers. Blue sky. Blue water. Bluebirds. So the grandfather said:

"'We could paint the rocking chair blue.'

"So the grandfather and the father scraped off the old yellow paint. They rubbed the pine wood smooth with sandstone. They bought a pot of blue paint at the store——"

"Great-granny," Ann interrupted, "this is your doll that I am rocking; your doll with a china head, a dotted muslin dress, and a blue sash. And I rock the barn pussy's kittens in this chair. This is a brick-end house. Were you that girl?"

"Now, how did you guess?" laughed Great-granny Brown.

"Oh, the blue rocking chair told me," Ann laughed back.

Creak, creak, went the blue rocking chair, alive—rocking Ann and Great-granny Brown's doll over the kitchen floor, finishing the story as it rocked.

A Tree of Apples

Written and Illustrated by Lois Lenski

"HAVE a chaw of sassafras!" said Jeddy. "Don't mind if I do," replied Becky. "I'm right partial to sassafras."

Jeddy Hinsdale was a shy, awkward boy whose legs and arms protruded beyond his tight-fitting clothes. He dug deep into his pocket and pulled forth a handful of treasures—a broken-handled knife, a piece of slate pencil, a jew's-harp, some nuts and stones, and last but not least, a piece of washed and scraped sassafras root.

"Here 'tis!" he said, solemnly, holding it out.

Becky took it and put it to her mouth. She began to chew. The sharp sting of the spicy root was pleasant on her tongue.

"It's real strong," she said. Then, putting the root in her pocket, she added, "I'll keep it till after school."

"Oh, chew it! I can get lots more," said Jeddy, boldly, "if you want it, that is. I know where there's lots more down in Cedar Holler. . . ."

Jerome and Tobias Hubbard dashed by. Jeddy did not stop to finish his sentence, but rushed on with the boys. The day was dark and cloudy. It had rained heavily at breakfast time and that meant that most of the boys would be in school. On clear days during the summer term, most of them were kept at home to work in the fields or do other necessary tasks.

As she passed a small house at the corner where the side road branched off the highway, Becky looked up anxiously. It was the home of a widow, Mrs. Ruth Hodges, known to the whole neighborhood as "Aunty Ruth." Her granddaughter, Sally Barber, was ten years old and Becky's best friend. Becky looked now to see if Sally or the teacher, Miss Belinda Ludlow, who was boarding there this week, might be coming out. But she saw no signs of life and knew they must already have gone. She liked to walk to school with them, especially since Fanny's departure. It seemed a long time since Fanny went to Happy Valley and Becky continued to miss her.

"Hurry, Cindy Jane!" cried Becky. She turned to call her little sisters, who were trailing down the road behind her. "Hurry, Polly Prue and Sar'an!"

At the bottom of the hill stood the Fifth District school building. The house of Captain Pennyfeather, a stone's throw away, was the only human dwelling near. The school building was small, of unpainted gray clapboards, with a broad, unhewn rock beneath the door for a step. It stood in a low, damp spot, half in

Captain Pennyfeather's field and half in the road, in the exact geographical center of the district.

As Becky and her sisters came up, she saw Sally Barber and a group of girls standing in the wet dooryard, talking together. Julie Ann Janeway was in the center.

Julie Ann Janeway came to school regularly now and the girls never tired of looking at her. She had such a variety of pretty clothes, there was always something new to see. Even the big girls were impressed, and every day eyed her from top to toe. She was so beautiful, they could not help looking at her. They listened to her talk, too, for even the way she said her words was different and she had amazing tales to tell.

Becky leaned over the heads of several little girls and stared at Julie Ann. She wore a new apron today. It was white

satin and had bright flowers of every color embroidered on it. But that was not all. Julie Ann held out her hand and something sparkled on it. Becky drew in her breath sharply when she saw a gold ring on her finger.

"Yes, these are my birthday presents," said Julie Ann, proudly. "My grandmother sent them from Hartford for my birthday—my satin apron and my ring." She smoothed her apron with the hand that wore the ring.

"A ring!" cried Euphemia Hubbard, pushing forward.

"Yes, a gold ring—real gold," said Julie Ann. She slid it up and down her finger, while the girls watched, speechless.

"But it's too big for you!" cried Sally Barber. "Won't it drop off?"

"Oh, no!" cried Julie Ann. "Well, it is a little large now," she went on. "My grandmother got it that way on purpose.

That's because I'm growing. My finger will soon be fat enough to fit it. You see, a gold ring lasts forever 'n' ever. I expect to keep this one all my life. A gold ring will never wear out!"

"My Ma had a gold bead necklace once," said Lyddy Burton, a tall, quiet girl. "But she lost it when she went on a journey and never found it again."

"Well!" snapped Julie. "I shan't lose my ring even if I do go on a journey and even if I did, I am certain I should find it again!"

"How do you know?" asked Lizy Hubbard with a grin.

Suddenly a boy's voice called: "Watch out! Run!"

The girls forgot Julie Ann's birthday presents as they looked up. All eyes turned in one direction. Near Captain Pennyfeather's house, beside the fence which separated his yard from the school yard, stood a large apple tree, covered with small, yellow sweet apples, called pumpkin sweetings. The tree was full of boys. In response to their vigorous shaking, a shower of apples fell to the ground.

"Watch out! She's coming!" shouted Tobias Hubbard, astride the fence.

Mrs. Pennyfeather, broom in hand, came rushing out of the kitchen door. The boys jumped down, filling hands and pockets with apples, then leaped over the fence to safety. Mrs. Pennyfeather shook her fist and shouted. Then she went back into the house and slammed the door behind her.

The bell rang and all the children passed into the school room. The stolen apples were passed around and soon appeared on most of the desks. The first thing that Miss Belinda did was to ask Tobias Hubbard to read the Apple Fable.

Tobias took his blue-backed speller in hand, rose awkwardly and read:

Of the BOY that stole APPLES.

An old Man found a rude Boy upon one of his trees stealing Apples, and desired him to come down; but the young Sauce-box told him plainly that he would not.

"Won't you?" said the old Man. "Then I will fetch you down;" so he pulled up some tufts of Grass and threw at him; but this only made the Youngster laugh, to think the old Man should pretend to beat him down from the tree with grass only.

Tobias paused to draw breath. A titter ran around the room. Then he continued:

"Well, well," said the old Man. "If neither words nor grass will do, I must try what virtue there is in Stones": so the old Man pelted him heartily with stones, which soon made the young Chap hasten down from the tree and beg the old Man's pardon.

MORAL
"If good words and gentle means will not reclaim the wicked, they must be dealt with in a more severe manner."

Tobias coughed once or twice, then sat down. The tittering began but stopped suddenly, for in through the door walked Captain Pennyfeather, tall, dark and very angry. He stormed and fumed over the theft of his apples, while the children, boys and all, cowered in their seats. Then he turned to Miss Belinda and asked her what she was going to do about it.

Miss Belinda stood timidly behind her desk, as if she, too, were afraid. The huge size of Captain Pennyfeather made her look very small.

"Will all those . . . will all those who took Captain Pennyfeather's apples please rise?" she asked in a trembling voice.

Silence filled the room. Even the tiny children on the low benches in front made not a sound. A shuffle was heard and a boy rose to his feet. It was Jeddy Hinsdale. His face was pale and he began to stammer: "I . . . er . . . we . . ." Then Tobias Hubbard, in the seat behind, pulled him smartly by the coat tail. Jeddy sat down abruptly.

Miss Belinda waited a moment. Then she asked Becky to gather up the apples from the desks. From the entry she brought two lunch baskets which she had emptied of their contents. One or two of the boys grabbed an apple and stowed it into a safe pocket. Presenting the filled baskets, Miss Belinda apologized for the boys.

Captain Pennyfeather, frowning heavily, stopped at the door and said: "A change of teachers is needed here. I shall see the school committee about it." Then he stalked out.

All through the nooning hour it rained. The children sat about uncomfortably, talking in whispers about the Pennyfeathers. When the afternoon session began, Julie Ann Janeway stood up, flushed and excited, and Becky knew that Miss Belinda's troubles were not yet over.

"Oh, teacher! Teacher!" cried Julie Ann. "My ring is gone! My gold ring is gone!"

"Gone?" asked Miss Belinda, with a sinking heart. Becky saw that she turned pale.

"My beautiful gold ring! Somebody has stolen it!" Julie Ann did not look beautiful any more. Her curls were very stringy and her face was streaked with tears.

Miss Belinda questioned all the boys and girls, but no one had seen the ring. Miss Belinda was at her wits' end. Why was the child so foolish as to wear such finery to school? Ring or no ring, work must proceed.

Then Euphemia Hubbard walked up to Miss Belinda's desk, *Dobell's* Arithmetic in hand. Feemy was thirteen and the smartest girl in school. She loved arithmetic and boasted that she knew more about it than her teacher. She liked to ask questions which she knew Miss Belinda could not answer.

Feemy bent over Miss Belinda's desk, open book in hand. She asked her question in a loud voice, as she pointed to a spot on the page.

Miss Belinda jumped to her feet and spoke in a stern voice: "Euphemia Hubbard! Is that not Julie Ann's ring on your finger?"

A hubbub of excitement filled the room as the children stared in amazement.

"Yes, ma'am!" admitted Feemy. She grinned at her sister, Lizy, in the back of the room. "Lizy found it. Julie Ann's grandma got it too loose," she declared. "It dropped right off her finger into the mud, while the boys was a-stealin' the apples."

"Why did you not say you had it, Euphemia, when I first inquired?" asked Miss Belinda.

Feemy giggled. Then she said sullenly: "If Lizy hadn't a picked it up, 'twould'a been tramped on in the mud."

After school, Becky sent the little girls on home with Sally Barber and waited for Miss Belinda. It was the teacher's last day at Aunty Ruth's. She was coming to board at the parsonage for the next two weeks and Becky wanted to help her carry her bundles.

When they reached the Hodges house, Miss Belinda sat down on the doorstep suddenly as if she were very tired. Becky sat down, too, and put her arm about her teacher's waist. Then she saw that Miss Belinda was crying. She took her hand and held it tight. What a dreadful day it had been!

"I suppose . . ." said Miss Belinda, tearfully, "Captain Pennyfeather was right. A change of teachers is needed. I . . . just . . . can't go on!"

"Oh, Miss Belinda!" cried Becky. "You won't . . . go away and leave us! I always like the summer term the best, because you are the teacher. Why, I would stop going to school right away if you left!"

"Aw, please don't, Miss Belinda!"

Becky was surprised to hear a boy's voice close at hand. She looked up and there was Jeddy Hinsdale. He must have come quietly up the road behind them. He twisted and turned his hat in his clumsy hands. Then he said, "Don't go and leave us! The boys didn't mean anything!"

The door behind them opened and Sally and Aunty Ruth came out.

"I declare! It's a shame!" cried Aunty Ruth. She was a small energetic, quick-moving woman, with sharp dark eyes.

And she was known as a woman who did not fear to speak her mind. "That Pennyfeather! I never saw the beat of him!" Sally had told her grandmother all about it. "And those Hubbard girls! They just try to do all they can to plague you."

"It just seems like I can't . . . go on teaching," said Miss Belinda, sadly. "Why, I'm all worn out just from today. How can I go back tomorrow and face them?"

"The sun will be shining tomorrow," said Aunty Ruth cheerfully, "and all the boys will have to stay at home and work. Things always look better after a good night's sleep, anyhow. As for the apple fights, I'll tell you what I'll do. Do you see that tree down there by the fence? That's a *Seek-no-further* apple tree and it's loaded with apples. I'll *give* that tree to the 5th district school children!"

"Give them the tree?" asked Miss Belinda, puzzled.

"Yes!" said Aunty Ruth, her eyes snapping. "For their very own! There will be apples enough to last them a long, long time."

Becky and Sally and Jeddy jumped up and down happily. "A tree of apples for the 5th district school!" they cried. "How wonderful! A tree for our very own!"

"I'll put up a sign on the tree," said Aunt Ruth, nodding her head vigorously. "It will say:

NOTICE CHILDREN OF
THE 5th DISTRICT SCHOOL
Help Yourselves to Apples
This Tree Belongs to YOU!"

"Why, Aunty Ruth!" cried Miss Belinda, forgetting her sadness. "You are doing a wonderful thing—an unheard-of thing! Your name will go down in the history of Blueberry Corners! Your grandchildren and great-grandchildren will talk about this. Other people have always had fights with school children to keep them from stealing their apples. But you have given them a tree for their own!"

"Stuff and nonsense!" cried Aunty Ruth. "There's nothing wonderful about it. I just think children should have all the apples they can eat. So there!"

Miss Belinda gathered up her belongings and said goodbye to Aunty Ruth and Sally and Jeddy Hinsdale. She and Becky walked slowly to the parsonage.

Becky looked at Miss Belinda and knew that she was happy again. She knew that her teacher no longer feared the rest of the summer term. She could go on teaching, for every day she would see rows of Aunty Ruth's shiny, rosy-cheeked apples, sitting on the children's desks and her own. The apples would always be a reminder. Becky knew that Miss Belinda's courage had come back to her, strengthened and renewed by the love of her good friends.

Becky thought of Mrs. Hodges' bright smile and cheerful unselfish ways. What a wonderful woman she was! No wonder everybody called her "Aunty Ruth." She was "Aunty" to all, because she had more than enough love in her heart to go round.

Barnum's First Circus

By Laura Benét

"Phineas," remarked his father, pushing back his coffee cup and carefully wiping the ends of his walrus mustache, "you can tend store for me mebbe two or three days. The mare's going to take your mother and me to the county seat." He looked across the table at his thirteen-year-old son with decision.

Phineas Taylor Barnum, a stocky, broad-shouldered lad bursting with vitality, stopped munching a doughnut and his eyes danced. This piece of news was too good to be true. He had often helped his father in the store, but to have it in charge . . . that would be wonderful!

"Yes, sir," he answered, respectfully.

His father went briskly on with the tale of his instructions: "If Noah Totten's drinking, don't give him credit. And don't give the Widow Sweeney any, neither. Cash in hand is the rule, unless circumstances is a mite unusual. Seeing apples is good this year, you can take two or three barrels in exchange for groceries. But, remember, business is likely to be brisk and you're to tend to your job and not talk your head off. You've got a good head on your shoulders when you choose to use it. That's all. And don't make me use that strap hanging up in the barn when I come back Saturday." His own keen eyes twinkled slightly.

Having delivered this ultimatum, Barnum Senior, citizen of the town of Bethel, Connecticut, went to "hitch up." Barnum Junior, rejoicing in his unexpected freedom from school, put on his hat and took his way to his father's small corner store that was the town's greatest resource.

The day being October and a chill wind blowing, he began his business day by doing what his father would have said was needless extravagance. He started a fire in the rusty iron stove in the center of the store. The fire, made out of shavings, old boxes, and good hard cordwood, had not been going fifteen minutes before Phineas' first customer arrived.

It was the Widow Sweeney, shawled and bonneted, peering out of near-sighted pinkish-rimmed eyes that were much like a rabbit's. She slammed the store door behind her so that everything on the shelves rattled and, delighted by the good fire, crept near it, untying her bonnet strings.

"Well, if it ain't Barnum's boy!" she ejaculated in a pleased tone. "The son should be much easier to deal with than the father," she thought.

"Now, I want you," she continued, consulting a list, "to tie up a pound of white sugar and a parcel of apples and raisins and two pounds of coffee and a pound of rice and a pint of sorghum molasses."

Young Barnum went to the shelves and began weighing out the various articles, to which the Widow Sweeney kept adding other items. At last everything was ready. In his pleasantest tone, he stated: "One dollar, if you please, Missus Sweeney."

The widow started back. "No sass from you, Phineas Barnum. This is on credit, today. I'm a poor woman and I pay up my bills, all at once, twice a year."

"Pa said 'no credit'—that I was to take cash only," answered Pa's representative. "I'm sorry but you've got a long credit column already, Missus Sweeney."

Finding her first method of bluster did not work, the widow began to wheedle: "Now, you're a good boy and not raised for impudence. Haven't I got the nicest little calf only two weeks old that I was calculating on giving your Pa in payment if he'd continue my credit a while."

"Is it an all-right calf?" asked the youthful storekeeper bluntly.

"Of course it's all right. It's as pretty as can be. But it's got a curious failing—an extra eye."

"Oh!" Joy gleamed in Phineas' own eyes. If he could only get hold of that calf for purposes of his own! "Pa's been wanting a calf," he answered. "Is it a bull?"

"No, a heifer."

"Well, marm—" He hesitated, the thought of his father's ready strap at the back of his mind, but decided he'd have to take a chance. "If you'll let me stop around tonight and see it when I close up store, I can let you have these things now."

The delighted widow assented, warmed herself thoroughly at the stove, and then went on her way. Meanwhile, Phineas Barnum resolved inwardly to "show off" that three-eyed calf behind their barn at a penny a peep—or maybe he'd make it two cents for a look. What a find for the show he was planning!

His next customer was a red-headed boy, younger than himself, who painfully lugged in two pecks of apples to be exchanged for potatoes. As he set the half-bushel basket down with a thump, a snake glided across the uneven, splintered floor toward the heat.

"Hi, help me get him, Phin! He must-a got out of my pocket!" screeched Hiram Fletcher.

Young Barnum recaptured the snake in a wink, stowing him in a small and dark box. "Can you do tricks with him?" he inquired interestedly.

"Only caught him yesterday, so how'm I to know?" said Hiram, surprised at the idea.

"Bring him around to my house Saturday afternoon. Meet me behind the barn. We'll have a circus," said Phineas in an excited whisper. He saw three farmers entering, bent on leisurely purchases and conversation. "There's lots of things I can tell you, but I've got to tend store now."

Hiram chuckled. "I'll see you later and I'll get Rafe and George and Buckle Ewing, too."

Farmers were apt to stay indefinitely on such a raw day. Phineas prepared for them by fetching out a couple of rickety wooden stools (the third could perch on the molasses barrel) and mending the fire. He brought out a jug of new cider.

"Hey, Phineas," said the first farmer, Ezra Drean, a hard-bitten Yankee with rugged features and a long jaw. "Give me a plug of chewing tobacco?"

The busy young storekeeper cut it and was paid. "One nickel more," he requested briskly.

Ezra dumped his weather-beaten purse out on the counter for inspection. Not a cent was in it.

"I'll give you a hopping bean instead, boy!" he offered. "I know you like tricks."

"But does it really hop? Lemme see for sure."

Ezra winked at the other men and produced a small brown object from his pocket. Placing it on the bottom of a broken cracker box, he carried it to the stove. Yes, the heat caused it to skip about here and there on the piece of board. The dance was uncanny. The farmers stood and watched interestedly.

"Ain't seen a contraption like that in a month of Sundays," said the oldest of the three, Mose Painter.

Phineas put it carefully into his pocket. "Thank you kindly," he capitulated, and the bean owner joined his friends at the fire. The other two farmers, whom Barnum's son knew to be prosperous, would buy later and pay good greenbacks. They didn't need to bargain.

Phineas returned to ladle out brown sugar for Eliza Streeter.

"Look out for that sugar, now," said the stout woman, tartly. "You ain't giving me good measure, pressed down and running over, as the scripture says. Don't you be skimping!"

The boy nodded amiably and overweighed the brown sugar, though he knew what his father would have said. The sugar, damp from recent wet weather, packed down easily.

As he waited on children, giggling schoolgirls, shrewd New England matrons (for the store had filled up), Phineas caught snatches of conversation from the group of farmers.

"Just try walking easy by that mill, come twilight, and you'll hear a voice, a high, queer voice, like a spirit's," was one statement.

"I swan. I didn't know the old mill was haunted."

"Well, 'tis, and Steve Carter's lost his watch chain and swears he had it when he was going by there, week or so ago."

"Time some one got to the bottom of this," said Mose Painter.

Then they began discussing Simon Pearce's affairs. "That dog of his ran through town the other day looking mighty suspicious. It might be mad and folks should look out for it."

The very same evening Phineas, who had been to see Widow Sweeney's three-eyed calf and agreed on a transfer, took a walk past the old Franklin mill on the village outskirts. He didn't believe what the men at the store had said, and, anyway, he was more curious than afraid. In the moonlight the stone mill looked as peaceful as the stream that flowed beside it. Suddenly, from an upper window of the mill came conversational tones.

"Good boy," uttered a clipped, mocking voice, and then a dark shadow flew past him. Something with straw clinging to it jingled at his feet. Squatting on a stone, Phineas drew from his pocket a bit of bread and a cheese rind he kept for just such emergencies. The shadow drew nearer and perched on his finger. It was a raven!

"Good night," it said, "good night, good night. Have no fear, no fear."

Adroitly Phineas caught it, slipped it into a bag he had brought, and picked up the object on the ground. It was nothing less than Steve Carter's gold watch chain! What a surprise Steve would have on Saturday.

The raven would be a great addition to the side-show for which Phineas could not yet persuade Amos Tutt, the man with the longest beard in the village, to be the Bearded Giant. But this raven was a find and he could teach it to talk in no time. It must have flown over from some other township where some one else had begun its education. He might rent a skull for it to perch on, if there was one handy. There was never going to be another exhibition like this one. No, sir!

Next morning Phineas had Hiram and George, his brother and side-partner, take a brisk turn about Bethel. One went east, one west, until they covered the town. In their hands they carried a pile of hand-printed advertisements that were stuck under front doors or pushed at any one they happened to meet.

After three long days of storekeeping, Phineas had collected a goodly sum in his father's till as well as half-a-dozen barrels of fall pippins. Now it was Saturday noon. His father was still away, but he'd done his level best and at three o'clock he planned to close up the store until evening.

"Barnum's Saturday Show" was opening at four o'clock for a nickel's admission and a penny apiece extra for special side-shows. Of course it couldn't begin until Phineas appeared.

The crowd that gathered at the back of the Barnums' barn at four o'clock that day was enormous. At a rude turnstile made of two crossed laths stood Barnum's boy himself, hair tousled, face red with excitement.

"This way, ladies and gentlemen," he shouted, "to see the Three-Eyed Calf, the only specimen of its kind in captivity. Meet Jupiter, the Domestic Snake that snuggles up to you like an infant! See the Magic Bean worked by Unseen Force, and Lupo the Raven, that talks and brings forth gold. Last chance, cash and tickets!"

"That boy of Barnum's has the gift of gab," said the tired mother of two fretting children. "First-rate showman! He'll make money or I miss my guess."

Farmers, curious to see, were driving up in carts and buggies, with children between their knees. Big boys were stamping in leading younger brothers and sisters by the hand.

"This way, this way, to the calf. Put your money on the Three-Eyed Calf," called one of Barnum's assistants.

He was instantly corrected by Phineas who shouted, "Say a lot more, Hi, about its unusual points—like this: 'The One and Only Calf in Captivity that has an Extra Eye'!"

Meantime a fearless brother, younger than Phineas, was riding Zeke, the runaway colt, around a chalked ring, sticking on its back despite frantic kickings and plungings. This feature, the only ten-cent one, was marvelously popular. When Bethel's crop of dimes had been taken in, the raven was produced.

"Step up here," announced the showman to late comers, "plenty of room to stand. Step up!" Then, "What do you like best, Lupo?" he asked the raven which he held up on an improvised stand.

"Gold," said Lupo in a hoarse and impressive tone.

"What next to that?"

"Chain," croaked the raven.

"And then?"

"Gold chain."

"Now. Tell the gentleman whose watch chain you took that you're sorry."

"Sor-ry," croaked the raven, and Steve

Carter, eyes popping, was beckoned forward to receive his missing watch chain. "I *swan*," was all he could say.

As a final feature, the hopping bean began gamboling briskly on a table. Young Phineas had learned exactly how much heat to give it from his warm, perspiring palm.

Home-made doughnuts and cider were being circulated to the still admiring crowd when hoofs were heard approaching and a tired mare came into view on the far side of the barn. In the buggy were the substantial shoulders of Pa Barnum, his wife by his side.

Barnum Senior's astonishment when he saw the gathering on the lot back of his barn was followed by a grim expression about the jaw. That fool boy of his, who was so keen on freaks and shows, had gone and closed up the store (yes, it was shut and silent when he passed it) and lost the tide of the late Saturday afternoon trade. He'd show him! He could not help being perked up over his son's talents, but he'd have to teach him a lesson for all that.

"Phineas," he called in tones to wake the dead, "you come here and stop this fooling."

Some little distance away he seemed to see a familiar form, to hear a familiar voice saying "Calf."

Calf! Was it possible there was a new

295

heifer? Excitedly, Barnum stopped the buggy, threw the reins to his wife, got out and stamped over to the circus enclosure.

"Nickel, please, Mister Barnum," requested the gate-keeper. Inwardly raging, Barnum paid it and continued his search.

"Excuse me, folks," he kept saying until suddenly, in a pen near him, he saw one of the finest little heifer calves. It was sound in wind and limb, the only defect being a curious third eye immediately over the regular one on the left side.

"Where on earth did Phineas . . . ?"

Then father and son met face to face. Young Barnum's look was as bland as cream. "Hey, Pa," he said. "See the calf you got from the Widow Sweeney."

"How much did you have to give for it?" roared his father.

"Not a penny. It was a present in payment."

"Well—and what do you have to say about closing the store and losing my Saturday afternoon trade?"

"I was going to reopen this evening," said Phineas confidently, "and what I've taken in here on entrances will make up for any loss. I've got a good sight of money in here, Pa, and it's all yours!" He gleefully rattled the contents of a tin can.

Parent looked at son with sudden added respect.

"You've not cheated any one to get hold of these critters?" Barnum Senior indicated in one sweeping gesture, the calf, the raven, the snake and the colt. "I nearly stepped on that blamed snake," he exploded as it wiggled near his boots.

"No, Pa, I didn't cheat. I only quit the store an hour or so."

His father scratched his head. "You always had smartness in you," he said.

Young Barnum looked triumphantly around. The crowd was scattering. His father had made up with him and gone peering into this box and that pen to see what else he could see.

But, somehow, the barn lot wasn't quite large enough. Some day there must be a big white tent pegged down at the corners —or maybe a hall. In his imagination such a hall swelled and grew bigger until he had it peopled with weird shapes. He'd like a family of dwarfs—a mummy—a giant—and a voice that would fill space with its ringing music and make echoes come out of the air. Some day he'd have that, too!

CIRCUS PARADE

By James S. Tippett

HERE it comes! Here it comes!
I can hear the music playing;
I can hear the beating drums.
On parade! On parade!
Gaily plumed a horse and rider
Lead the circus cavalcade.
Knights in armor with their banners
Calmly riding by;
Horses hung with velvet trappings,
Stepping proudly high;
Circus wagons slowly clanking,
Drawn by six horse teams,
Red and gold and set with mirrors
Where the sunlight gleams;
Yawning lions in their cages;

Polar bear with swinging head;
Restless tiger pacing pacing
Back and forth with noiseless tread;
Horses snorting and cavorting
With wild yelling cowboy bands;
Dressed-up monkeys riding ponies,
Bowing as we clap our hands;
Herds of elephants and camels,
Marching one by one;
Troops of painted clowns advancing,
Playing tricks, and making fun.
At the end the steam calliope
Comes in playing all too soon,
Saying the parade is over
As it pipes its wildest tune.

Fung's Fourth

By *Lavinia Davis*

IT WAS the Fourth of July and a perfectly beautiful day. It was cool and clear and the sunlight on the lake in the park broke up into a hundred dancing little sparklers.

Wang Fung hurried to the meeting place at the end of one of the park paths. He could see that Bonny and Pierre and Amos and Marta were all ahead of him. Fung ran as fast as his short fat little legs could paddle. All his life Fung had heard stories about the Fourth of July. He knew that the Fourth of July was Independence Day. He knew it was the day that meant you could be free and happy in America.

"Hurry, Fung," shouted the boys.

"Hurry up, Fung," Tim O'Grady called louder than any of the others. "We're going to have a parade."

They started their parade right then and there around all the statues in the park. They walked by two's so as not to disturb other people and they made a fine long line. First of all they came to the statue of Count Casimir Pulaski.

"And who in the world was he?" asked Tim spelling out the name.

Jan Matchak stepped out of line and his dark eyes beamed with pride. "Why, he was a Pole," he said, "like my people. He came over here to help America get free. He was a General in the Revolutionary War."

Fung looked at Jan as they started to march on. Fung liked to see people happy and Jan looked very happy indeed. Fung didn't blame him. It must be grand to pass a statue of one of your father's countrymen who was a General in the American army.

They marched on past the lake and up the hill until they came to a statue of the Marquis de Lafayette. This time nobody had to ask who he was but Pierre told them anyhow.

Pierre stuttered and it took him quite a long time to tell his story but Fung waited for the very last word. It was rude to interrupt when people talked about their ancestors and for today, anyway, Lafayette, who was French, was a sort of ancestor of Pierre's.

They came to the statue of Columbus, and John, Tony, and Rosa who were all

Italians, took turns telling about him. Finally they came to the big statue of Carl Schurz, and little Marta Ludwig, whose family had just come from Germany, told about him. "Carl Schurz was German," Marta said. "And he came to America to be free. Then he was American as I am."

Little Fung liked Marta's speech so much he thought about it all through their picnic lunch. He wished he could point to something and say it was American the way he was.

It didn't have to be a statue. In fact, when the police marched in the park parade after lunch, Tim pointed out that most of them were Irish-Americans the way he was. Fung envied Tim even more than Marta.

Even the games they played after the parade seemed to belong to the other children more than to Fung. There was "Taffy was a Welshman" and "Ach du lieber Augustin" and "London Bridge is Falling Down." By the time it was suppertime, Fung felt just the least little bit lonely.

It wasn't anyone's fault. All the other children were as friendly as could be. "Be sure and come back tonight, Fung," several had called. "Be sure and come back for the celebration."

As Fung walked home, he wasn't at all sure that he wanted to come back to the celebration. It would be like the statues and the policemen and the games. It would be Scotch-American or Swedish-American or French-American but never Chinese-American.

Fung ate his supper of rice without saying much. "You had better have a rest before you go out again," Fung's mother said. "You look tired."

"Perhaps I won't go out," Fung said.

Fung's mother shook her head. "Oh, but that wouldn't be polite," she said. "Mrs. Kung Li promised last week to take you tonight and you said you wanted to go. It would be rude not to."

Fung went to his rest feeling just a bit cross. Mother was right, of course. He had told Mrs. Kung he would go. And he had wanted to go. It was just that now he had had too much of things being American this and American that and never American from China.

When he was finally out in the dark with Mrs. Kung, Fung was glad he had come. For one thing, the park looked strange and exciting at night. The statues looked big and scary and even the trees seemed mysterious. Fung stayed close to Mrs. Kung until they got to the lake where the celebration was to be.

Then he saw Pierre and Amos and Marta and lots of other children with their mothers and fathers or grown-up friends. Fung started to say "Hello" but before he could get it out of his mouth the celebration started. It was a fireworks celebration put on by the city. Fung's "Hello" was just a round "O" of surprise and pleasure as he watched the first rocket swirling up into the sky.

There was another rocket and another, then a giant salute that spangled the sky with a golden spray of fire. Then there were pinwheels and wonderful red, white, and blue balls of light that dropped down, down, down to earth on little white parachutes. There were more rockets and then a whole polar bear made of little lights and a beautiful flashing waterfall. Finally at the very end, there was a great big beautiful American Flag.

Mrs. Kung clapped her hands and Fung clapped his hands and all the other children and grown-ups clapped their hands.

"Oh boy, that was great," Amos said.

"Sure was," said Tim. "Who'd you suppose ever thought of fireworks?"

Fung knew. He hadn't thought of it before but he did know. His little oval face broadened into a grin. "Why, the Chinese," he said. "My father's countrymen thought of it. They thought up fire-works many, many years ago."

"That. is right," said Mrs. Kung as everyone jostled against everyone else on the way home.

"That is truly right," said Marta's mother.

"Sure 'tis right," said Police Sergeant O'Grady who was Tim's father.

Fung didn't say another word. But how happy he was! The fireworks were Chinese. The Fourth of July was American. Fireworks on the Fourth of July made a perfect Chinese-American celebration. Fung felt that the country from which his father came had given a wonderful present to the country where he lived— the country he loved tonight more than he ever had before.

Willie's Good Recess

By Lavinia Davis

WILLOUGHBY RUFUS SNOW was small and dark and, right now, he was cold and unhappy. He was the smallest boy in the second grade of a big public school. He was the only black boy and he was the only boy who wasn't enjoying recess.

The second grade, along with three other grades, always had recess in the great big high-ceilinged gym. The gym was awfully big. Bigger than three good-sized barns. It was also cold. Willie Snow, who had left the nice warm climate of Georgia only three weeks ago, shivered and felt very cold and lonely indeed.

None of the other children seemed to mind the gym being cold. They liked it because they moved so fast they kept warm anyway. Some played dodge ball, others played bat ball. And at one end of the gym a whole lot of them roller-skated with a loud grinding noise of skates.

Willie watched them from out of one corner. He didn't know how to play dodge ball. He didn't know how to play bat ball, and he didn't even own a pair of roller-skates. Willie shivered and wished he were back in Georgia where the sun was warm and the children were his friends.

Finally Willie got so cold that his teeth chattered and he had to move around to get warm. He walked around the huge gym until he came to the stage at one end. Willie was just going to walk past when he saw the big drum. Sometimes the high school orchestra left their instruments on the stage between rehearsals and this was one of those times.

Willie walked straight up to that drum. It was big and beautiful with School Band painted in red letters on the sides. Willie looked at it and looked at it, and just then Willie's teacher came by. Willie looked up at the teacher and then he looked at the drum. "Please, Miss Carter," Willie said almost without meaning to, "could I play that drum?"

"Yes," said Miss Carter. "If you are very, very careful."

Miss Carter walked on past the stage but Willie didn't see her go. He didn't see anything but that great big beautiful drum that drew him like a magnet. He picked up a drumstick and tapped the drum very lightly. There was a surprised little "boom" like the croak of a bull frog.

Willie beamed. He tapped the drum harder. "Boom!" That was a good sharp boom like the slam of a door. This time Willie really swung the drumstick. BB-OOO-MM. The deep shivery sound grew like thunder. Willie stopped the noise with his hand, though it sounded wonderful. He held the drumsticks lightly now and tapped very gently. The

beam on Willie's face grew wider. Willie was feeling his way. *Tap-tappa-tap*. Slowly, gradually the tune came. It was as though the drumsticks were leading and Willie's small swaying body just naturally followed.

The tune unfolded in Willie's mind. He no longer heard the shouts of the other children. All Willie heard was a song his father used to sing.

Willie Snow hummed the words to himself and beat the strong familiar tune on the drum. When he got to the chorus Willie had forgotten everything except the big drum and the wonderful rolling sounds that came from it.

Willie wasn't cold any more. Willie wasn't small any more, and he certainly wasn't lonely. Willie was part of a great big wonderful flood of sound that was coming out of that drum.

When the clanging bell that meant the end of recess finally sounded out over the gym and even over the roll of Willie's drum, he was surprised. He was so surprised that he just stood with a drumstick in each hand while the last rumble of the drum melted away with the clanging of the bell.

Then Willie saw Miss Carter and the other children. They had stopped playing ball. They had stopped roller-skating. They had even stopped shouting and talking. They had all crowded around the edge of the platform and were looking up at Willie. Now, all of a sudden they broke into a great noisy burst of applause that was even bigger and noisier than the school bell.

He didn't know what to make of it. He looked at Miss Carter and she was clapping too. Finally she stopped and moved over beside him. "Thank you, Willie," she said. "Thank you very much. We all loved the concert."

Willie gave a little gasp of surprise.

They were clapping for him! All those big children, who were used to this big school, were clapping for him and the sounds he brought out of that fine, round drum! They too liked that drum and the good song Willie's father used to sing.

Willie stood on one foot and then on the other but he didn't know what to say. "Did you have a good recess?" Miss Carter asked. Willie nodded his head excitedly.

"Oh yes, Miss Carter," he said. "I did."

"So did we all," said Miss Carter. "Thanks to you, Willie."

On the way upstairs Johnny Griswold gave him a little poke. "Say, Willie, how's chances to teach me how to roll that drum?" he asked.

Willie grinned. "Sure thing, Johnny, if you show me how to play dodge ball."

"It's a deal. Tomorrow at recess."

Willie was feeling very good indeed.

Elizabeth Ann Fails in an Examination

By Dorothy Canfield Fisher

SOMETHING perfectly dreadful had happened in school that day. The Superintendent, the all-important, seldom-seen Superintendent, came to visit the school and the children were given some examinations so he could see how they were getting on.

Now, you know what an examination did to Elizabeth Ann. Or haven't I told you yet?

Well, if I haven't, it's because words fail me. If there is anything horrid that an examination *did*n't do to Elizabeth Ann, I have yet to hear of it. It began years ago, before ever she went to school, when she heard Aunt Frances talking about how *she* had dreaded examinations when she was a child, and how they dried up her mouth and made her ears ring and her head ache and her knees get all weak and her mind a perfect blank, so that she didn't know what two and two made. Of

course Elizabeth Ann didn't feel *all* those things right off at her first examination, but by the time she had had several and had rushed to tell Aunt Frances about how awful they were and the two of them had sympathized with one another and compared symptoms and then wept about her resulting low marks, why, she not only had all the symptoms Aunt Frances had ever had, but a good many more of her own invention.

Well, she had had them all and had them hard this afternoon, when the Superintendent was there. Her mouth had gone dry and her knees had shaken and her elbows had felt as though they had no more bones in them than so much jelly, and her eyes had smarted, and oh, what answers she had made! That dreadful tight panic had clutched at her throat whenever the Superintendent had looked at her, and she had disgraced herself ten times over. She went hot and cold to think of it, and felt quite sick with hurt vanity. She who did so well every day and was so much looked up to by her classmates, what *must* they be thinking of her! To tell the truth, she had been crying as she walked along through the woods, because she was so sorry for herself. Her eyes were all red still, and her throat sore from the big lump in it.

And now she would live it all over again as she told the Putney cousins. For of course they must be told. She had always told Aunt Frances everything that happened in school. It happened that Aunt Abigail had been taking a nap when she got home from school, and so she had come out to the sap-house, where Cousin Ann and Uncle Henry were making syrup, to have it over with as soon as possible. She went up to the little slab house now, dragging her feet and hanging her head, and opened the door.

Cousin Ann, in a very short old skirt and a man's coat and high rubber boots, was just poking some more wood into the big fire which blazed furiously under the broad, flat pan where the sap was boiling. The rough, brown hut was filled with white steam and that sweetest of all odors, hot maple syrup. Cousin Ann turned her head, her face red with the heat of the fire, and nodded at the child.

"Hello, Betsy, you're just in time. I've saved out a cupful of hot syrup for you, all ready to wax."

Betsy hardly heard this, although she had been wild about waxed sugar on snow ever since her very first taste of it. "Cousin Ann," she said unhappily, "the Superintendent visited our school this afternoon."

"Did he?" said Cousin Ann, dipping a thermometer into the boiling syrup.

"Yes, and we had *examinations!*" said Betsy.

"Did you?" said Cousin Ann, holding the thermometer up to the light and looking at it.

"And you know how perfectly awful examinations make you feel," said Betsy, very near to tears again.

"Why, no," said Cousin Ann, sorting over syrup tins. "They never made me feel awful. I thought they were sort of fun."

"*Fun!*" cried Betsy, indignantly, staring through the beginnings of her tears.

"Why, yes. Like taking a dare, don't you know. Somebody stumps you to jump off the hitching-post, and you do it to show 'em. I always used to think examinations were like that. Somebody stumps you to spell 'pneumonia,' and you do it to show 'em. Here's your cup of syrup. You'd better go right out and wax it while it's hot."

Elizabeth Ann automatically took the cup in her hand, but she did not look at it. "But supposing you get so scared you can't spell 'pneumonia' or anything else!" she said feelingly. "That's what happened to me. You know how your mouth gets all dry and your knees . . ." She stopped. Cousin Ann had said she did *not* know all about those things. "Well, anyhow, I got so scared I could hardly stand *up!* And I made the most awful mistakes—things I know just as *well!* I spelled 'doubt' without any b and 'separate' with an e, and I said Iowa was bounded on the north by *Wisconsin,* and I . . ."

"Oh, well," said Cousin Ann, "it doesn't matter if you really know the right answers, does it? That's the important thing."

This was an idea which had never in all her life entered Betsy's brain and she did not take it in now. She only shook her head miserably and went on in a doleful tone. "And I said 13 and 8 are *22!* and I wrote March without any capital M, and I . . ."

"Look here, Betsy, do you *want* to tell me all this?" Cousin Ann spoke in the quick, ringing voice she had once in a while which made everybody, from old Shep up, open his eyes and get his wits about him. Betsy gathered hers and thought hard; and she came to an unexpected conclusion. No, she didn't really want to tell Cousin Ann all about it. Why was she doing it? Because she thought that was the thing to do. "Because if you don't really want to," went on Cousin Ann, "I don't see that it's doing anybody any good. I guess Hemlock Mountain will stand right there just the same even if you did forget to put a b in 'doubt.' And your syrup will be too cool to wax right if you don't take it out pretty soon."

She turned back to stoke the fire, and Elizabeth Ann, in a daze, found herself walking out of the door. It fell shut after her, and there she was under the clear, pale-blue sky, with the sun just hovering over the rim of Hemlock Mountain. She looked up at the big mountains, all blue and silver with shadows and snow, and wondered what in the world Cousin Ann had meant. Of course Hemlock Mountain would stand there just the same. But what of it? What did that have to do with her arithmetic, with anything? She had failed in her examination, hadn't she?

She found a clean white snow-bank under a pine-tree, and, setting her cup of syrup down in a safe place, began to pat the snow down hard to make the right bed for the waxing of the syrup. The sun, very hot for that late March day, brought out strongly the tarry perfume of the big pine-tree. Near her the sap dripped musically into a bucket, already half full, hung

on a maple-tree. A blue-jay rushed suddenly through the upper branches of the wood, his screaming and chattering voice sounding like noisy children at play.

Elizabeth Ann took up her cup and poured some of the thick, hot syrup out on the hard snow, making loops and curves as she poured. It stiffened and hardened at once, and she lifted up a great coil of it, threw her head back, and let it drop into her mouth. Concentrated sweetness of summer days was in that mouthful, part of it still hot and aromatic, part of it icy and wet with melting snow. She crunched it all together into a delicious, big lump and sucked on it dreamily, her eyes on the rim of Hemlock Mountain, high above her there, the snow on it bright golden in the sunlight. Uncle Henry had promised to take her up to the top as soon as the snow went off. She wondered what the top of a mountain would be like. Uncle Henry had said the main thing was that you could see so much of the world at once. He said it was

too queer the way your own house and big barn and great fields looked like little toy things that weren't of any account. It was because you could see so much more than just the . . .

She heard an imploring whine, and a cold nose was thrust into her hand! Why, there was old Shep begging for his share of waxed sugar. He loved it, though it did stick to his teeth so! She poured out another lot and gave half of it to Shep. It immediately stuck his jaws together tight, and he began pawing at his mouth and shaking his head till Betsy had to laugh. Then he managed to pull his jaws apart and chewed loudly and visibly, tossing his head, opening his mouth wide till Betsy could see the sticky, brown candy draped in melting festoons all over his big white teeth and red gullet. Then with a gulp he had swallowed it all down and was whining for more, striking softly at the little girl's skirt with his forepaw. "Oh, you eat it too fast!" cried Betsy, but she shared her next lot with him too. The sun had gone down over Hemlock Mountain by this time, and the big slope above her was all deep blue shadow. The mountain looked much higher now as the dusk began to fall, and loomed up bigger and bigger as though it reached to the sky. It was no wonder houses looked small from its top. Betsy ate the last of her sugar, looking up at the quiet giant there, towering grandly above her. There was no lump in her throat now. Although she still thought she did not know what in the world Cousin Ann meant by saying that about Hemlock Mountain and her examination, it's my opinion that she had made a good beginning of an understanding.

She was just picking up her cup to take it back to the sap-house when Shep growled a little and stood with his ears and tail up, looking down the road. Something was coming down that road in the blue, clear twilight, something that was making a very queer noise. It sounded almost like somebody crying. It *was* somebody crying! It was a child crying. It was a little, little girl. . . . Betsy could see her now . . . stumbling along and crying as though her heart would break. Why, it was little Molly, her own particular charge at school, whose reading lesson she heard every day. Betsy and Shep ran to meet her. "What's the matter, Molly? What's the matter?" Betsy knelt down and put her arms around the weeping child. "Did you fall down? Did you hurt you? What are you doing 'way off here? Did you lose your way?"

"I don't want to go away! I don't want to go away!" said Molly over and over, clinging tightly to Betsy. It was a long time before Betsy could quiet her enough to find out what had happened. Then she made out between Molly's sobs that her mother had been taken suddenly sick and had to go away to a hospital, and that left nobody at home to take care of Molly, and she was to be sent away to some strange relatives in the city who didn't want her at all and who said so.

Elizabeth Ann knew all about that! Her heart swelled big with sympathy. For a moment she stood again out on the sidewalk in front of the Lathrop house with old Mrs. Lathrop's ungracious white head bobbing from a window, and knew again that ghastly feeling of being unwanted. She knew why little Molly was crying! And she shut her hands together hard and made up her mind that she *would* help her out!

Do you know what she did, right off, without thinking about it? She didn't go and look up Aunt Abigail. She didn't wait till Uncle Henry came back from his round of emptying sap buckets into the big tub on his sled. As fast as her feet could carry her she flew back to Cousin Ann in the sap-house. I can't tell you (except again that Cousin Ann was Cousin Ann) why it was that Betsy ran so fast to her and was so sure that everything would be all right as soon as Cousin Ann knew about it; but whatever the reason was it was a good one, for, though Cousin Ann did not stop to kiss Molly or even to look at her more than one sharp first glance, she said after a moment's pause, during which she filled a syrup can and screwed the cover down very tight: "Well, if her folks will let her stay, how would you like to have Molly come and stay with us till her mother gets back from the hospital? Now you've got a room of your own, I guess you could have her sleep with you."

"Oh, Molly, Molly, *Molly!*" shouted Betsy, jumping up and down, and then hugging the little girl with all her might. "Oh, it will be like having a little sister!"

Cousin Ann sounded a dry, warning note: "Don't be too sure her folks will let her. We don't know about them yet."

Betsy ran to her, and caught her hand, looking up at her with shining eyes. "Cousin Ann, if *you* go to see them and ask them, they will!"

This made even Cousin Ann give a little abashed smile of pleasure, although she made her face grave again at once and said: "You'd better go along back to the house now, Betsy. It's time for you to help Mother with the supper."

The two children trotted back along the darkening wood road, Shep running before them, little Molly clinging fast to the older child's hand. "Aren't you ever afraid, Betsy, in the woods this way?" she asked admiringly.

"Oh, no!" said Betsy, protectingly; "there's nothing to be afraid of, except getting off on the wrong fork of the road, near the Wolf Pit."

"Oh, *ow!*" said Molly, scringing. "What's the Wolf Pit? What a name!"

Betsy laughed. She tried to make her laugh sound brave like Cousin Ann's, which always seemed so scornful of being afraid. As a matter of fact, she was beginning to fear that they *had* made the wrong turn, and she was not quite sure that she could find the way home. But she put this out of her mind and walked along very fast, peering ahead into the dusk. "It hasn't anything to do with wolves," she said in answer to Molly's question; "anyhow, not now. It's just a big, deep hole in the ground where a

309

brook had dug out a cave. . . . Uncle Henry told me all about it when he showed it to me . . . and then part of the roof caved in; sometimes there's ice in the corner of the covered part all the summer, Aunt Abigail says."

"Why do you call it the Wolf Pit?" asked Molly, walking very close to Betsy and holding very tightly to her hand.

"Oh, long, ever so long ago, when the first settlers came up here, they heard a wolf howling all night, and when it didn't stop in the morning, they came up here on the mountain and found a wolf had fallen in and couldn't get out."

"I hope they killed him!" said Molly.

"Gracious! that was more than a hundred years ago," said Betsy. She was not thinking of what she was saying. She was thinking that if they *were* on the right road they ought to be home by this time. She was thinking that the right road ran downhill to the house all the way, and that this certainly seemed to be going up a little. She was wondering what had become of Shep. "Stand here just a minute, Molly," she said. "I want . . . I just want to go ahead a little bit and see . . . and see . . ." She darted on around a curve of the road and stood still, her heart sinking. The road turned there and led straight up the mountain!

For just a moment the little girl felt a wild impulse to burst out in a shriek for Aunt Frances, and to run crazily away, anywhere so long as she was running. But the thought of Molly standing back there, trustfully waiting to be taken care of, shut Betsy's lips together hard

before her scream of fright got out. She stood still, thinking. Now she mustn't get frightened. All they had to do was to walk back along the road till they came to the fork and then make the right turn. But what if they didn't get back to the turn till it was so dark they couldn't see it . . . ? Well, she mustn't think of that. She ran back, calling, "Come on, Molly," in a tone she tried to make as firm as Cousin Ann's. "I guess we have made the wrong turn after all. We'd better . . ."

But there was no Molly there. In the brief moment Betsy had stood thinking, Molly had disappeared. The long, shadowy wood road held not a trace of her.

Then Betsy *was* frightened and then she *did* begin to scream, at the top of her voice, "Molly! Molly!" She was beside herself with terror, and started back hastily to hear Molly's voice, very faint, apparently coming from the ground.

"Ow! Ow! Betsy! Get me out!"

"Where *are* you?" shrieked Betsy.

"I don't know!" came Molly's sobbing voice. "I just moved the least little bit out of the road, and slipped on the ice and began to slide and I couldn't stop myself and I fell down into a deep hole!"

Betsy's head felt as though her hair were standing up straight on end with horror. Molly must have fallen down into the Wolf Pit! Yes, they were quite near it. She remembered now that big white-birch tree stood right at the place where the brook tumbled over the edge and fell into it. Although she was dreadfully afraid of falling in herself, she went cautiously over to this tree, feeling her way

with her foot to make sure she did not slip, and peered down into the cavernous gloom below. Yes, there was Molly's little face, just a white speck. The child was crying, sobbing, and holding up her arms to Betsy.

"Are you hurt, Molly?"

"No. I fell into a big snow-bank, but I'm all frozen and I want to get out!"

Betsy held on to the birch-tree. Her head whirled. What *should* she do! "Look here, Molly," she called down, "I'm going to run back along to the right road and back to the house and get Uncle Henry. He'll come with a rope and get you out!"

At this Molly's crying rose to a frantic scream. "Oh, Betsy, don't leave me here alone! Don't! Don't! The wolves will get me! Betsy, *don't* leave me alone!" The child was wild with terror.

"But I *can't* get you out myself!" screamed back Betsy, crying herself. Her teeth were chattering with the cold.

"Don't go! Don't go!" came up from the darkness of the pit in a piteous howl. Betsy made a great effort and stopped crying. She sat down on a stone and tried to think. And this is what came into her mind as a guide: "What would Cousin Ann do if she were here? She wouldn't cry. She would *think* of something."

311

Betsy looked around her desperately. The first thing she saw was the big limb of a pine-tree, broken off by the wind, which half lay and half slantingly stood up against a tree a little distance above the mouth of the pit. It had been there so long that the needles had dried and fallen off, and the skeleton of the branch with the broken stubs looked like . . . yes, it looked like a ladder! *That* was what Cousin Ann would have done!

"Wait a minute! Wait a minute, Molly!" she called wildly down the pit, warm all over in excitement. "Now listen. You go off there in a corner, where the ground makes a sort of roof. I'm going to throw down something you can climb up on, maybe."

"Ow! Ow, it'll hit me!" cried poor little Molly, more and more frightened. But she scrambled off under her shelter obediently, while Betsy struggled with the branch. It was so firmly imbedded in the snow that at first she could not budge it at all. But after she cleared that away and pried hard with the stick she was using as a lever she felt it give a little. She bore down with all her might, throwing her weight again and again on her lever, and finally felt the big branch move. After that it was easier, as its course was downhill over the snow to the mouth of the pit. Glowing, and pushing, wet with perspiration, she slowly maneuvered it along to the edge, turned it squarely, gave it a great shove, and leaned over anxiously. Then she gave a great sigh of relief! Just as she had hoped, it went down sharp end first and stuck fast in the snow which had

saved Molly from broken bones. She was so out of breath with her work that for a moment she could not speak. Then, "Molly, there! Now I guess you can climb up to where I can reach you."

Molly made a rush for any way out of her prison, and climbed, like the practiced squirrel that she was, up from one stub to another to the top of the branch. She was still below the edge of the pit there, but Betsy lay flat down on the snow and held out her hands. Molly took hold hard, and, digging her toes into the snow, slowly wormed her way up to the surface of the ground.

It was then, at that very moment, that Shep came bounding up to them, barking loudly, and after him Cousin Ann striding along in her rubber boots, with a lantern in her hand and a rather anxious look on her face.

She stopped short and looked at the two little girls, covered with snow, their faces flaming with excitement, and at the black hole gaping behind them. "I always *told* Father we ought to put a fence around that pit," she said in a matter-of-fact voice. "Some day a sheep's going to fall down there. Shep came along to the house without you, and we thought most likely you'd taken the wrong turn."

Betsy felt terribly aggrieved. She wanted to be petted and praised for her heroism. She wanted Cousin Ann to *realize* . . . oh, if Aunt Frances were only there, *she* would realize . . . !

"I fell down in the hole, and Betsy wanted to go and get Mr. Putney, but I wouldn't let her, and so she threw down a big branch and I climbed out," explained Molly, who, now that her danger was past, took Betsy's action quite as a matter of course.

"Oh, that was how it happened," said Cousin Ann. She looked down the hole and saw the big branch, and looked back and saw the long trail of crushed snow where Betsy had dragged it. "Well, now, that was quite a good idea for a little girl to have," she said briefly. "I guess you'll do to take care of Molly all right!"

She spoke in her usual voice and immediately drew the children after her, but Betsy's heart was singing joyfully as she trotted along clasping Cousin Ann's strong hand. Now she knew that Cousin Ann realized. . . . She trotted fast, smiling to herself in the darkness.

"What made you think of doing that?" asked Cousin Ann presently, as they approached the house.

"Why, I tried to think what *you* would have done if you'd been there," said Betsy.

"Oh!" said Cousin Ann. "Well . . ." She didn't say another word, but Betsy, glancing up into her face as they stepped into the lighted room, saw an expression that made her give a little skip and hop of joy. She had *pleased* Cousin Ann.

That night, as she lay in her bed, her arm over Molly cuddled up warm beside her, she remembered, ever so faintly, as something of no importance, that she had failed in an examination that afternoon.

mary stevens

Rococo Skates

By Marjorie Fischer

TWENTY pairs of shoes clattered up the marble steps inside the Metropolitan Museum. The class was having Art today, and Miss Ryan had taken them to see the pictures. Miss Ryan walked beside the line, looking forward and back along the double row of children.

Mary Ann was at the very end of the line, even behind Frances, the girl she was supposed to be walking with, who was her best friend in a way. Miss Ryan looked back at Mary Ann and her glasses caught the light, so that for a second you couldn't see Miss Ryan's eyes.

"We can't have any loitering, Mary Ann," said Miss Ryan. "Close up the line."

Mary Ann stepped up and then fell back again. This would be a good place to roller skate, she thought; the floors were hard wood, and today most of the galleries were empty. You could go shooting down the galleries and around corners yelling like anything. You could stop yourself with statues so big and heavy they couldn't fall. You'd go swinging around the statue with the force of your rush, just holding lightly with one hand to the statue, and then you'd take off again, rolling, shooting, yelling. If you had skates, you could. Mary Ann didn't have any skates. Skates were what she had particularly wanted for a long time.

Sometimes when she was in the park—if she had skates—she wouldn't just shoot along, she'd swing, she'd glide, almost like dancing, and then she could play tag with Frances and the other kids who had skates. Maybe next Christmas—but Christmas was a long way off, and so was her birthday.

The twenty pairs of shoes clattered along the galleries. Here and there Miss Ryan would hold up her hand, the shoes stood still, and Miss Ryan told them about this picture or that, her glasses sometimes reflecting the pictures very small and curved, as if her glasses were mirrors.

Miss Ryan stopped before a medium-sized picture of a table with a bottle of wine, a loaf of bread, a knife, and a basket of fruit. It wasn't bad, Mary Ann thought, leaning. Then she stood straight. Right at one side of the picture was another picture on an easel. It was a medium-sized picture of a table with a bottle of wine, a loaf of bread, a knife, and a basket of fruit. It was, in fact, a copy of the picture on the wall and so exactly like it that, except for the frame around it, nobody could have told one from the other.

"How is that, Miss Ryan?"

"Artists get permission from the Museum to come in and copy," said Miss Ryan. "This is a very famous picture, so naturally artists copy it."

"I'd never," said Mary Ann. "I'd rather do my own, even if it was bad."

Mary Ann loitered behind the class, standing before the easel and looking from one picture to the other. Maybe the paint was still wet on the copy, she thought. It would be easy enough to find out, but of course she shouldn't do that. Her right hand reached out all by itself, and her forefinger pressed against the picture on the easel. Oh, heavens! It *was* wet. She felt the paint slide a little under her finger.

Mary Ann hurriedly caught up with Frances and stepped along beside her.

"I saw you," whispered Frances. "You're just lucky Miss Ryan didn't see. Did it leave a mark?"

Mary Ann didn't answer. She walked along beside Frances, not leaning at all and breathing rather fast.

Miss Ryan walked on, with twenty pairs of shoes clopping behind her. They walked and stopped, walked and stopped. The pictures were like windows, Mary Ann thought, and through them you saw how people used to look. Then they went through rooms full of furniture, and you could see how people used to sit and write and sew and sleep. There was one enormous bed with a canopy over it, and the canopy of green silk was held up with carved golden Cupids leaping through the air and holding carved wreaths of flowers.

"This is Rococo furniture," said Miss Ryan.

Rococo, Mary Ann thought to herself. It might be the name of something to play, or a pigeon cooing, or something you shouted as you slid along on roller skates.

"Rococo," Mary Ann said out loud, and Frances looked at her and repeated it after her.

"Rococo," said Frances.

"Rococo," said Mary Ann, trying it out as a pigeon.

Mary Ann and Frances began to laugh. They hit against each other as they walked. "Rococo!" they said, and swayed away. They walked and looked, walked and looked. Mary Ann began to lean again. She was *tired*.

"All right, children," Miss Ryan said at last; "that's enough for today. You may turn right around as you are and we'll find our way out."

The class turned, and Mary Ann and Frances were at the head of the line. They walked along, past the furniture—"Rococo!" said Mary Ann and Frances, swaying against each other. They walked past pictures and pictures. Now they were in the room where the picture on the easel had been.

"Look," said Frances, "the copy's gone."

Mary Ann was next to the wall. She leaned along as she walked, and when she came to the medium-sized picture of the table with the bottle of wine, the loaf of bread, the knife, and the basket of fruit, she gave such a loud cry that everyone stopped.

"Look!" cried Mary Ann. "It's the other one. The real one's been stolen!"

"How can you tell?" said Frances.

"Quick!" cried Mary Ann. "We've got to tell someone important."

Miss Ryan came between Mary Ann and Frances.

"What is the meaning of all this noise?" she said.

"The picture!" said Mary Ann. "The real picture's been stolen. This is the one that was on the easel."

"Nonsense," said Miss Ryan.

"Honestly!" cried Mary Ann. "We must tell the head of the Museum right away."

"Come along, now," said Miss Ryan. "I never heard such nonsense in my life."

By this time one or two people in other galleries had heard the racket and were standing about trying to find out what had happened. A guard in a blue uniform strolled in and told everyone to keep quiet —this was the Museum, in case they'd forgotten.

Miss Ryan was getting ready to march them straight out; Mary Ann saw that. Miss Ryan would never believe her, and in the meantime the picture would be gone.

"I must tell someone," cried Mary Ann. She spun about, before everyone, not knowing where to go. She began to run, back along the way she had come, because the class and Miss Ryan and the other people and the guard were on the other side. She ran past pictures and pictures, dodging people or bumping against them, and everyone turned to look, and then—there came the clatter of nineteen

pairs of shoes, running along the galleries after her.

Mary Ann came to the furniture room, and there were two guards coming towards her, one from each doorway, and she ran around two chairs and a desk, and there were the guards still coming toward her, and the nineteen pairs of shoes clopping along faster and faster. She sprang over the rope around the Rococo bed, and the guards came nearer. They reached out their hands for her, and she leaped on to the bed and stood on it. How hard the mattress was, like a board! She ran a little one way on the bed, under the canopy, and as both guards ran to get her, she doubled about, leaped from the bed, sprang over the rope, and made off again, with everyone clopping after her.

She ran out into a marble hall, and at her left she saw a door marked—marked—why, it was marked Office of the Director. The DIRECTOR. She turned about and swung open the heavy door and dashed inside, just as everyone caught up with her.

"A picture's been stolen," gasped Mary Ann to the people in the office. "I know it's been stolen. You just come along with me and I'll show you. No one believes me, Miss Ryan or not even Frances, but I'll show you. Only, hurry!"

While she was talking a nice old man had come out of an inner office, and Miss Ryan and four guards had come through the outer door.

317

"Let's just go along and have a look to make sure," said the nice old man. "It's pretty hard to steal a picture here, but just to make sure."

Back they went, all of them, first the nice old man and Mary Ann, then Frances and Miss Ryan, and then the class, and the other people, and the guards. When they got to the picture the nice old man put on a pair of glasses with a black ribbon attached to them, and he looked at the picture very carefully. After quite a while he turned to Mary Ann.

"This is a very good copy," said the nice old man, "but it is a copy. The real picture has been stolen. I am going back to my office now. Won't you wait for me outside?"

While they waited for the nice old man, Miss Ryan told Mary Ann that she quite understood how it was, that Mary Ann had really *had* to run. When the nice old man came out he had a great book bound in blue leather in his arms.

"This is for you, Mary Ann," he said. "It has colored pictures of most of the pictures in the Museum. It even has the stolen picture. If it had not been for you the theft might not have been noticed until the picture had been taken out of the country. You have done a very remarkable thing; almost anyone would have been fooled by that copy."

"I guess I couldn't be fooled," said Mary Ann.

"Here's the book then, Mary Ann," said the nice old man.

Mary Ann took the great book bound in blue leather and said thank you politely. The nice old man watched her.

"Maybe there was something you specially wanted, Mary Ann," he said, "besides the book."

"She wants roller skates," Frances burst out.

"Roller skates it is," said the nice old man, and he called a nice young man from his office.

In a few minutes Mary Ann and Frances were going down the steps outside the Museum with the nice young man. The rest of the class and Miss Ryan stood and watched Mary Ann and Frances climb into a beautiful automobile and waved to them as they drove away.

"How did you know about that copy, Mary Ann?" asked the nice young man as they drove along.

"I pushed the copy with my finger and it left a mark," said Mary Ann. "Right in the middle of the basket."

"Oh, so that was how," said Frances. "But I wouldn't tell on you."

"Neither would I," said the nice young man. "What do you say, Mary Ann and Frances, skates first or sodas first?"

"Sodas," said Frances.

"Skates," said Mary Ann, "she's got skates. Anyway, I marked the picture."

"Oh, all right," said Frances.

"I thought we could make up a new game," said Mary Ann. "Rococo Skates."

"What!" said the nice young man.

"Something like tag on skates," said Mary Ann.

High Water in Arkansas!

By Charles J. Finger

WM. MOYERS

Perhaps you heard Tad North's voice over the radio a short time ago. The program ended suddenly, you remember. He had been presented with a medal because of the part he played in the flood. Then someone asked him to talk into the microphone and tell what happened.

"But I didn't do anything," he said. "It just all came about like it did."

No persuasion could get him to say more, to be photographed, to be interviewed, or to regard himself as a hero. There he was, a freckled, healthy, straight-limbed boy of thirteen, in faded blue overalls. He took the medal shyly, thanked the giver, said those few words into the microphone, and then withdrew. Some few knew that the affair had to do with the Arkansas River flood, but no one, not even the local newspaper, got it exactly right.

This is how it was.

Proctor K. North, Tad's father, owned the ferryboat that went back and forth between Proctor's Landing and the other side. It was not much of a craft to look at, being little more than a roughly made platform built on two flatboats, and just large enough to take a couple of Model T Fords if they were parked close, and carefully. It was propelled by a little gasoline engine on a very small flatboat lashed alongside. Except when "school kept" (and it kept for only twelve weeks a year in that district) Tad ran the engine. He took great pride in it and had

319

run it, off and on, since he was nine. That makes four years' experience. His father, Proctor K., was captain as well as owner, steersman, fare-collector, also comforter for nervous tourists. And tourists often were nervous when they saw the steep clay bank, the ramshackle ferry, the rickety gangway, the swift river, and the road up the levee on the other side which had two hairpin turns.

"Is it safe?" some of them would ask.

"Safe as a hornet's nest," Proctor K. would assure them. "Why, it's been on the job ever since I came from the war in France, and it's like to be here when me and you isn't." Then, with his mind on business, he would say, with rough hand extended for the money, "Two bits for the car, and a dime for every passenger. Forty cents if you come back. We don't give no tickets, but we'll remember your face all right."

Proctor K. had made that speech so often, that Tad, who had seen no other ferry except that up at Cuming's Crossing (which was almost a twin), wondered if ferry-owners in places like New York, and Seattle, and Norfolk had to assure doubtful passengers.

Well, last spring it was high water in Arkansas. On the fourth day people began to call it flood stage, with more coming, and the ferry business was down to nothing. The lower branches of the willows along the river banks were burdened with floating sticks, corn stalks, and odds and ends. All the morning, snags had been drifting down; once a haystack, then a hen coop with two doubtful hens

for sailors, then a dead pig, then a mile-long tangle of corn stalks. Hourly the river rose, became yellower and yellower, noisier, angrier, wider. About nine o'clock, Proctor K. said, "I guess we'll call it a day, Tad, and lay up."

"Meanin' it's dangerous?" asked Tad.

"Not what you'd call plumb dangerous, Tad, only the way I look at things is that a pocketful of caution is worth more'n a hundred sacks of take-a-chance. What isn't wisdom is danger, always."

Tad nodded, considered, then asked, "What about Sim's delivery truck, the bread and all that?"

Proctor K. looked at the racing clouds, looked down river and up river, then said, "Why, *if* he comes, and the roads can't be none too good considerin', it'll be within the next hour. Of course we'll take him over. If he doesn't come by then, why, folks'll have to bake fer themselves like they did when I was a boy. But the roads'll be like pancake batter if I know mutton from goat."

But in spite of the worst kind of roads, Sim's delivery truck was no more than twenty minutes late, and, as usual, Sim was cheerful. His Scottie, Susie, was as cheerful as her master and announced her coming with joyous barks. As soon as the truck was aboard, she capered about the deck and barked at the water in a frenzy of enthusiasm.

"Maybe I ought to tie her up for once, she's that excited," said Sim, doubtfully. "Dogs, they know when anything's out of the usual quicker'n some men. Why, she's been worked up all mornin' since we took on some groceries for Bernses what he phoned over for just a little afore the 'phone went out. Dogs, they know things."

Sim went across the gangway to lend a hand to Proctor K., who was preparing to cast off the line. Tad, testing his engine, thought it would be a pity to tie Susie, seeing how she enjoyed things.

Then things happened. A rabbit appeared on the bank. Susie gave a sharp hunting cry, scampered across the gangway and started up the bank in chase. Tad looked up to see the dog silhouetted against the sky on the top of the levee, heard Sim say, "Dag gum it! I knew I ought to have tied her. Wait a bit! I'll be back!" Then Sim went running up the bank and Proctor K., after taking a half-hitch round the post to hold the ferryboat, followed.

That was the moment when the second thing happened. No one saw it.

Down stream, not floating nor even in sight, because it had long been water-logged, came rolling the stump of a tree. Now and then one of its roots came above water, vicious looking hooked roots they were, ready to do mischief. One of them reaching high, caught at the rope and dragged it under water at the moment when the end of the tree trunk struck the ferryboat and drove it sideways. Feeling the shock, Tad seized an oar to prevent being driven against the bank. At the same moment he saw the post dragged out of the soft earth and start riverwards.

Almost before he realized what had happened, twenty feet of yellow water separated ferryboat from river bank. Tad saw Sim on the bank with Susie under his arm, saw Proctor K. at the water's edge, saw the willows sliding strangely northwards and Sim and Proctor K. sliding with them. Then he knew he was adrift, and panic seized him. But his panic was for a moment only. In a trice he had his engine going, but almost immediately he knew how useless it was.

"What isn't wisdom is danger," ran through his mind. So he stopped the motor. He must not waste gasoline which might come in useful, though he could not tell how or when. The ferryboat was in the grip of the current and already sweeping round Union Point and into one of the many horseshoe-shaped lakes between Proctor's Crossing and the place where the Arkansas River joined the Mississippi.

"Tad, you've got to think straight," he told himself.

He got on the ferryboat, walked to the rope which was trailing in the river, hauled it in and coiled it ready for use. He examined the chocks under the tires of the delivery truck to make sure the auto would ride well, for if that rolled or slid—! He shook his head as he thought of possibilities. Next he took his ragged coat and covered the engine. Tad felt that if he got wet it would do no harm, but the engine was another matter. Then, believing all in order, he climbed to the roof of the truck to take observations.

What he saw was a world strange, yet familiar—strange when he looked at things near, familiar when he looked far off. The Arkansas River was a band of tossing water, ugly yellow, roaring, with leaping waves where the swift current broke on snags which were held fast on mud banks. If the ferryboat struck one of those—! It was like a nightmare to think of what might be, and like a pleasant dream to look at the sun shining brightly, to hear a thousand birds chattering. Then he saw the Mason place, the house now on a little island; washing hanging out to dry on another little island, only the barn roof above water.

nearer, he saw a Negro woman waving a white cloth, and three children seated on the roof.

Then Tad became breathless. Ahead, in the line the shantyboat would take, was a long and wicked looking wave which told its tale of jammed snags. Into that tangle the ark with its four passengers must certainly drift. There was no escape. Tad knew what would happen, how the shantyboat would catch broadside on, how it would tilt, how the water piling against it would pour in, how the boat would founder, how the disaster would

It was then, for the first time, that he realized he was not alone on that flooded river. Ahead was a shantyboat, a sort of little Noah's ark, one of those rough-made floating houses in which people live who fish for mussels, gathering shells to sell to button factories. Tad felt happy enough to sing when he thought that there might be a man, or men on board; but the hope waned when, drawing

mean a swift end for woman and children. All that came to him in a few moments. Then Tad became active.

Down he ran to his engine and started it. Back he ran to the steering oar and tugged to change the course, no matter how slightly, so that the drift of the ferryboat would be near the shantyboat. If the engine held out, if no swirl swept the ferry back into midstream, and, most

322

important, if the woman knew what to do and did it at the right moment when he threw the rope, there might be a chance. There were many "ifs."

"Catch! Make fast!" shouted Tad as he flung the rope. He saw the woman bend forward to catch the flying rope, saw the three frightened children on the roof, heard his little engine chugging bravely, saw how the woman, used to river ways, caught the rope, took a swift turn round the bollard post, and he knew the trick was done.

Getting the ark alongside, and holding it there while the woman and children got on board, was fairly easy. Then Tad shut his engine down, and there were explanations. Also there were rejoicings when Tad, wondering if it was honest to do so, opened the door of Sim's delivery truck and took out bread and doughnuts for the children. They stuffed rather than ate, so ravenous they were.

"Lawdy! Lawdy! Two days they got never a bite," said the mother. Then she turned to Tad and asked, "Is you all alone on this rescue boat?"

So Tad had to explain. "This isn't a rescue boat," he said. "I'm adrift like you all. An accident."

"Lawdy! Lawdy! Why, it's no accident at all, mister captain." She persisted in giving him that title. "Why, don't you see it's the Lawd's work? He sent that rabbit. He sent that dog. He sent you down the river to us."

She munched some bread herself, regarding the swift moving panorama of trees and drift and distant highlands.

"He done arranged it all, captain. Two bends in the river and it's Cypress Bend where I was in the high water in '32. Good Lawd's sendin' us all there."

And what with the whirling waters, racing bayous and islands of slush, they were in sight of Cypress Island when Tad thought they were still miles away. They saw four shanties, dots that were men and women, a raging river at the cut-off and white breakers ahead. If the little engine could force the ferryboat into still water behind the island, there was hope. The next minute or two meant quick work. Tad sent Nancy to the ferry steering oar, opened the rear door of the delivery truck and bundled the children in where they would be safe, ran to his boat alongside and started the engine. Immediately they were in wild water and racing like an express train, the world full of noise.

Once the ferryboat pivoted on a hidden snag and the shantyboat tore loose and went down stream on its side. Once the engine fluttered, as if it had done its best and, wearied, could do no more. But they won. The ferryboat slid into calmer water in the lee of the island, and into the water, waist deep, ran some of the marooned islanders. They laid hands on the ferryboat and pulled it inshore, while the engine chug-chugged bravely.

"You made it," said one of the men, a tall, bronzed fellow.

"More mouths to fill and nothin' much to give 'em," said another, laughing.

"I tell you the Lawd knows His business and don't do it half way," declared

Nancy, and pointed to the stores in the delivery wagon.

The marooned share-croppers were willing to believe that a little later when, with a blazing fire for comfort, all of them were feasting on Sim's bread and doughnuts, sardines and canned salmon, pork and beans, bacon, condensed milk, cheese, crackers, and much more. And when one of the share-croppers wondered who was going to repay Sim, Nancy relieved her own mind, even if she did not relieve Tad's by saying again, "The Lawd don't do things half way! It'll come out right." And as it turned out, Nancy was a good prophet.

All that was the part of the adventure which few people knew, except those on the rescue boat sent down from Helena, which arrived five days later. We, on that relief steamboat, expected to find famished people on Cypress Bend. Instead, there were fifteen high-hearted men, women and children, well fed and comfortable, a brave flag fluttering on a newly erected flagpole, and things in general wearing the air of a picnic rather than flood disaster.

When the relief supervisor and the Memphis newspaper man got Tad in a corner and said things about his good work, talking about a medal, Tad said exactly what he said a week later when they pushed him to the microphone:

"But I didn't do anything. It just all came about like it did."

WM. MOYERS

Space Ship to the Moon

By E. C. Reichert

"WHO WOULD like to go to the moon on a space ship?" asked Miss Rose, the second-grade teacher, as her class turned a corner in the museum hall. Twenty eager hands waved in the air in answer.

"Well, that is just what we are going to do, or *nearly* going to do," continued Miss Rose. "In the next room we are to see a motion picture that will show us how space ships operate, and the guide will tell us all about a trip to the moon."

Sally and Billy could hardly wait to see the picture. Sally nudged Billy and whispered, "I wonder if it will be like the ones we have seen at home on television?"

"I don't know but I'll bet it will be fun," answered Billy.

Excitedly, the class walked into the large theater with comfortable seats and a white screen at the front. The guide went forward and said, "We are going to turn off the lights, and you will see a movie showing how a space ship leaves the earth and goes to the moon and back."

The room was darkened, and the children sat forward on their seats with their eyes fixed on the screen. The guide began, "In this first scene you can see our space ship. You will notice that it does not have wings like an airplane. Can anyone tell me why?"

One of the boys shouted, "Because it is a rocket. It doesn't need wings. It's steered by a gyroscope."

"Right!" said the guide. "That boy knows about space ships. Now, then, notice the holes in the tail. What are they for?"

"They're for the jet blasts to shoot out," said Billy. "The ship gets its power from an atomic engine. I read about it."

"Fine!" said the guide, and he continued, "This diagram shows how the ship has a double hull, much like a thermos bottle. That's how it can stand the very hot and very cold temperatures it must go through. Now we shall see the space ship take off, and *if you will use your imagination, I think you can all go along.*"

Sally and Billy saw the ship on the launching platform. Suddenly they heard a loud WHOOSH! Straight out into space the ship sailed, leaving trails of smoke.

* * * *

Sally and Billy could all but feel the motion of the ship. They heard a man say, "You may unfasten your safety belts. From now on you won't feel any more jars or jolts. We'll ride as easily as a boat does on a calm sea." They unfastened their belts and sat back to enjoy the smooth ride.

"I don't think I know your name," Sally said. "Are you the pilot?"

The man smiled and answered, "I'm

one of the pilots, as you call them, but we call ourselves 'astronauts.' I'm Dan."

Billy said, "We're happy to know you, Dan."

"I hope you don't mind questions," Sally continued. "I have about a million to ask you."

"I'll be glad to answer questions," replied Dan, "but right now I think you should look out of the window. You can see the earth dropping away from us, and in just a minute something very exciting will happen."

Sally and Billy looked through the heavy plate-glass window and saw the earth dropping away so quickly that they no longer could see the space port from which they had set out. Only lakes and mountains stood out on the rounded surface of the earth.

"What is the very exciting thing, Dan?" asked Sally.

"Well," said Dan, "this is a stage-rocket ship. That means that we are riding in the nose of the ship in one rocket, and there is a bigger and separate rocket for a tail. After five minutes of flight we release the big rocket at our tail, and it parachutes back to earth. Walk up to the front of the ship and you can watch my partner, Bob, release it."

Sally and Billy ran to the front of the ship. Bob, the other astronaut, looked up and said, "Hi, there! Want to see our sky-fish lose its tail?"

He pulled back on a big lever at his feet. "Look out the window," he said. Sally and Billy saw the big tail rocket fall away from the ship and a huge parachute billow out behind it.

Bob leaned back and said, "We had to go 25,000 miles per hour for the first five minutes of our flight but now we can coast along. It will take five days to get to the moon. The first part of our trip is very fast, but from now on everything is easy."

Sally and Billy walked back to Dan, who showed them their bunks.

"When you aren't eating or sleeping," Dan said, "you might want to learn more about the moon and the stars. These books above your bunk will tell you a lot of interesting things about them."

The second day passed like the first.

On the third day, after lunch, Dan announced that there was a new adventure ahead. "In just one hour we will arrive at the orbital space station."

"Oh, I've read about that!" said Billy. "It's just like a little moon circling the earth."

"Yes," agreed Dan, "but with one big difference—men made the space station only a few years ago. It was built soon after the first successful space ship flights. It is a very useful place. We can refuel there and talk to the men who send weather reports back home."

Through the window the children watched a shiny object ahead grow larger. As they neared the space station, it looked just like a giant steel umbrella hanging in space.

"Why doesn't it fall back to earth?" asked Sally.

"It isn't that heavy," Dan answered, "and we are already a long way out in space. You know the earth holds everything in its orbit. That's why this is called an orbital station. It will always stay the same distance from the earth and will circle the earth just like a moon."

The ship slowly circled and edged up to the space station. When it was firmly anchored, Bob said, "We will need to wear space suits here. I'll get yours." He went to a closet and took out two suits that looked as if they were made of armor except that they had flexible joints at the elbows and knees and headpieces of plate glass.

"Do we have to wear these all the time we are here?" asked Sally.

"No," replied Bob. "Only when we are not in our ship or under the dome of the space station."

"The air here is too thin to breathe," explained Dan, "and your suits have oxygen tanks attached."

"How can we talk?" asked Billy.

"There's a microphone in the headpiece, and that little rod on top is an aerial," replied Dan.

"What if we fall off of the space station?" stammered Sally.

"We won't," Dan hastened to say. "And if we did, we can go in any direction by using the reaction pistols on the sides of the suits. If you pull the trigger on the pistol to your right, you will turn to the left; the other pistol will

send you in the opposite direction."

Sally and Billy put on their suits and helped each other tighten the heavy headpieces. The hatch of the space ship was opened, and they climbed out. While the ship was being refueled, they walked toward the dome in the middle of the station. It was enclosed by glass and topped by high radio and radar towers.

Once inside they removed their headpieces and were introduced to the men who manned the station. One was the radio operator, and he asked the children if they had any message they wished to send home. "Send our mother a message and tell her we are having a heavenly time!" they said.

"O.K.," said the radio operator.

"Now, back to the ship," Dan ordered. "It's time we took off again for the moon."

Back in the ship Sally and Billy got out of their space suits and watched the ship drift away from the space station. They saw the earth getting smaller and smaller, far behind the station, and the moon getting larger and nearer.

On the fourth day Dan said, "Tomorrow is the big day—the day we land on the moon."

The next morning the space ship, instead of going forward and landing like an airplane, backed into the moon with its rocket power as brakes. Soon it was on the ground.

"Here we are!" Dan called. "All out for the moon—but first climb into your space suits."

As soon as they were out of the ship,

the walkie-talkie aerials on their suits were sparking questions back and forth.

"What big mountains there are up here!" said Billy.

"Isn't it funny there isn't anything growing?" asked Sally. "Just rock dust as far as you can see."

"There's more than rocks to see," answered Dan. "Look this way and you will see the Lunar Space Station." Sure enough, under a huge glass dome that seemed to stretch for blocks, they saw men moving about. The radio and radar towers loomed high above. In the distance they could see men working in glass-enclosed trucks.

"Now walk slowly and follow me," said Dan. And then came the biggest surprise of all. As Billy stepped forward, to his amazement he jumped nearly ten feet up in the air.

"What happened?" he gasped.

Both Dan and Bob laughed. "You haven't grown any new leg muscles," said Bob. "Everyone can jump high here. The pull of gravity is so much less than on earth. Be careful, though, until you get used to it, or you will fall."

Inside the Lunar Space Station Dan told them to take off their space suits. Sally and Billy met the men who worked in the space port and asked them questions. Then they saw a tremendous rocket ship backing under the glass dome by using its small rockets under the nose of the ship.

"What's that?" asked Billy.

"That is one of the bigger ships that goes on to other planets," Bob explained. "The moon is used mostly as a stopping-off place for flights into farther space. Mining is also an important industry here. Strange and valuable minerals are being discovered all the time. Some are sent back to earth because they are a cheap source of atomic fuel for rocket ships."

"Why is everything under glass or underground here?" asked Billy.

"Because the temperature on the moon varies from much colder at night than it ever gets at the North Pole, to much hotter in the daytime than it gets on the hottest part of the earth," Dan answered.

Sally and Billy stayed two days on the moon and explored every place they could. One day they went into a uranium mine. Too soon the time came for their return trip to the earth. Once again the space ship flew through the sky toward the orbital station, and on the fifth day they arrived at the space port on earth.

* * * *

Suddenly there was a flash of light, and Sally and Billy jumped.

"We are back on earth," they heard a voice say. They rubbed their eyes and blinked. It was the museum guide talking, and the theater lights had been turned on. Sally gasped, and Billy said, "Whew! That was an exciting trip."

That night, as Sally was getting ready for bed, she looked out of the window and said to Billy, "Look at the beautiful moon! Just think what fun we had at the museum today up there looking down at the earth."

"Yes," Billy answered. "But I'm glad we live where there are trees and grass even if we can't jump as high as we could on the moon."

"Me too!" agreed Sally.

Christmas Stories
and Christmas Verses

Christmas Everywhere

By Phillips Brooks

EVERYWHERE, everywhere, Christmas tonight!
Christmas in lands of the fir-tree and pine,
Christmas in lands of the palm-tree and vine,
Christmas where snow peaks stand solemn and white,
Christmas where cornfields stand sunny and bright.

Christmas where old men are patient and gray,
Christmas where peace, like a dove in his flight,
Broods o'er brave men in the thick of the fight;
Everywhere, everywhere, Christmas tonight!
For the Christ-child who comes is the Master of all;
No palace too great, no cottage too small.

THE GIFT

By Christina Rossetti

WHAT can I give Him,
  Poor as I am?
If I were a shepherd
  I would bring a lamb.
If I were a Wise Man
  I would do my part.
Yet what can I give Him?
  Give my heart.

The Christmas Apple

By Ruth Sawyer

ONCE upon a time there lived in the Tyrol a little clock-maker by the name of Hermann Joseph. He lived in one little room with a bench for his work, and a chest for his wood, and his tools, and a cupboard for dishes, and a trundle-bed under the bench. Besides these there was a stool, and that was all—excepting the clocks.

There were hundreds of clocks: little and big, carved and plain, some with wooden faces and some with porcelain ones—shelf clocks, cuckoo clocks, clocks with chimes and clocks without; and they all hung on the walls, covering them quite up. In front of his one little window there was a little shelf, and on this Hermann put all his best clocks to show the passers-by. Often they would stop and look and some one would say, "See, Hermann Joseph has made a new clock. It is finer than any of the rest!"

Then if it happened that anybody was wanting a clock he would come in and buy it.

I said Hermann was a little clock-maker. That was because his back was bent and his legs were crooked, making him very short and funny to look at. But there was no kinder face than his in all the city, and the children loved him. Whenever a toy was broken or a doll had lost an arm or a leg or an eye its careless mother would carry it straight to Hermann's little shop.

"The little one needs mending," she would say. "Can you do it now for me?"

And whatever work Hermann was doing, he would always put it aside to mend the broken toy or doll, and never a penny would he take for the mending.

"Go put it by till Christmas-time," he would always say.

Now it was the custom in that long ago for those who lived in the city to bring gifts to the great cathedral on Christmas and lay them before the Holy Mother and Child. People saved all through the year that they might have something wonderful to bring on that day; and there was a saying among them that when a gift was brought that pleased the Christ Child more than any other He would reach down from Mary's arms and take it.

This was but a saying, of course. Old Mr. Graff, the oldest man in the city, could not remember that it had ever really happened; and there were many who laughed at the very idea. But children often talked about it, and the poets made beautiful verses about it; and often when a rich gift was placed beside the altar the watchers would whisper among themselves, "Perhaps now we shall see the miracle."

333

URSULA KOERING

Those who had no gifts to bring went to the cathedral just the same on Christmas Eve to see the gifts of the others and hear the carols and watch the burning of the waxen tapers. The little clockmaker was one of these. Often he was stopped and some one would ask, "How is it that you never bring a gift?" Once the Bishop himself questioned him: "Poorer than thou have brought offerings to the Child. Where is thy gift?"

Then it was that Hermann had answered: "Wait; you shall see. I, too, shall bring a gift some day."

The truth of it was that the little clockmaker was so busy giving things away all the year that there was never anything left at Christmas-time. But he had a won-

derful idea on which he was working every minute that he could spare time from his clocks. It had taken him years and years; no one knew anything about it but Trude, his neighbor's daughter, and Trude had grown from a baby into a little house-mother, and still the gift was not finished.

It was to be a clock, the most wonderful and beautiful clock ever made; every part of it to be fashioned with loving care. The case, the works, the weights, the hands, and the face, all had taken years of labor. He had spent years carving the case and hands, years perfecting the works; and now Hermann saw that with a little more haste and time he could finish it for the coming Christmas.

He mended the children's toys as before, but he gave up making his regular clocks, so there were fewer to sell, and often his cupboard was empty and he went supperless to bed. But that only made him a little thinner and his face a little kinder; and meantime the gift clock became more and more beautiful.

It was fashioned after a rude stable with rafters, stall, and crib. The Holy Mother knelt beside the manger in which a tiny Christ Child lay, while through the open door the hours came. Three were kings and three were shepherds and three were soldiers and three were angels; and when the hours struck, they knelt in adoration before the sleeping Child, while the silver chimes played the "Magnificat."

"You see," said the clock-maker to Trude, "it is not just on Sundays and holidays that we should remember to worship the Christ Child and bring Him gifts—but every day, every hour."

The days went by like clouds scudding before a winter wind and the clock was finished at last. So happy was Hermann with his work that he put the gift clock on the shelf before the little window to show the passers-by. There were crowds looking at it all day long, and many would whisper, "Do you think this can be the gift Hermann has spoken of—his offering on Christmas Eve to the Church?"

The day before Christmas came. Hermann cleaned up his little shop, wound all his clocks, brushed his clothes, and then went over the gift clock again to be sure everything was perfect.

"It will not look bad beside the other gifts," he thought happily. In fact he was so happy that he gave away all but one penny to the blind beggar who passed his door; and then, remembering that he had eaten nothing since breakfast, he spent that last penny for a Christmas apple to eat with a crust of bread he had. He was putting them in the cupboard to eat after he was dressed, when the door opened and Trude was standing there crying.

"Child, child, what is the matter?" And he gathered her into his arms.

" 'Tis father. He is hurt, and all the money that was put by for the tree and sweets and toys has gone to the doctor. And now, how can I tell the children? Already they have lighted the candle at the window and are waiting for Kris Kringle to come."

The clock-maker laughed merrily.

"Come, come, little one, all will be well. Hermann will sell a clock for you. Some house in the city must need a clock; and in a wink we shall have money enough for the tree and the toys. Go home and sing."

He buttoned on his greatcoat and, picking out the best of the old clocks, he went out. He went first to the rich merchants, but their houses were full of clocks; then to the journeymen, but they said his clock was old-fashioned. He even stood on the corner of the streets and in the square, crying, "A clock—a good clock for sale," but no one paid any attention to him. At last he gathered up his courage and went to the richest man in the city.

"Will your Excellency buy a clock?" he said, trembling at his own boldness. "I would not ask, but it is Christmas and I am needing to buy happiness for some children." The rich man smiled.

"Yes, I will buy a clock, but not that one. I will pay a thousand dollars for the clock you have had in your window these four days past."

"But, your Excellency, that is impossible!" And poor Hermann trembled harder than ever.

"Poof! Nothing is impossible. That clock or none. Go home and I will send for it in half an hour, and pay you the thousand dollars."

The little clock-maker stumbled out.

"Anything but that—anything but that!" he kept mumbling over and over to himself on his way home. But as he passed the neighbor's house he saw the children at the window with their lighted candle and he heard Trude singing.

And so it happened that the servant who came from the rich man carried the gift clock away with him. But the clock-maker would take but five of the thousand dollars in payment. And as the servant disappeared up the street the chimes commenced to ring from the great cathedral, and the streets suddenly became noisy with the many people going thither, bearing their Christmas offerings.

"I have gone empty-handed before," said the little clock-maker, sadly. "I can go empty-handed once again." And again he buttoned up his greatcoat.

As he turned to shut his cupboard door behind him his eyes fell on the Christmas apple and an odd little smile crept into the corners of his mouth and lighted his eyes.

"It is all I have—my dinner for two days. I will carry that to the Christ Child. It is better, after all, than going empty-handed."

How full of peace and beauty was the great cathedral when Hermann entered it! There were a thousand tapers burning and everywhere the sweet scent of the Christmas greens—and the laden altar before the Holy Mother and Child.

There were richer gifts than had been brought for many years: marvelously wrought vessels from the greatest silver-smiths; cloth of gold and cloth of silk brought from the East by the merchants; poets had brought their songs illuminated on rolls of heavy parchment; painters had brought their pictures of saints and the Holy Family; even the King himself had brought his crown and scepter to lay before the Child. And after all these offerings came the little clock-maker, walking slowly down the long, dim aisle, holding tight to his Christmas apple.

The people saw him and a murmur hummed a moment indistinctly through the church and then grew clear and articulate:

"Shame! See, he is too mean to bring his clock! He hoards it as a miser hoards his gold. See what he brings! Shame!"

The words reached Hermann and he stumbled on blindly, his head dropped forward on his breast, his hands groping the way. The distance seemed interminable. Now he knew he was past the

seats; now his feet touched the first step, and there were seven to climb to the altar. Would his feet never reach the top?

"One, two, three," he counted to himself, then tripped and almost fell. "Four, five, six." He was nearly there. There was but one more.

The murmur of shame died away and in its place rose one of wonder and awe. Soon the words became intelligible:

"The miracle! It is the miracle!"

The people knelt in the big cathedral; the Bishop raised his hands in prayer. And the little clock-maker, stumbling to the last step, looked up through dim eyes and saw the Child leaning toward him, far down from Mary's arms, with hands outstretched to take his gift.

URSULA KOERING

337

Away in a Manger

By Martin Luther

AWAY in a manger,
  No crib for His bed,
The little Lord Jesus
  Laid down His sweet head.

The stars in the bright sky
  Looked down where He lay,
The little Lord Jesus
  Asleep in the hay.

The cattle are lowing,
  The poor Baby wakes,
But little Lord Jesus,
  No crying He makes.

I love Thee, Lord Jesus;
  Look down from the sky,
And stay by my crib,
  Watching *my* lullaby.

LONG, LONG AGO

WINDS through the olive trees
  Softly did blow
Round little Bethlehem
  Long, long ago.

Sheep on the hillside lay
  Whiter than snow;
Shepherds were watching them,
  Long, long ago.

Then from the happy sky,
  Angels bent low,
Singing their songs of joy,
  Long, long ago.

For in a manger bed,
  Cradled we know,
Christ came to Bethlehem,
  Long, long ago.

SONG FOR CHRISTMAS

By Eugene Field

WHY do bells of Christmas ring?
Why do little children sing?

Once a lovely shining star,
Seen by shepherds from afar,
Gently moved until its light
Made a manger's cradle bright.

There a darling Baby lay
Pillowed soft upon the hay;
And its Mother sung and smiled:
"This is Christ, the holy Child!"

Therefore bells for Christmas ring,
Therefore little children sing.

Surprise

By Laura Ingalls Wilder

THIS wonderful surprise came, over sixty years ago, to two little girls on the bank of Plum Creek in western Minnesota.

The winter was mild, without much snow. But chill winds blew across the prairie, and the best place for little girls was in the cozy house.

Father was gone outdoors all day. He hauled logs and chopped them into wood for the stove. He followed frozen Plum Creek far upstream, where nobody lived, and set traps along the banks for muskrat and otter and mink.

Every morning Laura and Mary studied their books and worked sums on the slate. Every afternoon Mother heard their lessons. She said they were good little scholars, and she was sure that when they went to school again they would find they had kept up with their classes.

Every Sunday they went to Sunday School. There they saw a number of other children, among them Nellie Oleson. Laura did not like Nellie Oleson. She remembered that Nellie had talked about Father being nothing but a country man, and she burned hot inside. And Nellie Oleson had a fur cape, something Laura, who was a thin, cold little thing, had always wanted.

One happy Sunday was the Sunday when the Reverend Alden came from eastern Minnesota to preach in this western church. He preached for a long time, while Laura looked at his soft blue eyes and watched his beard wagging. She hoped he would speak to her after church. And he did.

"Here are my little country girls, Mary and Laura!" he said. He remembered their names.

Laura was wearing her new dress that day. The skirt was long enough, and the sleeves were long, too. They made her coat sleeves look shorter than ever, but the red braid on the cuffs was pretty.

"What a pretty new dress, Laura!" the Reverend Alden said.

Laura almost forgave Nellie Oleson that day.

One afternoon Mother said there would be no lessons, because they must all get ready to go to town that night. Laura and Mary were astonished.

"But we never go to town at night!" Mary said.

"There must always be a first time," said Mother.

"But why must there be, Mother?" Laura asked. "Why are we going to town at night?"

"It's a surprise," said Mother. "Now, no more questions. We must all take baths and be our very nicest."

In the middle of the week, Mother

brought in the washtub and heated water for Mary's bath. Then again for Laura's bath, and again for Carrie's. There had never been such scrubbing and scampering, such a changing to fresh drawers and petticoats, such brushing of shoes and braiding of hair and tying on of hair ribbons. There had never been such a wondering.

Supper was early. After supper, Father bathed in the bedroom. Laura and Mary put on their new dresses. They knew better than to ask any more questions, but they wondered and whispered together.

The wagon box was full of clean hay. Father put Mary and Laura into it and wrapped blankets around them. He climbed to the seat beside Mother, who held Carrie on her lap, and drove away toward town.

URSULA KOERING

341

The stars were small and frosty in the dark sky. The horses' feet clippety-clopped, and the wagon rattled over the hard ground.

Father heard something else. "Whoa!" he said, pulling up the reins. Sam and David stopped. There was nothing but vast, dark coldness and stillness, pricked by the stars. Then the stillness blossomed into the loveliest sound.

The clear notes sounded, and sounded again and again.

No one moved. Only Sam and David tinkled their bits together and breathed. Those two notes went on, full and loud, soft and low. They seemed to be the stars singing.

Too soon Mother murmured, "We'd better be getting on, Charles," and the wagon rattled on. Still through its rattling Laura could hear those swaying notes.

"Oh, Father, what is it?" she asked, and Father said, "It's the new church bell, Laura."

The town seemed asleep. The stores were dark as Father drove past them. Then Laura exclaimed, "Oh, look at the church! How pretty the church is!"

The church was full of light. Light spilled out of all its windows and ran out into the darkness from the door when it opened to let someone in. Laura almost jumped out from under the blankets before she remembered that she must never stand up in the wagon when the horses were going.

Father drove to the church steps and helped them all out. He told them to go in, but they waited in the cold until he

had covered Sam and David with their blankets. Then he came, and they all went into the church together.

Laura's mouth fell open and her eyes stretched to look at what she saw. She held Mary's hand tightly, and they followed Mother and Father. They sat down. Then Laura could look with all her might.

Standing in front of the crowded benches was a tree. Laura decided it must be a tree. She could see its trunk and branches. But she had never before seen such a tree.

Where leaves would be in summer, there were clusters and streamers of thin, green paper. Thick among them hung little sacks made of pink mosquito-bar. Laura was almost sure that she could see candy in them. From the branches hung packages wrapped in colored paper, red packages and pink packages and yellow packages, all tied with colored string. Silk scarves were draped among them. Red mittens hung by a cord that would go around your neck and keep them from being lost if you were wearing them. A pair of new shoes hung by their heels from a branch. Lavish strings of white popcorn were looped over all this.

Under the tree and leaning against it were all kinds of things. Laura saw a crinkly-bright washboard, a wooden tub, a churn and dasher, a sled made of new boards, a shovel, a long-handled pitch-fork.

Laura was too excited to speak. She squeezed Mary's hand tighter and tighter, and she looked up at Mother, wanting so much to know what that was. Mother smiled down at her and said, "That is a Christmas tree, girls. Do you think it is pretty?"

They could not answer. They nodded while they kept on looking at that wonderful tree. They were hardly even surprised to know that this was a Christmas program, though they had not expected Christmas yet, because there was not enough snow. Just then Laura saw the most wonderful thing of all. From a far branch of that tree hung a little fur cape and a muff!

The Reverend Alden was there. He preached about Christmas. Everyone stood up to sing, and Laura stood up, but she could not sing. Not a sound would come out of her throat. In the whole world, there couldn't be any other thing so wonderful to look at as that tree.

After the singing, Mr. Tower and Mr. Beadle began taking things off it and reading out names. Mrs. Tower and Miss Beadle brought those things down past the benches and gave them to the persons whose names were on them. Mrs. Tower was Laura's Sunday-school teacher, and Miss Beadle was her schoolteacher. They made it all seem more real.

Everything on that tree was a Christmas present for somebody!

When Laura knew that, the lamps and people and voices and even the tree began to whirl. They whirled faster, noisier, and more excitedly. Someone gave her a pink mosquito-bar bag. It did have candy in it, and a big popcorn ball. Mary had one, too. So did Carrie. Every girl and boy had one. Then Mary had a pair of blue mittens. Then Laura had a red pair.

Mother opened a big package, and there was a warm, big, brown and red plaid shawl for her. Father got a woolly muffler. Then Carrie had a rag doll with a china head. She screamed for joy. Through the laughing and talking and rustling of papers, Mr. Beadle and Mr. Tower went on shouting names.

The little fur cape and muff still hung on the tree, and Laura watched them. She wanted to look at them as long as she could until someone got them.

Laura did not expect anything more. But to Mary came a pretty little booklet with Bible pictures in it from Mrs. Tower.

Mr. Tower was taking the little fur cape and the muff from the tree. He read a name, but Laura could not hear it through all the joyful noise. She lost sight of the cape and muff, among all the people. They were gone now.

Then to Carrie came a cunning little brown-spotted, white china dog. But Carrie's arms and eyes were full of her doll, so Laura held and stroked and laughed over the sleek little dog.

"Merry Christmas, Laura!" Mrs. Beadle said, and in Laura's hand she put a beautiful little box. It was made of snow-white, gleaming china. On its top stood a wee, gold-colored teapot and a gold-colored tiny cup in a gold-colored saucer.

The top of the box lifted off. Inside was a nice place to keep a breastpin. Mother said it was a jewel box.

There had never been such a Christmas as this. It was such a large, rich Christmas —the whole church full of Christmas. There were so many lamps, so many people, so much noise and laughter, and so many happinesses in it. Laura felt full and bursting, as if that whole big, rich Christmas were inside her, and her mittens and her beautiful jewel box with the wee gold cup and saucer and teapot and her candy and her popcorn ball. And suddenly someone said, "These are for you, Laura."

Mrs. Tower stood smiling, holding out the little fur cape and muff.

"For me?" Laura said. "For me?" Then everything else vanished while, with both arms, she hugged the soft furs to her.

She hugged them tighter and tighter, trying to believe they were really hers, that silky-soft, brown fur cape and muff.

All around her Christmas went on, but Laura knew only the softness of those furs. People were going home. Carrie was standing on the bench while Mother fastened her coat and tied her hood. Mother was saying, "Thank you so much for the shawl, Brother Alden. It is just what I needed."

Father said, "And I thank you for the muffler. It will feel good when I come to town in the cold."

The Reverend Alden sat on the bench and asked, "And does Mary's coat fit?"

Laura had not noticed Mary's coat until then. Mary had on a new coat. It was long, and its sleeves came down to Mary's wrists. Mary buttoned it, and it fitted.

"And how does this little girl like her furs?" The Reverend Alden smiled. He drew Laura between his knees. He laid the fur cape around her shoulders and fastened it at the throat. He put the cord of the muff around her neck, and her hands went inside.

"There!" the Reverend Alden said. "Now my little country girls will be warm when they come to Sunday School."

"What do you say, Laura?" Mother asked, but the Reverend Alden said, "There is no need. The way her eyes are shining is enough."

Laura could not speak. The golden-brown fur cuddled her neck and softly hugged her shoulders. Down her front it hid the threadbare fastenings of her coat. The muff came far up her wrists and hid the shortness of her coat sleeves.

"She's a little brown bird with red trimmings," the Reverend Alden said.

Then Laura laughed. It was true. Her hair and her coat, her dress and the wonderful furs were brown. Her hood and mittens and the braid on her dress were red.

"I'll tell my church people back east about our little brown bird," said Reverend Alden. "You see, when I told them about our church out here, they said they must send a box for the Christmas tree. They all gave things they had. The little girls who sent your furs and Mary's coat needed larger ones."

URSULA KOERING

"Thank you, sir," said Laura. "And please, sir, tell them thank you, too." For when she could speak, her manners were as nice as Mary's.

Mr. and Mrs. Oleson were going home, too. Mr. Oleson's arms were full of things, and so were Nellie's and Willie's. No wickedness boiled up in Laura now. "Merry Christmas, Nellie," she said, her hands snuggled in the warm muff.

Then they all said good night and Merry Christmas to the Reverend Alden. Mary was so beautiful in her Christmas coat. Carrie was so pretty on Father's arm. Father and Mother were smiling so happily, and Laura was all gladness.

A Miserable Merry Christmas

By Lincoln Steffens

WHAT interested me in our new neighborhood was not the school, nor the room I was to have in the house all to myself, but the stable which was built back of the house. My father let me direct the making of a stall, a little smaller than the other stalls, for my pony, and I prayed and hoped and my sister Lou believed that that meant that I would get the pony, perhaps for Christmas. I pointed out to her that there were three other stalls and no horses at all. This I said in order that she should answer it. She could not. My father, sounded, said that some day we might have horses and a cow; meanwhile the stable added to the value of a house.

"Some day" is a pain to a boy who lives in and knows only "now." My good little sisters, to comfort me, remarked that Christmas was coming, but Christmas was always coming and grownups were always talking about it, asking what you wanted and then giving you what they wanted you to have. Though everybody knew what I wanted, I told them all again. My mother knew that I told God, too, every night. I wanted a pony, and to make sure that they understood, I declared that I wanted nothing else.

"Nothing but a pony?" my father asked.

"Nothing," I said.

"Not even a pair of high boots?"

That was hard. I did want boots, but I stuck to the pony. "No, not even boots."

"Nor candy? There ought to be something to fill your stocking with, and Santa Claus can't put a pony into a stocking."

That was true, and he couldn't lead a pony down the chimney, either. But no. "All I want is a pony," I said. "If I can't have a pony, give me nothing, nothing."

Now I had been looking myself for the pony I wanted, going to sales stables, inquiring of horsemen, and I had seen several that would do. My father let me "try" them. I tried so many ponies that I was learning fast to sit on a horse. I chose several, but my father always found some fault with each one. I was in despair. When Christmas was at hand I had given up all hope of a pony, and on Christmas Eve I hung up my stocking along with my sisters, of whom, by the way, I now had three. I haven't mentioned them, or their coming, because, you understand, they were girls, and girls, young girls, counted for nothing in my manly life. They did not mind me, either; they were so happy that Christmas Eve that I caught some of their merriment. I speculated on what I'd get; I hung up the biggest stocking I had, and we all went reluctantly to bed to wait till morning. Not to sleep; not right away. We were told that we must not only sleep promptly, we must not wake up till seven-thirty the next morning—or if we did, we must not go to the fireplace for our Christmas.

We did sleep that night, but we woke up at six A.M. We lay in our beds and debated through the open doors whether to obey till, say, half past six. Then we bolted. I don't know who started it, but there was a rush. We all disobeyed; we raced to get first to the fireplace in the front room downstairs. And there they were, the gifts, all sorts of wonderful things, mixed-up piles of presents; only as I disentangled the mess, I saw that my stocking was empty; it hung limp; not a thing in it; and under and around it—nothing. My sisters had knelt down each by her pile of gifts. They were squealing with delight, till they looked up and saw me standing there in my nightgown with nothing. They left their piles to come to me and look at my empty place. Nothing. They felt my stocking: nothing.

I don't remember whether I cried at that moment, but my sisters did. They ran with me back to my bed, and there we all cried till I became indignant. That helped some. I got up, dressed, and driving my sisters away, I went alone out into the yard, down to the stable, and there, all by myself, I wept. My mother came out to me by and by. She found me in my pony stall, sobbing on the floor, and she tried to comfort me. But I heard my father outside; he had come part way with her, and she was having some sort of angry words with him. She tried to comfort me; besought me to come to break-

WM. MOYERS

WM. MOYERS

fast. I could not; I wanted no comfort and no breakfast. She left me and went on into the house with more sharp words for my father.

I don't know what kind of breakfast the family had. My sisters said it was "awful." They were ashamed to enjoy their own toys. They came to me, and I was rude. I ran away from them. I went around to the front of the house, sat down on the steps, and, the crying over, I ached. I was wronged, I was hurt—I can feel now what I felt then. I am sure that if one could see the wounds upon our hearts, there would be found still upon mine a scar from that terrible Christmas morning. And my father, the practical joker, he must have been hurt, too, a little. I

saw him looking out of the window. He was watching me or something for an hour or two, drawing back the curtain ever so little lest I catch him. But I saw his face, and I think I can see now the anxiety upon it, the worried impatience.

After—I don't know how long—surely an hour or two—I was brought to the climax of my agony by the sight of a man riding a pony down the street, a pony and a brand new saddle; the most beautiful saddle I ever saw, and it was a boy's saddle. The man's feet were not in the stirrups; his legs were too long. The outfit was perfect; it was the realization of all my dreams, the answer to all my prayers. A fine new bridle, with a light curb bit. And the pony! As he drew near, I saw that the pony was really a small horse, what we called an Indian pony, a bay, with black mane and tail, and one white foot and a white star on his forehead. For such a horse as that I would have given, and forgiven, anything.

But the man, a disheveled fellow with a blackened eye and a fresh-cut face, came along, reading the numbers on the houses. As my hopes—my impossible hopes—rose, he looked at our door and passed by, he and the pony, and the saddle and the bridle. Too much. I fell upon the steps, and having wept before, I broke now into such a flood of tears that I was a floating wreck when I heard a voice.

"Say, kid," it said, "do you know a boy named Lennie Steffens?"

I looked up. It was the man on the pony, back again, at our horse block.

"Yes," I sobbed. "That's me."

"Well," he said, "then this is your horse. I've been looking all over for you and your house. Why don't you put your number where it can be seen?"

"Get down," I said, running to him.

The man went on saying something about "ought to have got here at seven o'clock; he told me to bring the nag here and tie him to your post and leave him for you . . ."

"Get down," I said.

He got down, and he boosted me up to the saddle. He offered to fit the stirrups to me, but I didn't want him to. I wanted to ride.

"What's the matter with you?" he said, angrily. "What are you crying for? Don't you like the horse? He's a dandy, this horse; I know him of old. He's fine at cattle; he'll drive 'em alone."

I hardly heard, I could scarcely wait, but he persisted. He adjusted the stirrups, and then, finally, off I rode, slowly, at a walk, so happy, so thrilled, that I did not know what I was doing. I did not look back at the house or the man. I rode off up the street, taking note of everything—of the reins, of the pony's long mane, of the carved leather saddle. I had never seen anything so beautiful. And mine! I was going to ride up past Miss Kay's house. But I noticed on the horn of the saddle some stains like raindrops, so I turned and trotted home, not to the house but to the stable. There was the family—father, mother, sisters—all waiting for me, all happy now. They had been putting in place the tools of my new business: blankets, currycomb, brush, pitchfork—everything, and there was hay in the loft.

"What did you come back so soon for?" somebody asked. "Why didn't you go on riding?"

I pointed to the stains. "I wasn't going to get my new saddle rained on," I said. And my father laughed. "It isn't raining," he said. "Those are not raindrops."

"They are tears," my mother gasped, and she gave my father a look which sent him off to the house. Worse still, my mother offered to wipe away the tears still running out of my eyes. I gave her such a look as she had given him, and she went after my father, drying her eyes.

My sisters remained and we all unsaddled the pony, put on his halter, led him to his stall, tied and fed him. It began really to rain; so all the rest of that memorable day we curried and combed that pony. The girls plaited his mane, forelock, and tail, while I pitchforked hay to him and curried and brushed, curried and brushed. For a change we brought him out to drink. We led him up and down, blanketed like a race horse; we took turns at that. But the best, most inexhaustible fun, was to clean him.

When we went reluctantly to our midday Christmas dinner, we smelt of horse, and my sisters had to wash their faces and hands. I was asked to, but I wouldn't, till my mother bade me look in the mirror. Then I washed up—quick. My face was caked with muddy lines of tears that had coursed over my cheeks to my mouth. Having washed away that shame, I ate my dinner, and as I ate I grew hungrier. It was my first meal that day, and as I filled up on the turkey and the stuffing, the cranberries and the pies, the fruit and the nuts—as I swelled, I could laugh. My mother said I still choked and sobbed now and then, but I laughed, too. I saw and enjoyed my sisters' presents till—I had to go out and attend to my pony, who was there, really and truly there, the promise, the beginning, of a happy double life. And—I went and looked to make sure—there was the saddle, too, and the bridle.

But that Christmas, which my father had planned so carefully, was it the best or the worst I ever knew? He often asked me that; I never could answer as a boy. I think now that it was both. It covered the whole distance from broken-hearted misery to bursting happiness—too fast. A grownup could hardly have stood it.

WM. MOYERS

CHRISTMAS BELLS
By Henry Wadsworth Longfellow

I heard the bells on Christmas day
Their old familiar carols play,
    And wild and sweet
    The words repeat,
Of "Peace on earth, good will to men!"

And thought how, as the day had come,
The belfries of all Christendom
    Had rolled along
    The unbroken song,
Of "Peace on earth, good will to men!"

Till ringing, singing on its way,
The world revolved from night to day,—
    A voice, a chime,
    A chant sublime,
Of "Peace on earth, good will to men!"

Then pealed the bells more loud and deep:
"God is not dead; nor doth He sleep!
    The wrong shall fail,
    The right prevail,
With peace on earth, good will to men!"

351

Mother Makes Christmas

By Cornelia Meigs

JUST because it was a dull gray after-noon, with low skies and a soft chill in the air, Sally Gilbertson had let the school bus rumble away and had chosen to walk home. Now it was not so very far from Christmas and still the first snow to come. It would begin this very after-noon, Sally felt sure, for people who live on Vermont farms are always weather-wise. Snow would make everything per-fect for the Christmas feast they were going to spread at her house—the white farmhouse at the top of the hill. It had been a hard year, she knew, with her father working harder and harder, and her mother trying not to look anxious. But only last week her father, George Gilbertson, had come in smiling to say,

"I've sold all the extra hay and the two colts, both to the same buyer from up north. So now we can feel a little easy again."

And her mother's prompt answer was, "Then I'm going to make Christmas."

In Vermont, if you say you will make Christmas, it means that you will hold the Christmas feast at your house and all the family from round about will come to it. Sally jumped up and down with delight. She was eleven years old, and as full of spirit and enterprise as one of the striped chipmunks that ran up and down the pasture stone wall.

As she came out of school and walked down the one short street of the town her mind was so full of plans that she hardly noticed anything about her. She passed the railroad station with scarcely a glance; the afternoon train was in and there was nothing to watch for. But sud-denly she heard feet running after her and looked around to see a tall boy, a little older than herself. He spoke rather breathlessly,

"I think you're the cousin I met five years ago. I'm Hugh Evans. Father and mother are traveling, so I came up to spend the vacation with Uncle Silas. He is——"

Just then Great-Uncle Silas came rat-tling down the street in his loose-jointed old buggy with the stout gray mare, Bess. He pulled up with a great whoa and motioned Hugh to get in, saying gruffly,

"Well, you got here, I see. I've got errands to do before I go out home. Get up, Bess." They clattered away.

How would a boy feel, Sally thought hotly, who came for his Christmas vaca-tion and was given so brief a greeting? Oh, dear, why must Uncle Silas be like that! But as she set out on the long tramp home her heart lightened and her feet scarcely knew they were on the ground as she went up the hill.

There are few things that one learns

URSULA KOERING

353

to love more than one's own home road. Sally loved hers, with its loop at the edge of the village, its curves around the head of Mr. Hopkins' little stream, its long straight uphill stretch with the valley lying ever wider and more distant below. She loved it at all seasons but perhaps most of all when the smooth slopes of brown and yellow fields began to show the first powdering of snow. A soft aimless flake wandered down, touched her cheek and melted and was followed by another. Then there was a thin veil of falling white which spread slowly over the whole hillside and hid the dark bulk of the mountains looming above. Nothing was ever so mysterious, so exciting or so curiously satisfying as this first downfall of snow. She lifted her face to the cool flakes as she walked along.

Sally was halfway up the hill when she heard the sound of wheels and the trot, trot of a horse's feet. She knew the thin rattle of those wheels, this was Great-Uncle Silas again, with his errands finished, jogging home. He drew up to offer her a ride. She felt shy and looked down as she climbed in. The boy with him seemed subdued by Uncle Silas' presence, too, for he gave her one quick, friendly look and did not say anything. At last Uncle Silas brought out the remark that Sally had been waiting for.

"Well, all the children look forward to the first snow. Now they have it." He said that every year.

Her house was beginning to show at the top of the hill, white behind the row of tall maples. She would get down at her own door, but before she did so she must give Uncle Silas his invitation.

"You must come for Christmas dinner at our house. Mother told me to ask you."

"Going to make Christmas, air ye?" Uncle Silas returned sourly. "And I'd like to know what you think you're going to make it on. Your father may think he sold his hay and his colts, but you can never be sure of such things until the money has passed. If I was as bad off as George Gilbertson, I wouldn't be making Christmas for nobody."

Sally's cheeks flamed. Her mother had told her often that she was too hasty, but she forgot it completely now.

"Of course we're going to do it. My father and mother both said so and they're never wrong. So you're to come. Both of you."

Uncle Silas said nothing; Bess heaved herself into motion again and they rolled away. Sally thought that Hugh looked back over his shoulder at her as they turned into the road.

The big farm kitchen was warm and bright as they sat down to supper. Her father had driven the car to town and came in late, with snow all over his coat.

"It's really coming down," he said as he took his place at the table. Sally's younger brother, Billy, settled himself in his chair.

"Gee, but I'm hungry," he said happily.

They had nearly finished supper when Sally's father pushed back his chair. "There is word going around town that the man who was here buying grain and

354

horses has gone back on every bargain he made. So I guess I haven't sold the colts and the hay."

Sally saw her mother's face change, saw it look almost frightened. It is so easy to step from good fortune to bad, all in a minute, when you live on a farm. The same thought was in every mind, even Billy's, when Mary Gilbertson put it into words.

"Then we have hardly anything to go on with. And we've asked at least twenty people to Christmas dinner."

"Twenty-two," said Sally in a little voice, but no one seemed to hear her.

On the wall opposite her place hung the round, gold-framed mirror with an eagle on it which had belonged to her grandmother. Sally was growing so big that she was beginning to be able to catch sight of herself in it, though for all the years before it had hung too high. Now, by a very little stretching she could see her whole head and shoulders, her flyaway hair, her sturdy chin, her dark eyes. Why, she was a big girl now, she was able to do all sorts of things she had not thought possible.

"I'll help you, mother, I can help. And Billy and I can help with the colts, they can eat up the hay, and in the spring they will be big horses. Oh, surely we can have Christmas. We have to." Her voice was desperate. She had told Uncle Silas and the new cousin that they would.

"I think we can manage," Mary Gilbertson said slowly. "Yes, we'll do it somehow."

It was a busy two weeks, so busy that Sally began to think that she had never before known what real work meant. But the work was fun because she knew she could do it. It was not for nothing that she had grown big enough to see herself in Granny's looking glass.

There was first of all the great problem of the Christmas dinner. What they would make it out of seemed at first a complete mystery. They had some young guinea hens.

"But they're so slim and small," her mother said. "People say they are choice eating, but they never would go around twenty hungry guests." But only the next day Mrs. Haskins, who raised poultry below the hill, came up to get some eggs and admired the guineas.

"I never seem to have enough to supply my customers down in the town," she said.

It was Sally's grand and sudden idea that they should trade the guineas for two of Mrs. Haskins' turkeys, to be collected the day before Christmas. The plan was good. Mrs. Haskins thought she had a mite too many turkeys and would be glad of the exchange. She went home with the basket of loud-voiced guineas in the back of her bumpy old car and the main dish for Christmas dinner was settled. The makings of the plum pudding were not so hard to find; the Corners store would give them raisins and citron and flour when they took in their pumpkins and squash. Things began to look hopeful, but there would be plenty of work to do.

Besides this the colts were Sally's job,

355

hers and Billy's. It was surprising how much waiting on young colts needed, water and grain brought to them in the morning, bedding down and feeding at night, turning out when the weather was good, bringing in when storms threatened. Sally loved to see the colts scamper down the pasture, stepping high in the crisp frozen snow, the breath from their noses going up in columns in the frosty air. They seemed to grow every day, turning from awkward, lanky babies into real horses. She and Billy were very proud of them.

There was one afternoon when Sally got home, a little tired after the long day in school, to be met at the door by her mother.

"Billy came home early, with a cold. Can you tend the colts?"

It was not so easy to go alone into the dark barn, to hang up the lantern, to get the hay fork and clamber up into the loft. The colts were stamping in their stalls and nickering for their supper. The hay was low in the part of the mow where they were used to getting it. She had to move the heavy ladder, but finally got it into a new place. It was not very steady—"But it will do—it will have to do," she said impatiently.

She began to climb up, but suddenly the foot of the ladder slid outward. She caught at a beam and held herself, but she could get neither up nor down. She hung there, wondering what she should do when all at once a voice spoke in the gloom below her, a voice she did not recognize.

"I came out to help you. Steady, I'll hold the ladder and you can get down." She scrambled down safely and saw in the lantern light that it was the visiting cousin, Hugh Evans. He took the fork from her hand and clambered up.

"Let me know when I have thrown down enough," he said. The hay began swishing down in great forkfuls. How good it was to have some real help!

Sally heard an odd sound, and saw her mother standing in the barn doorway, holding something white in her arms, something that struggled and quacked.

"Why, it's Uncle Silas' Josiah," she exclaimed. Josiah was a white duck so old that everyone knew him. Hugh leaned over to explain, a little unwillingly.

"Uncle Silas said it was to help out with the Christmas dinner," he said. "I wish—I wish a little you could keep him somewhere for the few years he will last. Josiah is a noble old bird, but I'll bet he would make tough eating."

Sally's mother nodded and laughed. "Certainly, we will give him a home," and she added what was in Sally's mind too. "You know how to pitch hay well for a city boy."

"Oh, I've learned to do it since I've been with Uncle Silas. May I come help you again?"

He came again and again, to help Sally and Billy and their father in the barn, and, when the work was done, to have a wild romp with his cousins all over the mountains of hay in the loft. But he always walked away looking serious and dignified. That was how one had to look

356

when one stayed in Uncle Silas Evans' house.

On Christmas morning everyone was up at sunrise, a glowing red sunrise behind the still, snow-wrapped mountains. There were gay gifts for the children; for Sally a red hood with rabbit's fur around the face, for Billy a small axe, shiny and sharp, a sign that he was a big boy and could be trusted with a keen edge. Then everyone began to "fly around." The two turkeys were ushered into the oven, the dried corn and squash and pickles and cake were made ready. The sauce for the plum pudding was a morning's occupation in itself. Sally felt very proud as she stirred and stirred. The kitchen was full of steam, of delicious smells, of bubbling and popping sounds coming from under every cover.

"Mother," said Sally suddenly, "what will Uncle Silas say about Josiah?"

"Uncle Silas will be glad enough to eat turkey, he won't ask about Josiah."

Guests began to arrive long before noon, Cousin Miranda Betts with her three small children, Cousin Tom Howe with his wife and his big son and bigger daughter. More came and more. All the women and most of the young girls put on aprons at once and began to help, or gave their assistance to Sally who was setting the table in the long living room. The work went forward steadily in a loud buzz of talk. Uncle Silas came in last, wrapped in half a dozen scarfs and

URSULA KOERING

357

two pairs of big mittens.

"The rest of you don't seem to be taking much notice, but it's going to storm before the day is over. This Christmas-card weather is too good to last."

Hugh came in behind him. He had brought a big bunch of arbor vitae and red berries to add to the other Christmas greens.

The oven was opened for the last time and the turkeys were brought out. Everything was ready. Suddenly the outer door of the kitchen was flung back and Billy stood on the threshold, his cheeks scarlet, his eyes wide with excitement.

"There's a big wind coming up. It blew the stable door open and the colts got out." The wind was big indeed, for it slammed the door behind him with a crash.

One of the women screamed, all the men jumped up, grabbed their wraps and ran out, Sally and Billy at their father's heels. The great pile of clouds, sweeping up the sky, spoke the truth of the storm which Uncle Silas had prophesied. Two dots, racing wildly across the pasture, told which way the excitable colts had dashed to freedom. Hugh plunged into the stable and came out leading Bess. Uncle Silas raised a shout of protest, but Tom Howe silenced him.

"Let the boy alone. He knows what he is about."

The colts had tried to run down the long slippery slope, but headed off by Hugh and the galloping Bess, they turned about and plunged into the woods.

"That's no place for them in this wind," George Gilbertson cried. "We'll have to drive them out."

Sally and Billy kept close behind their father as they dashed for the wood. The wind was screaming overhead now, filling the air with a cloud of dry snow. She saw Hugh slide off the back of the horse; she thought he motioned to her to go back, but she could not be stopped. The colts were standing, undecided, for an instant, and she and Billy ran up to them. She had caught hold of the forelock of the black one when, all at once, a great shattering crash almost stunned her and a whiff of snow blinded her.

When Sally opened her eyes, she and Billy and the two colts were tangled in a great tent of broken branches. One big maple had crashed down, carrying two others with it. They were sheltered by the tilt of the huge trunk, but were so fenced in that they could scarcely move.

"Hold him, Billy, don't let him plunge and hurt himself." She had caught the broken halter of the brown colt and put the end into Billy's hand. Then she raised a call, "Here we are. We're safe."

"Thank God for that," she heard her father's voice outside. "Now keep as still as you can. We'll chop a way in."

They stood very still, trying to soothe the horses, Billy as valiant as Sally, but his face a little pale. The noise of the driving axes sounded all about them. Sally heard Hugh's voice, knew that the fastest, fiercest strokes were his, heard him say, "Can you hold out?" Then a trunk beside them suddenly fell in two and Hugh stepped through the opening. He

358

URSULA KOERING

was so breathless that he could scarcely speak, but he took hold of the black colt. "I'll hold him now, Sally."

Yes, Sally was willing that he should. Her arm ached and her knees were weak. Another log rolled aside and her father pushed through to put his arm around her.

Christmas dinner was a little late, but it was a grand feast just the same. Sally was not allowed to help wait on the others as she had expected. The younger cousins took over that task and kept coming to her to ask, "Shall we do this, Cousin Sally? Is it right to do that?" It made her feel very grown up and proud.

When Uncle Silas was asked if he would prefer duck or turkey, he answered promptly, "Turkey, Mary. Leave the duck for the young ones," so that no questions were asked about Josiah. Cousin Tom Howe said the two colts were the likeliest-looking pair he had ever seen and were on the way to being valuable horses. When they got up from the table, Uncle Silas, in the midst of a silence, said solemnly,

"Your mother knows how to make Christmas, Sally." And Hugh behind him whispered to her,

"And so do you. I'm coming again, next year."

The Stork and the Holy Babe

A Christmas Ballad Found on the Fly-Leaf of a King's Prayer-Book, 1549

THE stork, she rose on Christmas Eve
And said unto her brood:
"I now must fare to Bethlehem
To see the Son of God."

She gave to each his dole of meat
And tucked them safely in,
And fair she flew and fast she flew
And came to Bethlehem.

"Now where is He of David's line?"
She asked at house and hall.
"He is not here," they softly spoke,
"But in the manger stall."

She found Him in the manger stall
With Mary, Holy Maid;
The gentle stork, she wept to see
The Babe so lowly laid.

Then from her snowy breast she plucked
The feathers white and warm
And strewed them on the manger crib
To keep the Babe from harm.

"Now blessèd be the gentle stork
Forever more," said He,
"For that she saw my lowly bed
And comfort gave to me.

"Full welcome shall she ever be
In hamlet and in hall
And called henceforth the blessèd bird,
The friend of babies all."

The Friendly Beasts

JESUS our brother, strong and good,
Was humbly born in a stable rude,
And the friendly beasts around Him stood,
Jesus our brother, strong and good.

"I," said the donkey shaggy and brown,
"I carried His mother up hill and down,
I carried her safely to Bethlehem town;
I," said the donkey, shaggy and brown.

"I," said the cow all white and red,
"I gave Him my manger for His bed,
I gave Him my hay to pillow His head,
I," said the cow all white and red.

"I," said the sheep with curly horn,
"I gave Him my wool for His blanket
  warm,
He wore my coat on Christmas morn;
I," said the sheep with curly horn.

"I," said the dove, from the rafters high,
"Cooed Him to sleep, my mate and I,
We cooed Him to sleep, my mate and I;
I," said the dove, from the rafters high.

And every beast, by some good spell,
In the stable dark was glad to tell,
Of the gift he gave Immanuel,
The gift he gave Immanuel.

Young Lucretia

By Mary E. Wilkins Freeman

WHO's that little gal goin' by?" said old Mrs. Emmons.

"That—why, that's young Lucretia, Mother," replied her daughter Ann, peering out of the window over her mother's shoulder. There was a fringe of flowering geraniums in the window; the two women had to stretch their heads over them.

"Poor little soul!" Mrs. Emmons remarked. "I pity that child."

"I don't see much to pity her for," Ann returned, in a voice high-pitched and sharply sweet; she was the soprano singer in the village choir. "I don't see that she isn't taken care of as well as most."

"Well, I don't know but she's taken care of, but I guess she don't get much coddlin'. Lucretia an' Maria ain't that kind—never was. I heard the other day they was goin' to have a Christmas-tree down to the schoolhouse. Now I'd be willin' to venture that child don't have a thing on it."

"Well, if she's kept clean and taught to behave, it amounts to a good deal more'n Christmas presents, I suppose." Ann sat down and turned a hem with vigor; she was a dressmaker.

"Well, I s'pose it does, but that little gal ought to have somethin'. Do you remember those little rag babies I used to make for you, Ann? I s'pose she'd be tickled with one. Some of that blue calico would be just the thing to make a dress of."

"Now, Mother, don't you fuss. She won't think anything of it."

"Yes, she would too. *You* used to." Old Mrs. Emmons, tall and tremulous, rose and went out of the room.

Ann began smoothing out some remnants of the blue calico on her lap. She selected one piece she thought would do for the dress.

Meanwhile young Lucretia went to school. It was quite a cold day, but she was warmly dressed. She wore her Aunt

362

Lucretia's red and green plaid shawl, which Aunt Lucretia had worn to meeting when she was herself a little girl, over her Aunt Maria's black cloth coat.

Young Lucretia wore, also, her Aunt Maria's black alpaca dress, which had been made smaller to fit, and her Aunt Lucretia's purple scarf over her head. She had mittens, and her Aunt Maria's thick wool stockings drawn over her shoes to keep the snow from her ankles.

If young Lucretia caught cold, it would not be her aunts' fault. She went along rather clumsily but quite merrily, holding her tin lunch box very steady.

Here and there along the road were sprigs of evergreen and ground-pine and hemlock. Lucretia glanced at them. She was nearly in sight of the schoolhouse when she reached Alma Ford's house, and Alma came out and joined her. Alma was trim and pretty in her fur-bordered winter coat and her scarlet hood.

"Hullo, Lucretia!" said Alma.

"Hullo!" responded Lucretia. Then the two girls trotted on together; the evergreen sprigs were growing thicker. "Did you go with the others to pick out the tree?" asked Lucretia.

"Yes; we went way up to the crossroads. They wouldn't let you go, would they?"

"No," said Lucretia, smiling broadly.

"I think it was *mean*," said Alma.

"They said they didn't approve of it," said Lucretia, in a voice which sounded like an echo of someone else's.

When they got to the schoolhouse it took her a long time to unroll herself from her many wrappings. There was not another child there who was dressed like her. Seen from behind, she looked like a small, tightly-built old lady.

Her sandy hair was braided in two tight tails, fastened by a green bow. Young Lucretia was a homely little girl, although her face was always radiantly good-humored. She was a good scholar, too, and could spell and add sums as fast as anybody in the school.

In the hall, where she took off her things, there was a great litter of evergreen and hemlock; in the farthest corner, lopped pitifully over on its side, was a fine hemlock tree. Lucretia looked at it, and her smiling face grew a little serious.

"That the Christmas tree there?" she said to the other girls when she went into the schoolroom. The teacher had not come, and there was such an uproar and jubilation that she could hardly make herself heard. She had to poke one of the girls two or three times before she could get her question answered.

"What did you say, Lucretia Raymond?" the girl asked.

"That the Christmas tree out there?"

"Course 'tis. Say, Lucretia, can you come and help us trim this evening? The boys are going to set up the tree, and we're going to trim. Can't you come?"

The other girls joined in: "Can't you come, Lucretia?"

Lucretia looked at them all, with her honest smile. "I don't believe I can," said she.

"Won't your aunts let you?"

"Don't believe they will."

363

Alma Ford stood back on her heels and threw back her chin. "Well, I don't care," said she. "I think your aunts are *awful mean*—so there!"

Lucretia's face grew pinker, and the laughter died out of it. She opened her lips, but before she had a chance to speak, Lois Green, one of the older girls and an authority in the school, added her testimony, "They are two mean, stingy old maids," she proclaimed.

"They're not neither," said Lucretia, unexpectedly. "You shan't say such things about my aunts, Lois Green."

"Oh, you can stick up for 'em if you want to," returned Lois. "If you want to be such a little gump, you can, an' nobody'll pity you. You know you won't get a single thing on this Christmas tree."

"I will, too," cried Lucretia, who could be fiery for all her sweetness.

All through the day it seemed to her, the more she thought of it, that she must go with the others to trim the schoolhouse, and she must have something on the Christmas tree. A keen sense of shame for her aunts and herself was over her; she felt as if she must keep up the family credit.

"I wish I could go to trim this evening," she said to Alma, as they were going home after school.

"Don't you think they'll let you?"

"I don't believe they'll approve of it," Lucretia answered with dignity.

"Say, Lucretia, do you s'pose it would make any difference if my mother should go up to your house and ask your aunts?"

Lucretia gave her a startled look. A vision of her aunts' indignation at such interference shot before her eyes. "Oh, I don't believe it would do a mite of good," said she fervently. "But Alma, you might come home with me while I ask."

"I will," said Alma eagerly. "Just wait a minute till I ask Mother if I can."

But it was all useless. Alma's pretty pleading little face as a supplement to Lucretia's, and her timorous "Please let Lucretia go" had no effect whatever.

"I don't approve of children being out nights," said Aunt Lucretia, and Aunt Maria supported her. "There's no use talking," said she. "You can't go, Lucretia. Not another word. Take your things off, and sit down and sew your square of patchwork. Alma, you'd better run right home; I guess your mother'll be wanting you to help." And Alma went.

"What made you bring that Ford girl in here to ask me?" Aunt Lucretia asked of young Lucretia.

"I don't know," stammered Lucretia over her patchwork.

"You'll never go anywhere any quicker for taking such means as that," said Aunt Lucretia.

"It would serve you right if we didn't let you go to the Christmas tree," declared Aunt Maria severely, and young Lucretia quaked. She had had the promise of going to the Christmas tree for a long time. It would be awful if she should lose that. She sewed very diligently on her patchwork.

Half an hour after supper she had the square all done and she carried it over to her Aunt Lucretia.

Aunt Lucretia put on her spectacles and looked closely at it. "You've sewed it very well," she said, finally. "You can sew well enough if you put your mind to it."

"That's what I've always told her," chimed in Aunt Maria. "There's no sense in her taking the kind of stitches she does sometimes. Now, Lucretia, it's time for you to go to bed."

Lucretia went lingeringly across the sitting-room, then across the dining-room, into the kitchen. It was quite a time before she got her candle lighted and came back, and then she stood about hesitantly.

"What are you waiting for?" Aunt Lucretia asked sharply. "Take care; you're tipping your candle over; you'll get the grease on the carpet."

"Why don't you mind what you're doing?" said Aunt Maria.

"They're going to have lots of presents on the Christmas tree," she remarked, tipping her candle again.

"Are you going to hold that candle straight or not?" cried Aunt Lucretia. "Who is going to have lots of presents?"

"All the other girls."

"Well, the other girls can have lots of presents. If their folks want to get presents for 'em they can," said Aunt Lucretia. "There's one thing about it, you won't get anything, and you needn't expect anything. I never approved of this giving presents Christmas, anyways. It's a foolish piece of business."

Young Lucretia's lips quivered so she could hardly speak. "They'll think—it's—

so funny if I don't have anything," she said.

"Let 'em think it's funny if they want to. You go to bed, and don't say any more about it. Mind you hold that candle straight."

Young Lucretia tried to hold the candle straight as she went upstairs, but it was hard work, her eyes were so misty.

It was a long time before she went to sleep that night. She cried first, then she meditated. After a while her lively imagination hit upon a plan for keeping up the family honor, hers and her aunts', before the eyes of the school.

The next day everything favored the plan. There was no school. In the afternoon both the aunts went to the sewing society. They had been gone about an hour when young Lucretia trudged down the road with her arms full of parcels. She stole so quietly and softly into the schoolhouse, where they were arranging the tree, that no one thought about it. She laid the parcels on a settee with some others, and stole out and ran home.

The Christmas Eve festivities at the schoolhouse were to begin at seven o'clock. There were to be some exercises, some recitations, and singing, then the presents. Right after supper that evening young Lucretia went up to her own room and came down in a surprisingly short time all dressed.

"Are you ready?" said Aunt Lucretia.

"Yes, ma'am," replied young Lucretia. She had her hand on the door.

"I don't believe you are half-dressed,"

said Aunt Maria. "Did you get your bow on straight?"

"Yes, ma'am."

"I think she'd better take her things off and let us be sure," said Aunt Lucretia. "I'm not goin' to have her down there with her clothes on any which way, and everybody making remarks. Take your jacket off, Lucretia."

"Oh, I got my bow on straight, *honest*," protested young Lucretia. She clutched the plaid shawl tightly together, but it was no use—off the things had to come. And young Lucretia had to put on her dress wrong side before; she had buttoned it in the back. There she stood, very much askew and uncomfortable about the shoulder seams and sleeves, and hung her head before her aunts.

"Lucretia Raymond, what *do* you mean, putting your dress on this way?"

"All the other girls wear theirs buttoned in the back."

"All the other girls! Well, you're not going to have yours buttoned in the back, and wear holes through that nice coat every time you lean back against a chair. I've a good mind not to let you go out at all. Stand around here!"

Young Lucretia's dress was sharply unbuttoned. She was jerked out of it, and it was turned around and fastened as Aunt Lucretia thought it should be. When she finally started, she felt sad and doubtful; but soon she was her own merry self.

There was no one more radiant than she all through the opening exercises. She listened to the speaking and the singing with the greatest appreciation and delight.

She sat up perfectly straight in her prim, stiff dress. She folded her small red hands before her, and her face was all smiles.

When the distribution of presents began her name was among the first to be called. She arose eagerly and went with a gay little prance down the aisle. She took the parcel the teacher handed to her and had begun her journey back when she suddenly saw her Aunt Lucretia and her Aunt Maria.

She had never dreamed of such a thing as her aunts coming; indeed, they had not thought of it themselves. A neighbor had come in and persuaded them, and they had agreed to come against all their principles.

Young Lucretia's name was called again and again. Every time she slunk more reluctantly and fearfully down to the tree; she knew her aunts' eyes were surveying her with more and more amazement.

After the presents were all distributed she sat perfectly still with hers around her. They lay on her desk, and the last was in her lap. She had not taken off a single wrapping. They were done up neatly in brown paper, and Lucretia's name was written on them.

Lucretia sat there. The other girls were in a hubbub of delight all around her, comparing their presents, but she sat perfectly still and watched her aunts coming. They came slowly; they stopped to speak to the teacher. Aunt Lucretia reached young Lucretia first.

"What are those packages you have there?" she demanded. "Why don't you undo them?" Young Lucretia just gazed miserably at her aunt and shook her head helplessly. "Why, what makes you act so, child?" cried Aunt Lucretia, getting alarmed. Then Aunt Maria came up, and there was quite a little group around young Lucretia. She began to cry.

"What on earth ails the child?" said Aunt Lucretia. She caught up one of the parcels and opened it; it was a book bound in red and gold. She held it close to her eyes; she turned it this way and that; she examined the fly-leaf. "Why," said she, "it's the old gift-book Aunt Susan gave me when I was eighteen years old! What in the world!"

Aunt Maria had undone another. "This is the *Floral Album*," she said tremulously, "the one we always keep in the north parlor on the table. Here's my name in it. I don't see——"

Aunt Lucretia speechlessly unmuffled a clove apple and a nautilus shell that had graced the parlor·shelf. Finally there appeared a little daintily dressed rag doll, its cheeks stained pink with cranberry juice. When Lucretia spied this last she was so surprised that she made a little grab at it.

"Oh," she sobbed, "somebody did hang this on for me! They did! It's mine!"

It never seemed to young Lucretia that she walked going home that night; she had a feeling that only her tiptoes occasionally brushed the earth as she went on rapidly with a tall aunt on either side. Not much was said. Once, in a lonely place in

367

the road, there was a volley of severe questions from her aunts, and young Lucretia burst out into a desperate wail.

"Oh!" she cried, "I was going to put 'em right back again. I haven't hurt 'em any. I was careful. I didn't s'pose you'd know it. They said you were cross and stingy and wouldn't hang anything on the tree for me, and I didn't want 'em to think you were. I wanted to make 'em think I had things like other children."

After they got home not much was said. The aunts were still too bewildered for many words. Lucretia was bidden to light her candle and go to bed. And then came a new grief. They took her new doll and put it away in the parlor with the clove apple, the nautilus shell, and the gift-book. Then the little girl's heart failed her; terror and the loss of the only comfort that had come to her on this pitiful Christmas Eve were too much.

"Oh," she wailed, "my rag doll! I want my—rag baby. Oh! oh! oh! I want her, I want her!"

Scolding had no effect. Young Lucretia sobbed out her complaint all the way upstairs, and her aunts could hear the pitiful little wail of "My rag baby, I want my rag doll," after she was in her room.

The two women looked at each other. They sat uneasily down by the fireplace.

"I must say I think you're rather hard on her, Lucretia," said Maria finally.

"I don't know as I've been any harder on her than you have," returned Lucretia. "I shouldn't have said to take away that rag doll if I'd said just what I thought."

"I think you had better take it up to her

then, to stop that crying," said Maria.

Lucretia hastened into the parlor without another word. She carried the rag doll upstairs to young Lucretia; then she came down to the pantry and got her a cookie.

"I thought the child had better have a little bite of something; she didn't eat scarcely a mite of supper," she explained to Maria. She had given young Lucretia's head a pat when she gave her the cookie, and told her to eat it and go right to sleep. The little girl hugged her rag doll and ate her cookie in bliss.

The aunts sat a while longer by the fire. Just before they left it for the night, Lucretia looked hesitatingly at Maria and said, "I s'pose you have noticed that wax doll down at White's store?"

"That big wax one with the pink dress?" asked Maria.

"Yes. There was a doll's bedstead there, too. I don't know as you noticed it."

"Yes, I think I did, now you speak of it. I noticed it the day I went for the gingham. There was a doll baby's carriage there, too."

The aunts looked at each other. "I s'pose it would be dreadful foolish," said Lucretia.

"She'd be most too tickled to live," remarked Maria.

"We can still buy 'em tonight if we hurry," said Lucretia. And that is exactly what they did.

The next day was Christmas. It was about three o'clock in the afternoon when old Mrs. Emmons went up the road to the Raymond house. She had a little parcel. When she came into the parlor there

was young Lucretia in a corner, so that the room should not get in a mess, with her wealth around her. She looked forth, a radiant little mother of dolls, from the midst of her doll's housekeeping.

"My sakes!" cried old Mrs. Emmons, "Isn't that *complete!* You've got a big wax doll, and a bedstead, and a baby carriage, and a table and a bureau. I declare! I don't know what I'd have thought when I was a little girl. And I've brought some pieces for you to make some more dresses for the rag baby if you want to."

Young Lucretia's eyes shone.

"You were real kind to think of it," said Aunt Lucretia, "and she'll take real comfort making the dresses. I'm glad you came in, Mrs. Emmons. I've been wanting to go to see you for a long time. I want to see Ann, too; I thought I'd see if she hadn't got a pattern of a dress that buttons up the back for Lucretia."

Young Lucretia's eyes shone more than ever, and she smiled out of her corner like a little star. Her world was a beautiful place and she loved everybody in it.

Christmas Every Day

By William Dean Howells

JANE came into her father's study, as she always did on Saturday mornings, and asked him to tell her a story. So he began: "Once there was a little pig—"

Jane put her hand over her father's mouth and stopped him at the word. She said she had heard little pig stories till she was sick of them.

"What kind of story *shall* I tell then?"

"About Christmas. It's getting to be the season. It's past Thanksgiving already."

"It seems to me," argued her father, "that I've told you stories about Christmas as often as I have about pigs."

"But Christmas is so much more interesting," protested Jane.

"Very well, then," agreed her father, "I'll tell you about the little girl who wanted it Christmas every day in the year. How would you like that?"

"Fine!" said Jane, as she nestled into his lap, ready for listening.

"Well, then this little pig— Oh, what are you pounding me for?"

"Because you said little pig instead of little girl!"

"I should like to know what's the difference between a little pig and a little girl who wanted it Christmas every day!"

"Daddy!" warned Jane. "If you don't go on, I'll *give* it to you!"

And at this her father began as fast as he could.

This is the story he told:

Once there was a little girl who liked Christmas so much she wanted it to be Christmas every day in the year. As soon as Thanksgiving was over she began to send post cards to the old Christmas Fairy to ask if she mightn't have it. For weeks she got no reply, but just the day before Christmas there arrived a letter for her from the Fairy, saying she might have her wish. It would be Christmas every day for a year.

The little girl was already greatly excited preparing for the old-fashioned once-a-year Christmas that was coming the next day, and perhaps the Fairy's letter didn't make such an impression on her as it would have made at some other time. She just decided to keep it to herself, and surprise everybody with it as it kept coming true; and then it slipped out of her mind altogether.

She went to bed early the night before, so as to let Santa Claus have a chance at the stockings; and in the morning she was up before anybody else. She found her stocking all lumpy with packages of candy and oranges and grapes and rubber balls and all kinds of small presents. Her mother's and father's stockings were filled with potatoes and pieces of coal wrapped up in tissue paper, just as they had always been, as a joke, on Christmas.

The little girl was the first to burst into the living room and look at the large presents laid out on the library-table—books and portfolios and boxes of stationery and bracelets and dolls and a little stove and dozens of handkerchiefs and a sled and skates and a snow-shovel and photograph-frames and little easels and boxes of water-colors and candies and a doll's house—and of course the big Christmas-tree, standing, lighted and laden with ornaments, in the middle of the floor.

The little girl had a splendid Christmas all day. She ate so much candy early in the morning that she did not want any breakfast, and all day presents kept pouring in that the expressman had not had time to deliver the night before.

The little girl went around giving the presents she had bought for other people, and when she came home she ate a dinner of turkey and dressing and cranberry sauce and sweet potatoes and plum-pudding and nuts and raisins and oranges and more candy. Then she went out and coasted on her sled, and came in with a stomach-ache, crying. And her father said he wouldn't have his house turned into that sort of fool's paradise another year. So they all had a very light supper, and pretty early everybody went to bed cross.

Here Jane pounded her father in the back again.

"Well, what now? Did I say pigs?"

"You made them *act* like pigs?"

"Well, didn't they?"

"No matter; you oughtn't to put it into a story."

"Very well, then, I'll take it all out."

The little girl slept very heavily, and she slept late, but she was awakened at last by other children dancing around her bed with their stockings full of presents in their hands.

"What is it?" said the little girl, and

mary stevens

371

she rubbed her eyes and tried to sit up.

"Christmas! Christmas! Christmas!" they shouted, and waved their stockings.

"Nonsense! Christmas was yesterday."

The children laughed. "We don't know about that. It's Christmas today, anyway. You come into the living room and see."

Then all at once it flashed on the little girl that the Fairy was keeping her promise, and her year of Christmases was beginning. She was dreadfully sleepy, but she sprang up like a lark—a lark that had overeaten itself and gone to bed cross— and darted into the living room. There it was again! Books and portfolios and boxes of stationery and bracelets—

"You needn't go over it all, Daddy; I guess I can remember what was there," said Jane.

But her father continued as though he hadn't heard:

Well, there was the Christmas-tree blazing away, and the family picking out their presents, but looking pretty sleepy, and the little girl's father very much puzzled, and her mother ready to cry.

"I'm sure I don't see how I'm to get rid of all these things," complained her mother, and her father said it seemed to him they had had something just like it the day before, but he supposed he must have dreamed it. This struck the little girl as a joke; and she ate so much candy she didn't want any breakfast, and she had turkey and cranberry for dinner, and then went out and coasted, and came in with a—

"Daddy!" interrupted Jane.

"What now?"

"What did you promise, you forgetful thing?"

"Oh! oh, yes!"

Well, the next day, it was the same thing over again, but everybody getting crosser; and at the end of a week's time so many people had lost their tempers you could pick up a lost temper anywhere; they all but covered the ground. Even when people tried to recover their tempers they usually got somebody else's, and it made the most dreadful mix-up.

The little girl began to get frightened, keeping the secret all to herself; she wanted to tell her mother, but she didn't dare to. And she was ashamed to ask the Fairy to take back her gift; it seemed ungrateful and ill-bred. So she thought she would try to stand it, but she hardly knew how she could, for a whole year.

It went on and on, and it was Christmas on St. Valentine's Day and Washington's Birthday and it didn't skip even the First of April, though everything was make-believe that day, and that was *some* relief!

After a while, coal and potatoes began to be awfully scarce because so many had been wrapped up in tissue paper to fool fathers and mothers with. Turkeys got to be about a thousand dollars apiece—

"Daddy!"

"What?"

"You're beginning to fib."

"Well, *two* thousand, then."

And they got to passing off almost anything for turkeys—even half-grown hum-

372

ming-birds—the real turkeys were so scarce. And cranberries—they asked a diamond apiece for cranberries. All the woods and orchards were cut down for Christmas-trees, and where they used to be, looked like a stubble-field, with all the tree-stumps. After a while people got so poor because of buying Christmas presents for one another that they couldn't get any new clothes, and they just wore their old ones to tatters. They got so poor that everybody had to go to the poorhouse, except the candy-makers and the gift-manufacturers and the expressmen; and *they* all got so rich and proud that they would hardly wait upon a person when he came to buy; it was perfectly shameful!

After this had gone on about three or four months, the little girl, whenever she came into the room in the morning and saw those great ugly lumpy stockings dangling at the fire-place, and the disgusting presents around everywhere, used to just sit down and burst out crying. In six months she was exhausted; she couldn't even cry any more; she just lay on the sofa and rolled her eyes and panted. About the beginning of October she took to sitting down on dolls, wherever she found them—French dolls, or any kind—she hated the sight of them so; and by Thanksgiving she just slammed her presents across the room.

By that time people didn't carry presents around nicely any more. They flung

mary stevens

373

them over the fence, or through the window. Instead of taking great pains to write pretty messages or Christmas cards, they wrote "Take it, you horrid thing!"

Nearly everybody had to build barns to hold their presents, but pretty soon the barns overflowed, and then they let them lie out in the rain, or anywhere. Sometimes the police came to tell them to shovel their presents off the sidewalk or they would be arrested.

"I thought you said everybody had gone to the poorhouse," interrupted Jane.

"They did go, at first," said her father. "But after a while the poorhouses got so full that they had to send the people back to their own houses."

Jane sighed and her father went on:

Now, just before the next Thanksgiving, it leaked out who had caused all these Christmases. The little girl had suffered so much that she had talked about it in her sleep; and after that, hardly anybody would play with her. People just despised her, because if it had not been for her greediness, it wouldn't have happened.

The little girl, frantic and sick of it all by this time, began to send letters to the Christmas Fairy, and then telegrams, asking her to stop this everlasting Christmas. But she got no reply, not one. Then she got to calling at the Fairy's house, but the girl who came to the door always said "She's not at home," or "She's at dinner," or something like that. And so it went on till it came to the old once-a-year Christmas Eve. The little girl fell asleep, and when she woke up in the morning—

"She found it was all nothing but a dream," suggested Jane.

"No, indeed!" said her father. "It was all true, every bit of it!"

"What *did* she find out then?"

"That it *wasn't* Christmas and wasn't ever going to be any more . . . Come on now, Jane, it's time for breakfast."

But Jane put her arms around her father's neck and held him fast.

"You shan't go if you're going to leave it *so!*" she said.

"How do you want it left?"

"Christmas once a year."

"All right," said her father. "We'll finish it that way."

There was the greatest rejoicing then, all over the country. When people met they kissed and cried for joy. The city trash-carts went around and gathered up all the candy and raisins and nuts, and dumped them into the river; and the whole United States, as far as Alaska, was ablaze with bonfires, where the children were burning up their presents of all kinds. They had the greatest time!

The little girl went to thank the old Fairy because she had stopped its being Christmas, and she said she hoped she would keep her promise and see that Christmas never, never came again.

But the Fairy frowned, and asked the little girl if she was sure she knew what she meant. This made her think it all over carefully again, and she said she would be willing to have it Christmas about once in a thousand years; and then she said a

mary stevens

hundred, and then she said ten, and at last she got down to one.

The Fairy said that was the good old way that had pleased people ever since Christmas began, and she agreed. Then the little girl said, "What're your shoes made of?" And the Fairy said, "Leather." And the little girl said, "Bargain's done forever," and skipped off and hippity-hopped the whole way home, she was so glad.

"How will that do?" asked Daddy.

"First-rate!" she exclaimed. But she hated to have the story stop. However, her mother put her head in at the door and asked her husband, "What on earth have you been telling Jane?"

"Oh, just a moral tale," said Daddy.

Jane caught him around the neck again and kissed him.

"*We* know," she cried. "Don't we, Daddy? But promise you won't tell!"

And he promised.

—*Adapted*

When the Mail Came Through

By *Armstrong Sperry*

IT HAD BEEN snowing hard all Christmas Eve, and now at daybreak a high wind still howled about the chimney of the old Vermont farmhouse. It rattled the shutters and growled at the windows and swept deep white drifts as high as the low-hanging eaves of the woodshed. But inside, all was snug and tight and warm.

Six generations of Barkers, thrifty and foresighted, had been born and raised in this house. The woodshed was stacked with split birch and hickory and oak. The pantry shelves were loaded with jars of canned goods and preserves. In the cellar there were pork in brine, barrels of potatoes, and enough carrots and cabbages to last the family till spring. Let winter winds howl!

There was no light anywhere except in the kitchen, where Bexy Barker had lighted the lamp on the shelf above the sink. With the pale gold braids pinned up around her head, Bexy looked older than her thirteen years. She bustled about, with no waste motion. She was a strong girl, with quiet wisdom. For a long time now she had had the responsibility of this kitchen—ever since Ma's arthritis got so bad. It was due to Bexy that the pantry shelves were so well stocked, and the younger children's meals so fortifying against the cold. But it was her fifteen-year-old brother, Cliff, who saw to the outside chores and kept the woodshed filled to the eaves, for their father was dead. Together, they were a fine team.

Cliff was pulling on his boots beside the stove. His hands looked too big for his thin arms. Still half asleep, he straightened and yawned. The yawn merged into a sigh. "Gee, I wish it was spring. Listen to that wind!"

"Ho!" scoffed Bexy. "You scared of a little cold weather?"

" 'Tain't that." The boy's words were slow in coming. Cliff wasn't one for easy talk. But now there seemed to be words pressing to be spoken, and he struggled with them. "D'you remember what Joe wrote in that last letter from the Pacific—about the south pasture?"

"Yes. He said he wanted you to break it up this spring and sow it to wheat."

"That's right," the boy replied, his eyes reflective. "Joe said it'd take a lot of bread to win this war. That's why I wish it was spring!" he finished eagerly. "So's I could get started on that pasture." Then, suddenly, the brightness seemed to go out of Cliff's face. "And now Joe won't never know I've done it."

"Don't say that!" Bexy reprimanded sharply. "He'll know you're doing his work just the same as if he was here. And he'll be so proud he'll burst his buttons. We've all got to do our part, every last one of us. Joe'll know."

"You believe that?"

"I know it." There was absolute faith and finality in the girl's words and, hearing them, Cliff took heart. "Guess I'd better get out and see to the cows," he said. "Some folks claim cattle are always restless on Christmas Eve. . . ."

An icy gust swept into the kitchen as Cliff opened the woodshed door, causing the lamp to flare and dim. Hastily the boy banged the door after him. Bexy stood listening to the sound of his retreating footsteps, and she felt a rush of pride in this brother of hers who had done a man's full work ever since Joe went away to war: plowing, harrowing, planting, harvesting, driving the surplus to market.

Cliff was head of his domain just as Bexy was of hers. Together they had held the family firm and seen to its needs; and, in so doing, each was adding his or her mite to the great need of America in this time of stress. Not just the need for grain and eggs and milk and meat, but the need for vigor and courage and faith. But, then, six generations of Barkers had been raised on these virtues, so it was small wonder that Bexy never gave such matters a thought. You just did whatever needed to be done, as well as you were able. The strength came from somewhere. That's all there was to it!

And standing there listening to Cliff's retreating footsteps, Bexy found her gaze being drawn toward the photograph that hung in a place of honor on the wall by the table—the last picture taken of Joe in his uniform of captain in the Marine Corps. Last Christmas Joe had been home on furlough, laughing with them, teasing the young ones, helping to decorate the tree, eating mountains of doughnuts and pancakes, and telling wondrous tales of the Pacific islands and of the people who live there. And tales, too, of fights with enemy planes high against the sun. But this Christmas. . . . A knot tightened in Bexy's throat and she brushed a hand across her eyes.

Determinedly the girl set about her tasks. Nothing should spoil this day if she could help it! She stuffed presents into the row of stockings that hung on nails above the wood box. Those stockings belonged to her four younger brothers and sisters, still sound asleep upstairs in the cold north bedroom. They'd be down any minute now—squabbling with one another over the gifts. There was a Scout knife for George, who was ten. A green lucite comb and brush for Julie, who was eight. A doll for Lola May, aged six. And a fuzzy bear for Jerry, the baby, who was four and mighty spoiled.

Bexy's hands were quick and capable. In no time the four stockings, stuffed with gifts and striped candy and nuts and oranges, looked like so many boa constrictors that had choked on a rabbit.

"Joe would want this Christmas to be happy for everyone," the girl said half aloud. "It's got to be. And we won't let Ma have a chance to be alone with her thoughts. . . ."

The stockings filled, there remained the other presents to be wrapped. Bexy did them all up in white tissue and tied

377

them with red ribbon that had been salvaged from other Christmases and sponged and pressed until almost as good as new. Then she placed the packages on the floor under the full-branched balsam tree that stood in one corner. The children had helped to trim the tree the night before, with festoons of strung cranberries and popcorn balls, and here and there a glitter of well-worn tinsel. A Star of Bethlehem that had crowned every Barker tree since Joe himself was a baby, glistened on the topmost branch. Like the rest of the room the Christmas tree seemed to hold its breath with waiting.

"There, it's lovely," Bexy sighed, backing off to survey the finished result. "Don't know as I ever saw a more handsome tree."

There was one thing Bexy had saved to do for the last and most important. Her breath came a little quicker as she broke off a branch of green, tied it with a bit of red ribbon and laid it across the top of Joe's photograph. Then she kissed a finger and pressed the kiss lightly against her soldier brother's cheek.

"That's for you, Joe. My gift to you."

And for a second it seemed that Joe smiled back at her, his quick, warm smile.

And standing there in the cozy kitchen with the wintry wind worrying at the shutters and causing the old house to tremble, there came over Bexy the remembrance of that terrible morning, six months ago now, when the letter had come from the War Department. . . .

URSULA KOERING

378

There hadn't been many words in that letter. It hadn't needed many . . . "missing in action. . . ."

For the thousandth time, "It can't be true," the girl thought desperately. "Not Joe. It can't be—"

Upstairs the first of the young ones was already stirring. Then George was piping: "Hi, fellers, it's Christmas! Come on, let's get downstairs!"

Then Bexy heard her mother's dry, restless cough in the front bedroom, and the girl's heart contracted. How brave her mother had been! Trying not to let the young ones know, trying to do her part. As if Bexy and Cliff couldn't guess what it cost her!

Cliff was returning from the barn now, clumping through the woodshed, and Bexy welcomed his return. She glanced up as he entered, his face scarlet with cold. He beat the snow off his coat and sought the warmth of the stove, rubbing his hands together at a great rate.

"Everything all right in spite of the snow?" Bexy inquired.

"Right as rain. But the cows did seem kind of uneasy—as if something important was going to happen. Maybe there's truth in that old tale, after all." Cliff paused, as if there were something on his mind he didn't know how to bring out. Bexy guessed what was worrying him but she waited for him to speak. Suddenly he was saying: "This is going to be a mighty hard day for Ma."

"Yes. . . . But we'll help her over it, Cliff, somehow."

The boy nodded. "Yup. We can do it,

Bexy. Here come the kids now. They'll help, too, or I'll take it out of their hides!"

There was a thud of bare feet on the stair, and a whirl like a minor tornado as the four youngest Barkers swept into the kitchen. Their voices shrilled in chorus as they reached for the stockings hanging behind the stove.

"Gee, look what I got!"

"A Scout knife. Oh boy!"

"Here, that's mine! Leggo!"

"It is not, is it, Bexy? Ain't that my stocking?"

"There, now!" Bexy moved swiftly into the threatened breach. "You young ones behave yourselves or I'll get the hairbrush out so it'll be handy. Lola May, you'll have an arm off that doll before night if you don't watch out. And, George, if you leave that Scout knife around so Jerry can cut himself; there'll be consequences for you, young man. Here, let me help you with that knot, Jerry—baby— You kids can get dressed after breakfast—"

"I woke up in the middle of the night," George announced. "I bet nobody else didn't wake up in the middle of the night."

"I almost did," declared Lola May, who had already undressed her doll and was combing out the flaxen hair.

"And I suppose you heard Santa Claus," Cliff joked at his younger brother.

"Nope!" came George's scoffing answer. "But I did hear somethin'. I heard the snowplow goin' through. Now Mr. Thatch can get through with the mail."

"Mail?" came Lola May's thin treble.

"Whoever would be writin' to us?"

"Huh!" George came back at her. "I guess we're mighty important. Didn't the War Department write to us once?"

"Be quiet!" Bexy cried out sharply, her heart sinking. For already she had heard her mother's slow step on the stair. Abashed at his sister's fierce rebuke, George fell to silent contemplation of the Scout knife. Suddenly silent, all the children glanced toward the door as their mother entered.

Mrs. Barker was a frail woman. Her shoulders were bent with hard farm work, her hands misshapen with arthritis. But she smiled at them all, a bright crooked smile that embraced each one, and held out her hands.

"Merry Christmas, my children!" she called.

And they ran to her, and she gathered them into her arms. Something in Bexy's heart caught and she felt a stinging on her eyelids. Ma was like that. You could always count on her.

"Merry Christmas, Ma!" Bexy called from her place at the stove. "I thought this'd be a good day for sausage and waffles. We never had better pork sausage than this year—"

Now the packages under the tree were being unwrapped: the gifts which meant so much to a family living on a remote farm in Vermont. Most of the gifts the Barkers had made surreptitiously for one another throughout the year, and the children had made things in school. Bexy had crocheted a set of tidies for her mother who, in turn, produced some aprons for

her oldest daughter, laboriously feather-stitched with her misshapen fingers. There were heavy knitted socks for the boys, a necktie for Cliff. Everyone talked at once until you could scarcely have heard yourself think in the old Barker kitchen. Bexy was stirring the waffle batter furiously while the double iron heated and the tempting odor of frying sausage filled the room.

Suddenly, cutting across the sound of their voices, there came the shrill pipe of a whistle down the road. Startled, instantly silent, they stared at one another, not speaking.

"What's that?" faltered Bexy finally. But she knew—

Cliff sprang to his feet, flung on his jacket. "That's Mr. Thatch!" he stammered in his excitement. "It's mail— Christmas mail for us!" He was out the door before anyone could speak a word. Bexy saw that her mother's face paled and drew in lines of grief. She would never hear the postman's whistle without remembering that morning, six months ago. . . . And the girl found herself listening with every nerve for Cliff's returning step on the porch. Suddenly the kitchen door was flung open again. Cliff was there, his face as white as the envelope he held in his hand. Slowly Mrs. Barker came to her feet. But Bexy was ahead of her mother.

"Who's it for?" she demanded.

Cliff gulped. "It's—it's addressed to Ma."

"I'll read it," Bexy announced matter-of-factly. "You haven't your glasses, Ma"

"Where's it from?" The woman's words were low and tense.

Now it was Bexy's turn to gulp. She stared at the inscription in the upper left-hand corner of the envelope. "Land," she gasped, "it's from the White House, in Washington!" Her fingers were shaking as she tore open the envelope.

"Read it! Read it!" the children were all shouting at once.

Bexy's eye raced across the single page. Slowly then she brought out the words. "It says:—

"'My dear Mrs. Barker: This letter should reach you on Christmas Day, and with it come my happiest felicitations. I know that it will make you a proud and joyful mother. Your son Joseph Barker, reported missing in action six months ago, effected an escape from the enemy in November. At present he is recuperating in Japan from malaria, but it is expected that by June he will be able to come to Washington where, my dear Mrs. Barker, I hope you will find it possible to be present when I bestow upon him in person the Congressional Medal of Honor for heroism and valor almost unsurpassed in this war. I remain, my dear Mrs. Barker—'"

Bexy's voice faltered and died.

"What is it?" Cliff almost shouted. "Finish what it says—"

"It's signed," Bexy quavered, "by the President of the United States! There, now, Ma, what are you crying for? Joe's most as good as home, and he's a hero!"

"You're cryin' yourself," scoffed George, knuckling a tear out of his own eye. "Only sissies cry."

Then everyone was laughing and crying at once, and the letter was almost torn to pieces by eager fingers.

"Land sakes, the coffee's boiling over!" Bexy cried, making a dash for the stove.

"And the waffles are burning," Cliff grinned. "A body'd think we never had a letter before."

"The cat's got into the cream pitcher," crowed Lola May with delight.

"Come now, come all of you," Bexy cried, flushed with excitement and the warmth of the stove. "Everything's ready, and there are two waffles to start on—"

They all took their places, then looked toward their mother who sat at the head of the table. Mrs. Barker's face was white but her lips were smiling, and in her eyes was a light they had never seen before. Slowly then she clasped her hands on the table edge and bowed her head. The children folded their own hands and cast down their eyes. Into the silence their mother's words, low at first, came with gathering strength:

"We thank Thee, Lord, for this day's great blessing. We thank Thee for the fruits of the earth, and for the strength Thou hast granted us to harvest them. From our hearts we thank Thee—" her voice faltered for a second, then resumed, "we thank Thee for Thy Son born this day, who gave His life, that all men might be free. Amen. . . ."

They raised their heads and smiled happily into one another's eyes.

"It's only six months till June," Cliff

URSULA KOERING

mused. "Joe'll know now I've sowed the south pasture—"

"I told you he'd know," said Bexy quietly. "George, take your thumb out of the syrup pitcher! Lola May, don't try to put a whole waffle into your mouth at once. Joe won't think much of your manners when he gets home. Remember, he'll be having supper at the White House, like as not!"

When Joe gets home. . . . There's magic in the words, she thought happily. And, unseen by the others, Bexy blew a little kiss toward the photograph.

Perhaps no one else knew it, but Bexy knew: Joe smiled back at her!

To a Christmas Tree

By Frances Frost

O BALSAM TREE, that lately held
The stars like nesting birds among
Your emerald branches, listen now
To children's voices sweet with song!

You talker with the wind, and friend
Of fox and fawn and silver mouse,
Bearing your tinsel and your gifts,
Glow softly now within this house,

Bringing your fragrance to our hearts,
Assuring us that wars will cease.
For a Child's bright birthday shine with
faith,
O tree of loveliness and peace!

We Will Sing a New Song

By Ernest Rhys

WE will sing a new song
That sounds like the old: *Noël.*

We will tell an old tale
That has often been told: *Noël.*

We will build a tall town:
We will watch for the star: *Noël.*

We will build a new world
Without War.

CHRISTMAS IN THE HEART

IT IS Christmas in the mansion,
    Yule-log fires and silken frocks;
It is Christmas in the cottage,
    Mother's filling little socks.

It is Christmas on the highway,
    In the thronging, busy mart;
But the dearest truest Christmas
    Is the Christmas in the heart.

WHEN CHRISTMAS IS OVER

By Corinna Marsh

WE'VE put away the ornaments,
And burned the Christmas tree;
The Christmas fun is over—but
The Christ Child, where is He?

He lives in gifts and toys we share
With children who have few
And in the acts of kindliness
We do the whole year through.